Due to an Earlier Incident

Due to an Earlier Incident

CHARLES BLACKWELL

NAYSAYER PRESS
Milwaukee

First Printing, 2019

ISBN 978-0-578-53289-9

Naysayer Press
Milwaukee, WI

Acknowledgement is made for permission to quote from the following works:

Excerpts from LET US NOW PRAISE FAMOUS MEN. Copyright 1939, 1940 by James Agee. Copyright © 1941 by James Agee and Walker Evans. Copyright © renewed 1969 by Mia Fritsch Agee and Walker Evans. Reprinted by permission of Houghton Mifflin Harcourt Publishing Company. All rights reserved.

Excerpt from "Wayward Girl," Hilton Als, *The New Yorker* © Conde Nast. Used with permission.

"Let's Face the Music and Dance" by Irving Berlin
© 1936 by Irving Berlin
All Rights Reserved, Used With Permission.

Republished with permission of University of Michigan Press, from *As If: An Autobiography* by Herbert Blau, 2012; permission conveyed through Copyright Clearance Center, Inc.

From THE CONSTANT GARDENER by John le Carré. Copyright © 2001 by David Cornwell. Reprinted with the permission of Scribner, a division of Simon & Schuster, Inc. All rights reserved.

Reprinted by permission of Farrar, Straus and Giroux:
Excerpt from "Out of Danger" from OUT OF DANGER by James Fenton. Copyright © 1994 by James Fenton.
Excerpts from "Memories of West Street and Lepke" "Skunk Hour" "For the Union Dead" "Waking Early Sunday Morning" "Man and Wife" from SELECTED POEMS by Robert Lowell. Copyright © 1976 by Robert Lowell.
Excerpts from "The Blade" and "The Rampage" from COLLECTED POEMS by C. K. Williams. Copyright © 2006 by C. K. Williams.

One haiku by Issa [Don't worry, spiders,/... .], one by Buson ["A tethered horse/... .] from THE ESSENTIAL HAIKU: VERSIONS OF BASHO, BUSON & ISSA. EDITED AND WITH AN INTRODUCTION by ROBERT HASS. Introduction and selection copyright © 1994 by Robert Hass. Reprinted by permission of HarperCollins Publishers.

Excerpts from "An Interview with Matthew Henriksen," originally published in *Bookslut* literary blog/webzine. Used by permission of Matthew Henriksen.

Back cover description and lines from "To a Child Trapped in a Barber Shop" from *Not This Pig* © 1968 by Philip Levine. Published by Wesleyan University Press. Used by permission. www.wesleyan.edu/wespress

FOR CAROLINE

In fact, and ignorant though I am, nothing, not even law, nor property, nor sexual ethics, nor fear, nor doubtlessness, nor even authority itself, all of which it is in the business of education to cleanse the brain of, can so nearly annihilate me with fury and with horror; as the spectacle of innocence, of defenselessness, of all human hope, brought steadily in each year by the millions into the machineries of the teachings of the world, in which the man who would conceive of and who would dare attempt even the beginnings of what "teaching" must be could not exist two months clear of a penitentiary: *assuming even that his own perceptions, were not a poison as deadly at least as those poisons he would presume to drive out*: or the very least of whose achievements, supposing he cared truly not only to hear himself speak but to be understood, would be a broken heart.

—James Agee, *Let Us Now Praise Famous Men* (Emphasis Mine)

Q. What do you hate most about living in New York?

A. The knowledge that, because it is impossible to conquer New York, you either have to die here or leave defeated. You cannot leave in triumph. Or, I mean, maybe you can, if you reach some kind of "emotional maturity," but good luck with that, everybody.

—Itamar Moses, Interview, *New York Magazine Daily Intelligencer*

CONTENTS

PART ONE

Maybe We Can Work Around That

No one should come to live in New York unless he is willing to be lucky.

E.B. White

An e-mail, dated June 8, 2004, sent to Belinda M----, Assistant Principal for English Language Arts at M---- L---- K----, Jr., High School, located near Lincoln Center, on the Upper West Side of Manhattan, in New York City, written in response to an earlier e-mail, subsequently lost, that included a vague suggestion of the possibility of a hypothetical interview for an actually (and, one understands now, recurrently) vacant teaching position:

Hi Belinda,

Thank you. I can come in next week. I've got this crazy five-and-a-half hour flight from Milwaukee to NYC via Atlanta (the cheapest I could get—it's expensive to fly one way) scheduled for Saturday, June 19, but I think that for a modest premium I can change the date, if not the route. How late this week do you think you could schedule an interview for me? Friday, maybe? Thursday? Please let me know as soon as possible, so I can get in touch with the airline and make the necessary arrangements.

Excitedly and nervously and gratefully yours,
Charles

The earlier e-mail, the one that included a vague suggestion of the possibility of a hypothetical interview, and was then subsequently lost, was lost because it had been archived in an old company account used, against company policy, for personal as well as professional communication, that had been closed before it—along with hundreds of other traces, remnants, and orthographic projections of an earlier life—could be downloaded and shored against their author's ruins. The lost e-mail had been written in response to an even earlier e-mail, only a copied and pasted fragment of which remains today, that included an earnest, and, in retrospect, touching, even tender, request for the possibility of an interview for a teaching position in an English Language Arts department described by Belinda M----, because of the long hours and constant meetings and great sacrifices required, as "a writing cult."

The Assistant Principal had offered this description of her department at a kind of mass interview cum information session, part of a larger job fair, conducted in a lofty and gloomy chalk-dusty classroom on the third floor of B---- and R---- High School, located in Harlem, New York City.

The classroom reminded me, Charles Blackwell, the author of the e-mail dated June 8, 2004, of an old church, but also of a sailing ship, or, more precisely, of a combination of the two I had read about somewhere, but couldn't remember where. While waiting for the service, or captain's briefing, to begin, I scribbled the following description in the little notebook I kept in the breast pocket of my blazer: "A classroom where rusted, repainted, and peeling radiators moaned plangent—a ghost ship's horn—and tall windows required a long pole with a hook at the end, a steady hand, and many years' practice to open and close their upper sashes; a large classroom, prow, or chancel, swash-churned, and ominous and solemn."

And in this ominous and solemn classroom, amid such swash, twenty or thirty or more earnest, and, in retrospect, touching, even tender, applicants, all of them younger than I was, younger by twenty years (younger, some of them, by twenty-five!), "sat crouching," in words inscribed in my little notebook, "as stooped novices, supplicants, or oarsmen, in carved and graffitied student desks gathered into a semi-circle around a kind of ambo, or quarterdeck," held by Belinda M---- and her assistant Assistant Principal, Maurice D----.

These novices/supplicants/oarsmen were New York City Teaching Fellows, former professionals in fields other than education and, more predominately, recent college graduates getting a first foot on the island, together forming a shadow workforce of shadow clerics, shadow mariners, recruited to teach "underserved populations" of at-risk schoolchildren housed by day in "hard-to-staff," "high needs" schools located mainly in the Bronx, but in the other boroughs as well, including Manhattan's Region 10, a broad and roiling diocese, encompassing parts of the Upper West Side and all of Harlem, Washington Heights, and Inwood, where the band of New York City Teaching Fellows gathered in the gloomy classroom had been set loose to find classrooms of their own in which they would earnestly and touchingly and tenderly hold forth while pursuing partially-subsidized graduate degrees in a teacher's training course at the City College of New York, also located in Region 10.

For about forty-five minutes that evening, Belinda M---- described, in sanguinary detail, the many opportunities her school offered for Teaching Fellows to work long hours, attend constant meetings, and make great sacrifices.

At the conclusion of the job fair, upon disembarking from the ghost ship, I noticed goose pimples rising on my forearms; I felt stirred, happy in anticipation and certain that by September this teaching position that I wanted so badly, or another teaching position I would also want so badly, would be mine.

Earlier that evening, fidgeting my way uptown on the C Eighth Avenue Local train, en route to B---- and R---- High School, nervous in anticipation, checking my breath on my hand, and fussing with the half-Windsor I never really learned to tie correctly—one corner always dragged[1]—I shared an otherwise almost empty car with a tall and slender young black man, fifteen or sixteen years old, "with curlicues / of marijuana in his hair," as Robert Lowell had written fifty years earlier about another young black man with whom he once found himself confined—except in Lowell's case not on the C train, but in the West Street Jailhouse. He was sitting on the edge of the bench, wearing a baseball cap cocked to the side—the young man, not Robert Lowell—lost in his thoughts, absently bouncing a basketball. Also present in the car was a young white woman, pretty, with blond hair. She was standing, although many seats were available, chewing a stick of gum that smelled all the way across the car of apples, bouncing her head to music she was piping into her ears, or maybe it was her hair that smelled of apples.

Everything I saw or heard in New York reminded me of a book, poem, song, play, or movie about New York, and, as I meditated on the bouncing ball, I thought for a moment of Amiri Baraka's play *Dutchman*, and, even though they didn't exactly fit the character descriptions, I imagined that the blond girl was Lula and the young man was Clay, and that an allegory of race and sex was about to be played out. Then, remembering why I was on the C train, and where I was going, I wondered if the young man would be my student in a few months, and I imagined that he, the young man, was Sidney Poitier, and that I was Glenn Ford, black student and white teacher playing out a different kind of allegory in the fifties classroom drama, *Blackboard Jungle*, while in the next car Ford's colleague at the hard-to-staff, high-needs high school where they both taught their underserved population of duck-assed JDs, a young math teacher, played by Richard Kiley, was having a nervous breakdown because his student—Vic Morrow, snarling and method-acting—had busted up his rare recording of Bix Biederbecke's "Jazz Me Blues."

---

[1] I later learned that the "half-Windsor" I thought I'd been tying all my life was, in fact, a four-in-hand, and the corner is supposed to drag.

Three and a half years later, when I was in the middle of having my own nervous breakdown, though by then the Diagnostic and Statistical Manual of Mental Disorders no longer used the term "nervous breakdown," and it wasn't a student who'd busted up my rare recordings, I found myself downtown, waiting on line to pay for a plastic basket full of second-hand books at the Strand Book Store, when a star-struck salesclerk, in clear breach of the unspoken New York City code of cool indifference to celebrity, excitedly directed customer attention to a movie star he had just served. I looked out the window, following the line of the salesclerk's arm as if it belonged to a saint in a Renaissance painting who was serenely pointing the way to salvation, and as my eyes adjusted to the sun, Jennifer Jason Leigh came into focus. She was standing on the corner of East 12th and Broadway, waiting for the light to change.

"What was she in?" a customer asked.

"*I Shot Andy Warhol*."

"No, that was Lily Tomlin."

"You mean Lili Taylor."

"Isn't Jennifer Jason Leigh somebody famous' daughter?"

"Tony Curtis'."

"No, you're thinking of Jamie Leigh Curtis."

"Vic Morrow. Jennifer Jason Leigh is Vic Morrow's daughter," I interjected, trying not to sound pedantic.

"Who's Vic Morrow?" someone asked.

As I recapitulated the highlights of Morrow's career for the curious book buyers at the Strand, I felt myself falling into a reverie, a swoon almost, as I remembered my *Blackboard Jungle* fantasy on the train to Harlem three and a half years earlier, and for a moment I felt in my body once again the happiness I'd felt that night, in the afterglow of the job fair when, standing on a corner of St. Nicholas Avenue on that warm moonlit evening of what seemed, by then, like twenty or twenty-five years earlier, I knew, at the age of forty-five, that I had found myself at last. But now, then, standing on line at the checkout counter of the Strand Book

Store, staring into the sunlight where only moments before Jennifer Jason Leigh had shone in her dazzling offbeat star quality, before darting off like a dragonfly from a warm rock near a cool stream, I lost the good feeling again, as I'd lost it so many times before, and, bracing myself, I fell into a different dream, a bad dream of all the bad feelings that had followed in the three and a half years since the job fair, the bad feelings that follow still; and I started to cry, all because Jennifer Jason Leigh was Vic Morrow's daughter. I half expected the clerk, when he saw my tears, to offer me a handkerchief from his sleeve, but there's no time for gallantry at the Strand check-out counters.

But this evening, the evening of the job fair, dreaming of the long hours I would work in the fall, the constant meetings I would attend, and the great sacrifices I would make, I felt happy; I decided to give the C train a miss, and walk from Harlem to the small hotel on West End Avenue where I was staying on this particular reconnaissance trip, one of many (it's expensive being a New York City Teaching Fellow).

Somewhere in Morningside Heights, about halfway between the Teacher's College of Columbia University and the Soldiers and Sailors Monument that I used to think was Grant's Tomb, I remembered that the combination church and ship I'd tried so hard to recollect earlier that evening was the New Bedford Whaleman's Chapel, described in detail in Chapter Eight of *Moby Dick*, the chapel where Ishmael receives, in Chapter Nine, fair warning of the dangers awaiting him at sea. And, like Melville's hero, my "hypos" having got the "upper hand of" me, and setting sail to assuage a vague and undefined "damp and drizzly November" in my soul, but in my case taking not to ship to see "the watery part of the world," but veering instead toward the very "insular city of the Manhattoes" from which Ishmael seeks escape, I was struck with a flashing presentiment of doom, as I thought of these words from the hymn Father Mapple offers as benediction to the congregation of sailors, and sailor's wives and widows, as he climbs his rope ladder and takes the pulpit:

I saw the opening maw of hell,
With endless pains and sorrows there;
Which none but they that feel can tell -
Oh, I was plunging to despair...

But the presentiment passed, and the endless pains and sorrows—and the plunge to despair!—were postponed for a few
months, and a couple of days later, upon my return to Milwaukee, Wisconsin, contemplating the new life that awaited me in
New York City, a new life of "building equity" by "invest[ing]
in 1.1 million futures," I dispatched an earnest, and, in retrospect, touching, even tender e-mail to Belinda M---, only a copied and pasted fragment of which remains today, that included
the following request:

> Please accept my application to join your writing cult. I don't
> mind panhandling at the airport (or staying after school to
> meet with you and my fellow cultists), and I'll bring my own
> incense. We met two nights ago at the B---- and R---- High
> School job fair, where you and Maurice D---- group-inter-
> viewed a bevy (a herd? a coven? oh yeah, a cohort) of New
> York City Teaching Fellows. I'm Charles (also known as Chip)
> Blackwell—middle-aged, (mostly) black hair, salt and pepper
> beard, third pledge from your right in the interview circle.
>
> I was very much impressed with you and Maurice, and all the
> encouraging things you were saying, the questions you asked,
> and the fact that you stayed at the job fair until closing time,
> allowing all Fellows the opportunity to interview. I walked
> away from the interview elated, with a buzz, feeling that feel-
> ing I often feel when I'm in New York City—the sense that life
> is full of possibilities, that there are smart, talented, and con-
> cerned people in the world who find the energy and the will
> to struggle and overcome impossible obstacles and do amaz-
> ing things. I just hope I'm one of those people.

You have my résumé. I'm attaching a copy of the "Why I Want to be a New York City Public Schoolteacher in A Thousand Words or Less" essay I included in my application to the New York City Teaching Fellows.

I'm in Milwaukee tying up loose ends at work, selling my house, and saying goodbye until June 21, when I begin my pre-service training and my wife and I take possession of our summer sublet on Orchard Street. I would love to accept your invitation to visit your school, but I don't think I can afford another trip to New York right now. I flew there in December to interview for the Teaching Fellows, in March to take the LAST and CST exams, and a few days ago for the job fair. Can I still be considered for the job if I can't make a spring visit?

A final e-mail from this exchange survives. Dated June 9, 2004, it captures one more moment in the accretion of time lost, fragmented, and digitally preserved, that serves now as a kind of ship's log, documenting my four years before the mast: a note from Belinda M----, Assistant Principal for English Language Arts at M---- L---- K----, Jr., High School, New York City, written in answer to an earlier response, dated June 8, 2004, to a vague suggestion of the possibility of a hypothetical interview for an actually (and recurrently) vacant teaching position; a laconic check on my prolix enthusiasm, engendering in my middle-aged, life-tempered, but still frangible heart the first, but not the last, pang of unrequited love I would feel before I'd completed my four-year tour of duty as a New York City public schoolteacher:

Are you saying you had already scheduled a flight on your own for your own purposes, on the 19th? If you have, maybe we can work around that.

Word Wall

Vsevolod Pudovkin called it "the plastic material," T. S. Eliot called it the "objective correlative," Alfred Hitchcock called it "the MacGuffin," and, according to the boys at Wikipedia, Pearl White, who played Pauline in *The Perils of Pauline*, called it "the weenie": Hamlet's "doublet all unbraced and stockings fouled," the cache of uranium in *Notorious*, the cask of Amontillado in "The Cask of Amontillado," the "intercostal clavicle" in *Bringing Up Baby*, or Marcel Proust's famous piece of madeleine soaked in its "decoction of lime-blossom"; that is to say, the object, image, or idea that propels a narrative, sets a plot in motion, and, for Eliot, acts as a formula for expressing an emotion in a work of the imagination, or, in the case of Proust, triggers something he called "involuntary memory." If it could be said that I had a weenie, it was the little notebook I always kept in the breast pocket of my blazer, the one in which I recorded my impressions of the ship/church/classroom, back at B---- and R---- High School.

Originally spiral-bound and college-ruled, until my wife explained to me that the sleek Moleskine numbers I'd been admiring at Harry W. Schwartz's Bookstore on Downer Avenue, in Milwaukee, the ones marketed as the sort of notebook wielded by the dashing and heroic Bruce Chatwin, as he faced down firing squads in Dahomey, or clumped across pampases to the world's end at Patagonia, were actually bound in oilcloth, and not the skin of a mole (I was trying very hard at the time to be a vegan), the weenie in question had been inspired by the journal George Eliot kept, the one she called her "Quarry," in which she wrote the preliminary sketches for *Middlemarch*. I had been an English major at college and fancied myself a "literary man," and I imagined I was writing preliminary sketches myself for my own nineteenth-century novel (cum confession, spiritual autobiography, *cri de coeur*, advertisement for myself, and *apologia pro vita sua*) that would do for the "No Child Left Behind Act of 2001" what *Middlemarch* had done for the "1832 Reform Act."

A few months after the job fair in Harlem, when my wife and I had relocated to New York City, and following two tense months of botched interviews and polite, but unequivocal rejection, I had finally claimed a quarterdeck of my own (and a moaning radiator and a long pole with a hook at the end), not at M---- L---- K----, Jr., High School, where I had, in my dreams of a new life, originally pictured myself (and where Belinda M---- would discover, upon further consideration, that she would not, after all, be able to work around me), even though, when I finally visited the campus for my interview, I hated the ugly poured concrete monolith, but on another plangent ghost ship, reminiscent of B---- and R---- High School, designed at the turn of the last century, in the gothic revival style (it even had gargoyles; boy did it have gargoyles), docked even farther uptown, in Inwood, a formerly Irish, but by the time I came to know it, largely Dominican outpost situated near the northernmost tip of Manhattan.

Facing down my own firing squad, tied to a mast in a gothic revival ghost ship, where for the next four years I would try to become a new Charles Blackwell—sprung, like an older and slightly less ostentatious Gatsby, from my own (dimly-perceived) Platonic conception of myself—I often entertained my students by relating a narrative set into motion by the little MacGuffin in my breast pocket, the notebook that, by then, however, I was using, in a sad and embarrassing perversion of its original purpose, to document the sins, transgressions, and misdeeds

24

that my sixth-graders, after a charming month-long idyll of sweetness and light, were committing with increasing frequency and recklessness. I was amassing evidence for the day I would make good my repeated bluffs to call their mothers and fathers and give them a "progress report." My students feared the call home above all other "interventions" because their parents were less fussy than the middle class (and the New York City Department of Education) about the ethics and efficacy of corporal punishment. The call home functioned, in the public school system, as a form of extraordinary rendition, in which corporal punishment was outsourced to parents and guardians in the developing world.

I never made any calls home, until my fourth, and final, year of teaching, when everything had changed, and even then only a few calls, because I didn't have any "follow-through" ("that state of grace," Nabokov calls it in *Speak, Memory*, but he was talking about his father's tennis game). This failure was noted by the hierarchy of administrators that paraded daily through my classroom, wielding objective correlatives of their own—big green canvass-bound ledgers with leather trim, if their bearers were higher in rank than assistant principal (or if they were ambitious assistant principals preparing to make their move), and the more familiar marbled composition book favored by the non-commissioned officers, the middle managers just glad to be the hell out of the classroom—in which these lofty personages, "the Great Chain of Being," I called them, recorded, in their never-ending and scientific pursuit of "data-driven instruction," every transgression, sin, and misdeed committed by the benighted day laborers and lay practitioners, applying their folk remedies, home truths, and mother wit, unsuitable because unquantifiable, to students in the classroom.

I had no follow-through, but I had discovered that the threat was almost always as good as a call, for the same reason that my students always forgave, if they didn't forget, and forgot, if they didn't forgive, their teacher's own transgressions, sins, and misdeeds: the riot acts I read them, the cruel, self-pitying tirades, the violent reproaches, all the hackneyed phrases and petty tyrannies that I, like all *parentis* (*in loco*, or in the flesh) had sworn I would never commit when I had children of my own. They were sassy, my students were, and they cracked like they were wise, and, let's face it, they could be stinkers when they wanted to be, but when you got to know them, and even before you got to know them, you understood how sweet, how loving, and, most importantly for me, how credulous they were. These were the "gifted and talented" students of the school, which is to say, in the context of the ghost ship, "gifted and talented" being a relative term, they were reading and doing math at pretty much grade level, or no more than a year behind; they were, in addition, relatively well-behaved ("relatively" being a relative term: no actual blood was ever let, or property destroyed; well, not *much* blood was let, not much property was destroyed).

All I had to do was pull out my little notebook, and keep my poker face, and my students believed, without any hard data (or even anecdotal evidence), that if they didn't start toeing the [insert bromide here] or minding their [insert cliché] and [insert platitude], their parents would be called and their squirming little posteriors would be effectively, if not necessarily extraordinarily, rendered.

The notebook, quarry, or account book, bound in paper or in oilcloth, served for four years as an objective correlative not only for my vocational imperative to discipline and punish, but also for my students' desire to uncover any hidden facts that might, if revealed, have shed light on the mysterious provenance of the peculiar old man (and my students made no niggling distinctions between middle-aged and senior citizen) who stood before them each weekday (teachers aren't allowed to sit), "modeling best practices" and "facilitating" "English Language Arts." In my efforts to satisfy my students' apparently inexhaustible curiosity, I was forthcoming to a fault; the little notebook was waved in the air, and used as a prop, when I began relating, in exaggerated detail, the improbable story of how I had come to be their teacher.

But the phrase "stood before them" might be less than precise. The tattered coat upon a(n aluminum) stick who, to the continual derision of my charges, always wore the same frayed charcoal blazer, buttoned-down white Oxford shirt, usually coffee-stained, and missing a button, but not either of the buttons that were buttoned down, pleated khaki trousers (no-iron, traditional fit, but with a "comfort waist"), worn at the knees and rolled at the ankles, and the same scuffed pair of "vegan" cap toe bluchers, more accurately *leaned* before them each weekday, propped against an ingeniously retractable and telescoping cane that enabled me, a lifelong overpronator, to walk when my arches had fallen, and my shins had splint, and, of course, when no longer lame, to ham it up by making like a vaudevillian doing the old soft shoe.

I had purchased the stick the same sad summer's day I'd also bought, because my near vision was failing me, a pair of thick-lensed reading glasses, horn-rimmed, with a magnification factor approaching that of an electron microscope, and a heavy chain like Jacob Marley or an eighties hip hop artist might have worn, so I could wear the appliance around my neck, and, once I started embellishing the story for my students' greater delectation, an ear horn, a truss, an oxygen tank, and a coronary stent, down aisle eight, in the alter kocker section of the Rite Aid drugstore on First Avenue and Fifth Street (I had always dreamed of being a real New Yorker and was at the time peppering my speech with Yiddish—Yiddish with a southern accent).

My students didn't know the phrase alter kocker, but they were familiar with a less scatological English equivalent: "old geezer." I myself had taught them the epithet, an epithet they gloried in applying to their teacher for the rest of the school year—and thereafter.

They knew this phrase, and many other words and phrases previously obscure to them, because aboard the ghost ship

where I was attempting to ply my new trade, teachers of all subjects were required by the Great Chain of Being, as part of ongoing efforts at "fostering a print-rich environment," to keep in
their classrooms a bulwark of print-richness that was called "the
Word Wall," in which new vocabulary written on index cards
was affixed, as best any teacher could, with gum, paste, glue,
putty, mucilage, sealing wax, and/or masking tape, to one of the
rough-surfaced cinderblock walls (because nothing would stick,
words were always flying off these walls, spinning, looping,
nose-diving, flapping about, and putting out eyes). Always ten
years behind my students in urban vernacular, but eager to
please them (they usually humored their teacher's corny attempts at street cred), if not so eager to please the Great Chain
(who, more and more, were coming to dictate all aspects of
teacher comportment, lesson planning, and even interior decoration), I had, in compliance with the Word Wall requirement,
built a construction paper brick wall, which I labeled, in imitation graffiti bubble letters, "WORD UP!" I also built—for myself—a wailing wall, to which I had daily recourse, and, for my
students—in a gesture of *noblesse oblige*—a "wall of democracy,"
as a medium for the "self-expression" of the younger generation,
with the motto, "Let a thousand flowers grow and a thousand
schools of thought contend," emblazoned at the top. (Please, if
you ever go into teaching, do not set up a wall of democracy in
your classroom.)

(Resistant as I was to the never-ending "innovations" of data-
driven instruction, or any of the other nostrums-of-the-week
promulgated in the celestial spheres that make up the higher re-
gions of the administrative *plenum formarum*, or to any interference at all in my classroom, I nevertheless found myself having
to hand the Great Chain some grudging props regarding the ef-
fectiveness of the Word Wall in building vocabulary when, one
day, shortly after I had installed mine, I heard some loud and
heated words bubbling forth from a familiar source of loud and
heated words, Esmyrna Renteria: "You touch my locker, Joshua,

and you're in for some serious *animadversion*."

Now, Esmyrna Renteria was a student I adored because she was always surprising and delighting me, and though she was in no way anything like the corrupt cop Harry Kello, played by the menacing Central Casting villain Emile Meyer in *Sweet Smell of Success*, perhaps the ultimate New York movie, Esmyrna's threat to Joshua put me immediately in mind of some words Kello growls—and simultaneously purrs—to Sidney Falco, played by Tony Curtis: "Come over here kid, I wanna chas*tise* ya." I would, by the way, later in my career, come in for some serious animadversion myself, when the Great Chain of Being sent its goons in to chastise *me*.)

The phrase "old geezer," which had caused some confusion when it came up in a story that I was reading to the class, was one of the first bricks laid in the Word Wall.

"Rumpled," "dawdling," "daft," "barmy," "tatterdemalion," "ramshackle," "tumbledown," and "meshuggener" were bricks that had also (by coincidence) been laid in those first few months, and when my students demanded to know how such a dawdling, daft, and barmy old ramshackle tumbledown tatterdemalion of a rumpled meshuggener as myself had wound up in New York City (actually, they could understand how a rumpled meshuggener—dawdling, daft, barmy, ramshackle, tumbledown, *or* old—would wind up, or originate, in New York City, but they needed a little back-story to account for how it is that *they* could ever have come to know such an abject creature personally, and even be on generally cordial terms with him), I was happy, thrilled even, to oblige them, and I pulled the little notebook out of my pocket and started my well-practiced oration.

The story that my students made me tell over and over, went, more or less, like this:

"I'll be honest with you kids," I would say, fiddling with my necktie, like Rodney Dangerfield used to fiddle with his, except Rodney Dangerfield knew how to tie a half-Windsor, and he got a lot more respect, "I've made a few mistakes, and I have a few regrets…"

"But, then again, too few to mention," some wise child would interrupt. My students liked to interrupt me.

"The first mistake I made was in November, 2002, when you lovely children were only four years old…"

"No way! We weren't four!"

"We were eight in 2002, Mr. Blackwell. Do the math."

"Some of us were nine."

"Hector was ten!" [Laughter.]

"I'm an English teacher, you know, not a math teacher. What do I know from subtraction? Anyway, as I was saying, it all started when I was four years old, barefoot, and living in a shotgun shack in Birmingham, Alabama, that my daddy bought on the G.I. Bill…"

"No, no, not that far back! This is a boring English Language Arts class, Mr. Blackwell, not a boring ancient history class."

"And we only have one period with you today, Mr. Blackwell! We have other classes, you know. You English teachers think English is the only subject that matters." [They were right about that; English teachers think English is the only subject that matters.]

"All right, all right. How does this story go? [I pause. I scratch my head. My students groan.] Oh yeah…the first mistake I made was coming to New York for a vacation in November 2002, because my mother-in-law was coming to Milwaukee for Thanksgiving—I'm sure I've told you a million times I used to live in Milwaukee—except I got the dates all wrong and accidentally booked my flight, *and* a hotel room, *and* bought tickets for three shows, and two operas, for the week before Thanksgiving, and so, as it turned out, I was still able to enjoy a lovely visit with the old battle…I mean with my mother-in-law…"

"That's what you get, Mr. Blackwell!"

"And besides, mother-in-law jokes are corny and they're sexist, too. Who do you think you are, Henny Youngman?"

"More like Myron Cohen, I'd say."

"He's the right age."

"All right, all right, you got me. I'm just going for some cheap laughs and maybe a drum roll, please. [I point to Pedro Gutierrez, who provides a drum roll, using two pencils, his desk, and the radiator.]

"Anyway, where was I? Oh yeah, my first mistake, which was coming to New York for a vacation when I could just as easily have gone to Panama City Beach, Florida, or Branson, Missouri, or Gatlinburg, Tennessee, and for a lot less money, but…"

"Or you could have gone to D.R., you know. You'd like it there."

"Punta Cana!"

"Puerto Plata!"

"You could have stayed at a resort!"

"Oh yeah, the Dominican Republic. I could have gone to the Dominican Republic…

"Now, the second mistake I made once I made the first mistake, was once I got to New York I had to be a big fat fancy pants and go to the opera, but not much of a big fancy pants, since instead of being the big spender I usually am—just ask my wife—I acted this time like a piker, which means a cheapskate [at this point I take out a magic marker, a blank card, and some scotch tape from my jacket pocket, and scribble "piker" on the card and tape it to the Word Wall; the card falls off the wall, and my students laugh; I laugh, too], and bought myself a cheap ticket in the Family Circle, 'cheap' being a relative term in New York—Row K, as a matter of fact, the last row before standing room, over by the real opera nerds leaning on their desks following the score. They can't even see the stage, even if they squint, from where they are. Basically my seat was five stories and six blocks from the stage. You'd have to use the Pythagorean Theorem—all you kids who love math and hate English—to figure just how far away from the stage I was.

"By the way, the opera I went to see was Richard Strauss' *Die*

Frau ohne Schatten, with a libretto by his long-time collaborator, Hugo von Hofmannsthal. *'Die Frau ohne Schatten'* is German for 'The Woman without a Shadow.' Now, this opera is all about a beautiful empress. An empress is kind of like a queen...[I add "libretto," "*Die Frau ohne Schatten*," and "empress" to the Word Wall; "libretto" and "*Die Frau ohne Schatten*" fall off immediately, to a couple of chuckles.]"

"We didn't ask you all that."

"Stay *on task*, Mr. B-well."

["Empress" falls off the wall.] "I know, I know, but hold on. You might be interested in this. Anyway, it turns out this empress used to be a gazelle, but her father, the King of the Spirit Realm, turned her into an empress for some reason. Because the empress wasn't really human, and just appears in human form, she doesn't cast a shadow—hence the name of the opera—and her father tells her that unless she figures out some way to get a shadow by the end of the twelfth moon, or the third act, whichever comes first, he'll turn her back into a gazelle, and what's more, he'll turn her husband into a stone. At least I *think* that's the plot; I got so immersed in the music and the costumes and the sets that I kept forgetting to read my Met Titles, and you can't rewind...

"Now the third mistake I made was..."

"Wait a minute; wait a minute, what happened to the empress?"

"Did she get a shadow?"

"What's a gazelle?"

"I thought you weren't interested."

At this point I would have to interrupt my narrative: first, to explain what a gazelle was, and sort of toss a piece of paper with "gazelle" written on it in the general direction of the Word Wall, and then in the course of explaining what a gazelle was somehow to wind up promising the class a trip to the Bronx Zoo to see one, and then the logistics of the trip would have to be discussed—for instance, Crystal, who lived in the Bronx, would want to know if she could meet the class at the zoo, and Ruben would have a cousin who just got out of juvenile detention, and he'd want to know if he could go, too, and then the class would have to help me figure out some angle for convincing the principal that the field trip had something to do with meeting New York State English Language Arts standards; and then to give the class a more detailed, if possibly inaccurate, synopsis of *Die Frau ohne Schatten*, because by then, once they understood a little better what a gazelle was, and had a tentative plan in place for going to see one, they wanted to know how the beautiful empress made out. (If you don't know the story, you can read a full synopsis in Kobbe's Opera Guide, or just google the title, but you'd better google the English title or you'll get a bunch of German web pages, but then maybe you read German...)

"Anyway," I continued, "the third mistake I made was taking the 1 train—or was it the 9?—instead of getting a taxi like I should have done, up to Lincoln Center. I mean, I was on the right train and everything—this was before Hop Stop, but I had an MTA map, and I knew how to take the subway. It's just that there was something on the train that...well, that...Wait a minute, I'm getting ahead of myself...

"The fourth mistake I made was looking *up* as I was riding in the subway car, instead of looking *down* like you're supposed to do, or reading *The New York Times* all folded up like origami the way some people do it, or even—blecch! [a vocabulary word from *MAD* magazine that I had just the week before put on the Word Wall]—reading the *New York Post*..."

"I like the *New York Post*!"

"...or a book..."

"Blecch!"

"...like real New Yorkers do, so they don't have to make eye contact with any dawdling, daft, and barmy old ramshackle tumbledown tatterdemalion meshuggeners..."

"Like you!"

"...like me—how did you know?—and because I was looking

up, I made my fifth mistake, I noticed an ad for something called 'The New York City Teaching Fellows,' an ad promising successful professionals and recent college graduates that by becoming a teacher they could 'Make a difference,' or 'Make an impression,' or 'Make a stink,' or something like that, and that they could 'build equity by invest[ing] in 1.1 million futures.'"

"What's equity?"

"It's the actor's union. Anyway, being a successful professional and everything, the sixth mistake I made was carrying around a little notebook and a pen in the breast pocket of my blazer. I think you know the blazer I mean."

"Yeah, we know the blazer you mean."

"For God's sake, Mr. Blackwell, get some new clothes!"

"Spruce up your wardrobe."

"Did he say *breast*?"

"And put some mousse in your hair!"

"Why would I put a moose in my hair?"

"Mousse, not moose! Don't be homophonebic [a standard gag in my classroom; the Word Wall was also filled with words my students and I had made up]."

"Anyway, I thought you guys liked my hair."

"We do. It's just that it would look so much better if you put some mousse in it, and, you know, if you combed it back. You look kind of old the way it is."

"Mr. Blackwell has good hair."

"Yeah, if he'd only take care of it." (Which was the same thing my mother used to say, except she'd say, "You have such *pretty* hair, if you'd only take care of it.")

"Anyway, the seventh mistake I made was not losing my pen, like I usually do.

"And the ninth mistake I made…"

"The eighth mistake, old geezer, can't you even count?"

"Is it the eighth? I always lose track when I'm counting my mistakes. I count them at night instead of sheep, but for some reason, I get insomnia instead…

"Oh yeah, the eighth mistake I made was writing down the address of the New York City Teaching Fellows website in the little notebook I carry in the *breast* pocket of my blazer, the *BREAST* pocket.

"The ninth mistake I made I made one year after the first mistake I made. It was in November 2003, when, after thinking about the thing for over for a year, and having about a million discussions about it with my wife, we decided I'd apply for the fellowship.

"The tenth mistake I made was writing an apparently convincing, or at least grammatical, 'Why I Want to be a Teacher in a Thousand Words or Less' essay, and getting myself invited to come to New York and interview to become a New York City Teaching Fellow.

"The eleventh mistake I made was being very, very charming and sincere at the interview—well, sincere...or charming, I can't remember—and then getting an e-mail saying I had the job. I was interviewed by a woman, by a very attractive woman, and you might not know this because after all you're just children, but I've always been kind of a lady's man..."

[Laughter. Disbelief.] "Yeah, right, you're a player, Mister B-Well."

"No way."

"All right, I'm lying about being a lady's man, but everything else I'm telling you is the *emmis* [another Word Wall word]."

"The *emmis*—get Blackwell! He thinks he's Jewish. He thinks he's a New Yorker!"

"You're not Jewish, Mr. Blackwell, so you can cut it out with the Yiddish."

"Anyway, you sound country when you say Yiddish words."

"Isn't '*emmis*' actually a Hebrew word?"

"It's a borrowing."

"Yiddish, Hebrew, or borrowing, Mr. Blackwell sounds like a hick when he says words in any language."

"*¡Ay dios mio!* Have you ever heard him try to speak Spanish?

Now *that's* hilarious!"

"Yeah, stop playacting. Anyway, let's face it; this whole coming to New York thing is a fantasy you're living..."

"He's having a midlife crisis."

"You can't really recreate yourself from your Platonic conception of yourself. You read *Gatsby*."

"I can try. After all, 'A man's reach must exceed his grasp, else what's a heaven for.'"

"Corny, and besides they don't let you teach Browning in the sixth grade. He's *canonical* for Christ's sake—a dead white man."

"Yeah, corny! [By the way, everything I said or did was "corny," even though my students were always laughing at my jokes.] And enough with the literary allusions. And obvious ones at that. You're not impressing anybody. You just sound pretentious."

"A dilettante." [Word Wall word]

"A *poseur*." [Word Wall word]

"Yeah, I know. I know...

"Anyway, the twelfth mistake I made was accepting the New York City Teaching Fellows' offer, and quitting a job I loved at the Kidz Clubhouse in Milwaukee, Wisconsin (except it's too cold in Milwaukee, way too cold), where I could have fun with kids all day without having to have a 'teaching point'—although my bosses, or at least my bosses' bosses, wanted me to have an 'outcomes logic model'—and I didn't have to carry around a grade book and tell kids to spit out their gun."

"Gum, Mr. Blackwell, gum. We're the relatively gifted and talented students. You're thinking of the duck-assed JDs downstairs in the 'Success Academy.'"

"I *said* 'gum,' didn't I? Anyway, the thirteenth mistake I made was flying to New York to take two tests you have to pass to be a schoolteacher in New York State: the Liberal Arts and Science Test and the Content Specialty Test, and passing both tests, which were really easy, but believe it or not, a lot of teachers fail them, you know, teachers who go to college to be teachers.

Which I don't even get—how anybody can go to college to be a teacher? I mean teaching's something you do when you fail at everything else you try."

"What do you do if you fail at being a teacher, Mr. Blackwell?"

"I'll let you know...Oh wait a minute; I think you write a memoir.

"Now, the fourteenth mistake I made was moving to New York. Wait a minute, I love New York!"

"And, don't lie, Mr. Blackwell, you love us, too. That's the *emmis!*"

They were right.

That was the *emmis*.

I mean, you know, up to a point.

Undisclosed Margins; Or, Starving to Become

I tried writing a first version of this piece in the usual disinterested academic style. I gave up after a few pages and after some thought decided to disclose a little of the undisclosed margins of that first essay. This decision was based on a certain program at least implicit in all feminist activity: the deconstruction of the opposition between the private and the public.

Gayatri Chakravorty Spivak

Now, if in my desire to satisfy my students' curiosity about my past I had wished to be forthcoming to an even greater fault, to the fault, indeed, of approaching full disclosure, if full disclosure, or disclosure of any kind, is possible in the fallen worlds engendered in what Nietzsche called the "prison-house of language" (where, he aphorized, "we find words only for what is already dead in our hearts," an appealingly morose phrase that I had quoted many times to my students, when, in "writers workshop," they despaired at the gulf between what they wanted to say and what they were able to say, a despair I shared; well, maybe my students didn't actually despair, but I did), I might also, while leaning on my aluminum stick and enumerating my mistakes, have read to them an annotated pastiche of the "Why I Want to be a Teacher in a Thousand Words or Less" essay I had sent a year earlier to the New York City Teaching Fellows. The annotation had been included as part of an assignment in "multi-genre" writing, along with a brunch invitation and a parody of the ubiquitous standardized tests that had become, for me, objective correlatives for the utilitarian joylessness of (reformed) public education. The copied, pasted, and retooled assignment had been cobbled together in odd moments when I wasn't working long hours, attending constant meetings, and making great sacrifices. I titled the assignment, "Triptych: 'Starving to Become,'" in homage to a charming mistake one of my students had made when trying to write "striving to become," an admittedly hackneyed phrase that I suggested when the student couldn't think of a way to start an essay I'd assigned the class, in violation of the Great Chain of Being's official edict against writing prompts, which research into best practices of data-driven instruction had exposed, along with textbooks and "direct instruction," as "inauthentic." The triptych had been submitted, in earnest (despite the sarcastic tone), as partial fulfillment of the requirements for a master's degree in English education at the City College of New York, in December of 2004.

If the original essay had not been necessarily altogether truthful in every single detail, the annotated edition would serve as an often self-lacerating corrective.

My longstanding habit of approaching full disclosure—and correcting myself to the point of self-laceration—as a means of partially fulfilling the requirements for various advanced degrees (and, in the process, of cannibalizing previously-submitted partial requirements—"same old soup, they just keep reheating it," the custodian at one of the universities I had attended used to say when you asked him how he was; "same old soup," he'd repeat for emphasis...), had begun approximately fifteen years prior to my writing the "Why I Want to be a Schoolteacher" essay, and sixteen years prior to my annotating it. This was when I was awarded the four-year Biermann Fellowship by the graduate program in Contemporary Critical and Cultural Studies at Milwaukee State University, an NCAA Division II seminary of advanced poststructuralist thought, where I—indolent, posturing, saturnine, dilatory—embarrassed myself, and gave my benefactors cause to regret their largesse, with my mediocre performance and frightened silence in advanced seminar.

If I'd learned to cite Nietzsche in the Contemporary Critical and Cultural Studies program, I'd learned also, in my loneliness and alienation, to cite, if just to myself, because it was kind of embarrassing, some plaintive lines of Joni Mitchell that spoke to my desolation,

> All the people at this party
> They've got a lot of style
> They've got stamps of many countries
> They've got passport smiles...

I played the song, called "People's Parties," from the *Court and Spark* album, over and over on my phonograph in the sad shag-carpeted nineteen-sixties space-age efficiency apartment that I'd rented for $375 a month (utilities included) not far from campus, adjusting the volume to lower and lower decibels each time I played it, in an effort to placate the sullen tool and die man occupying the cell next door. The tool and die man frequently, and often angrily, reminded me (a self-absorbed and privileged graduate student), that he, a working stiff, had to get up early the next morning, just as, years later, when I had joined the ranks of the working class myself and taken a position on an assembly line of my own, sponsored by the neo-Fordists at the New York City Department of Education, I would often find it necessary to ask *my* noisy and self-absorbed neighbors, first on the Lower East Side, and then, less frequently, on the Upper West Side of Manhattan, to turn down the decibels *they* were blasting; by the time I had finally made the inevitable move from the Upper West Side to Park Slope, in cozy brownstone Brooklyn (the type of neighborhood Lena Dunham calls "*Grown-Up* Brooklyn"), where hardworking urban professionals raised their overachieving children in absolute silence (at least on my block), I never had to remind anyone to be a good neighbor again.

The Joni Mitchell song that I pantomimed in front of my bathroom mirror, like countless other lonely little girls in similar situations, spoke to the alienation I felt stumbling about in a milieu of so many smart and stylish people, a coterie of something like the beautiful people: as beautiful, I suppose, as people can be in Milwaukee, Wisconsin. More beautiful, certainly, than I was. And smarter. And more stylish.

My fellow seminarians weren't listening to folksy Joni Mitchell in those days, though; their researches into the abyssal aporias of the postmodern condition required edgier, more up-to-date tunage. The soundtrack to their studies, and to their parties, as I remember it now, was supplied invariably by the Smiths, whose songs were always playing somewhere that year, reverberating in the speakers of home sound systems, and bleating from car radios as we, the seminarians, pretty little Hamlets all, cloaked, *de rigueur*, in black ink, poured ourselves into the hatchback of Tallulah McIlhenny's tiny little red-eyed two-seater coupé, the "Compact Pussycat" I called it, privately, after the pink *Wacky Races* hot rod Penelope Pitstop drove to the finish line on Hanna-Barbera Saturday mornings when I was a television-addled boy.

Thus crammed into the Compact Pussycat, thirty or forty of us at least, like college pranksters of old, we madcap semiologists would light out for some of our favorite slices of old Milwaukee: the Oriental Theater, for instance, a lavish movie palace built in 1927, extravagantly adorned with chandeliers, minarets, and giant statues of the Buddha, with lions, camels, and elephants rampaging everywhere, an archaeological relic miraculously still standing, if chopped (tastefully) into smaller auditoria, to take in a late showing of, say, *Dangerous Liaisons*, or *The Cook, The Thief, His Wife & Her Lover*, unless, of a Thursday night, one of the seminarians was hosting an evening of *Twin Peaks* at her house. The group would stop first, though, in case any reveler had fallen dry, at the Feathered Boa, to wet our whistles with an ironic martini or two (in the days when ordering a martini was considered ironic), or a Rob Roy, pink lady, or Champagne cocktail, and warm up the evening further by plugging some quarters into the vintage Wurlitzer, jammed with Frank and Dean and Sammy, and, my favorite, Miss Peggy Lee, asking the musical question that still haunts, "Is That All There Is?"

After the movie, peckish, and still requiring "atmosphere," we might make our way over the river to Nunzio's for some red-checkered tablecloths, candles in Chianti bottles, old-fashioned antipasto plates, thin-crusted pizza slathered with sweet and piquant red sauce, patted with fresh mozzarella, whipped with lattices of fresh basil, and served up with free-flowing carafes of homemade *vino rosso* that I imagined the pretty waitresses had stomped with their feet.

Sated, for the while, we would stop next at M. Hulot's or the Ostrich Club and dance each other to the end of love, until the lights came up and a final four a.m. sampling of the Spaniels' classic "Goodnite, Sweetheart, Goodnite" blasting over the loudspeakers intimated that the club was closing, and that it was time to go.

The night wasn't dead yet, though. Our next appointment was for a steam and a soak at the hot tub "collective," with saunas and steam rooms, a cold bath, massage tables, and a sensory deprivation tank (yikes!), that had been set up in the basement of an unassuming vinyl-sided duplex years before by some old hippies, and that continued to operate, on a subscription basis, in a location unknown to the general population: "Tantalus' Fleshpot," I called it, where the forthrightly unclothed bodies of all the pretty graduate students who had politely refused my tentative overtures earlier in the evening flashed, in such heartbreaking proximity, before my longing gaze.

Finally, forswearing dawn, and having danced and steamed and soaked up another appetite, one of the freshly laundered *bon vivants* would suggest breakfast, everyone else would agree, and we'd pile back into the Compact Pussycat and head out for the Horn of Plenty Diner, or the Pig and Whistle, and overtax the table in our booth with plate after steaming plate of ironic pigsin-the-blanket, tuna melts, Slim Jims, and Monte Christo sandwiches.

That I had come to be included in such semi-debauched postgraduate revelries, that I had any social life at all, was due solely to the beneficence of the very chic and very sexy Tallulah McIlhenny, who had taken me under her wing. Besides holding keys to the Compact Pussycat and to the secret basement full of hot tubs, Tallulah held keys to myriad other delightful secrets, and secret delights, as well. My entrée, my cicerone, to Milwaukee's *demimonde*, Tallulah was younger than I was by five or six years. (Because I'd finished my bachelor's degree five years later than the class with which I had entered university, I was finding myself, more and more, of statistical necessity, falling in with younger and younger crowds. As will be seen, when I got married, a scarce year after the events described in this chapter, I married a woman ten years younger than me; by the time, approximately fourteen years, and two career changes, after soaking in the hot tub, when I'd made my way uptown to supplicate in the graffiti-carved chair at the B---- and R---- job fair, the crowds, as has been noted, were twenty, and even twenty-five years younger.) Though she was younger than I was, Tallulah took me in tow, as a sort of a protégé.

By temperament gracious, Tallulah had assumed for herself a kind of role of unofficial social secretary/welcome wagon for the Program in Contemporary Critical and Cultural Studies, showing new students and visiting scholars around, taking them in tow, filling them in on the where to go and the what to do, making introductions, and maintaining a kind of fashionable salon in her rooms on Wakefield Street. In this capacity, Tallulah had befriended me early that first semester, when I felt so out of place and afraid I'd be found out, exposed as the *poseur* I knew myself to be. She became my guide to the celestial spheres of the Program in Contemporary Critical and Cultural Studies, and my guide also to the more earthly, and subterranean, realms of the city of Milwaukee, and with every hour that we passed together,

I became more and more attached to her, and my admiration grew.

Oh Tallulah McIlhenny: "Red hair and black leather, my favorite color scheme," as Richard Thompson crooned on a record I also played in those days, over and over, and also in diminishing volume, on my phonograph in the sad, shag-carpeted efficiency on Cambridge Street. Her hair was red (cut in a Louise Brooks bob, with bangs and a little flip at her chin; though I think it was Louise Brooks whose hair was cut in a Tallulah McIlhenny bob) and she wore black leather. She was very tall, but she wasn't "statuesque," if that's what you're thinking. She was, perhaps—what do you call it?—*lissome,* but not skinny like a model. Her figure was graceful, not voluptuous exactly; well, maybe a little voluptuous, but not in the va-va-va-voom mode; well, maybe a little in the va-va-va-voom mode, but lissome, willowy. She had a kind face, and a kind of funny face, roundish in spite of angular features, her smile very close to sardonic, but not quite. Her eyes, which were alive, beckoned, and then they turned away, dismissive, but ironically dismissive. And then they beckoned again. Her wit was mordant, but forgiving. (And mordant.) I never saw her cry. Something Henry Fonda said to Barbara Stanwyck in *The Lady Eve* applied to Tallulah: "You have the darndest way of bumping a fellow down and bouncing him up again." (Barbara Stanwyck had replied, as Tallulah might have, "and then bumping him down again.") Tallulah's fingers were long and elegant, and she used them to help her talk, to help her make her points, and she had many points to make, all fascinating, all surprising and delightful, but her longest and most elegant features were her legs. She had legs like Cyd Charisse had legs. And for the *coup de grace,* Tallulah was brilliant, and, in every way, *knowing.* She knew all about the free floating signifiers of Contemporary Critical and Cultural Studies, and the abyssal aporias, and she knew all the ironic spots for cocktails, the best antipasto plates, all the musicians in all the bands in all the clubs, and all the secret cellars; she knew the where to go, the what to do. Smart and sexy, my favorite color scheme. I was, of course, in love, or thought I was, but what's the difference between being in love and thinking you're in love?

And, after many an evening's revels, always the last to be dropped off, because I lived closest to Tallulah, maybe having gotten a kiss, maybe not, I would climb the stairs to my apartment, fumble for my latchkey (I was most likely a little drunk, or a lot drunk), and upon entering my room flip through my record collection for my Chet Baker LP, the one where Chet sings (heartrendingly). Turning the volume down very low, I'd drop the needle on the track called "I Fall in Love Too Easily," music by Jule Stein, lyrics by Sammy Cahn, and say to myself, softly, "You don't have a chance." Then I'd sing along or, I guess, pantomime along, because I can't sing.

Falling in love too easily had been a habit of mine since I was a kid, and for this reason I'd been a flop with chicks since 1966, when finding myself for the first time in the shadow of young girls in flower, or young girls who'd soon be in flower, I set the pattern that would, it seemed, forever rule my love life: I didn't know how to close the deal, whatever closing the deal might have meant at any particular age. In fact I hated the metaphor "closing the deal" altogether—or, for that matter, any trope grounded in business jargon. (More precisely, it was the tenor of the metaphor that I hated; the vehicle I liked, but I couldn't afford the sticker price.)

With one girl or another, I always *thought* I was going to be liked, or, later, loved, but invariably I managed to queer the deal, to scare the girl away, within grasp of my goal, or close to it.

The first girl I ever liked was called Brenda, but I can't remember her last name. She was cute, serene, and self-possessed, with big black eyes and a slightly Roman-looking nose. She gave me a pear in Vacation Bible School, the perfect gritty sweetness of which I always longed to taste again, and the standard against which I have judged pears all my life. I was five then, and I dreamed of rescuing Brenda from a burning building. But nothing ever caught fire.

Six years later, Vanessa Von Trier held my hand in the back of the bus, where all the cool kids sat, the kids eligible for handholding, on the ride all the way down to Montgomery, on a school field trip to see the First White House of the Confederacy, but after an exhausting day examining the relics of Jefferson Davis, Vanessa, apparently, thought better of her earlier indiscretion, and cuddled up with handsome, turtle-necked Ty Cuthbert for the long ride back to Birmingham, leaving me forlorn and forced to sit in the front of the bus, with the stuttering, the clubfooted, the hydrocephalic, and the polio victims wheezing in their iron lungs. I tried not to cry.

The next year, by applying myself, and combing my hair, and asking my mother to buy me a turtleneck, I had gotten pretty close to going steady with Cheri Chamberlain, a tall and skinny girl from Pennsylvania, who wore bangs I liked (I liked bangs) and a too-flowery fragrance I didn't like, not an A-list girl like Vanessa Von Trier, but presentable, acceptable, better than most of the other girls in the seventh grade, and *mine*, until Dwight Coombs alienated her affections with a series of obvious acts of forced bravado on the athletic field.

By the time I reached the eighth grade, my politics had changed: I'd repudiated Jefferson Davis, for instance, throwing my support to Black Power, and alarming my parents by tacking a poster of Angela Davis on the wall in my bedroom, the famous poster with the clenched fist and resplendent Afro. I scandalized my English teacher that year by writing a favorable book report on *Steal this Book!*, Abbie Hoffman's "manual of survival in the prison that is Amerika," and, late in the year, I led a (largely nonviolent) demonstration down the school corridors in support of Ho Chi Minh and the N.L.F., a demonstration that loudly assailed the principal's complicity in colonialist war against the people of Vietnam.

My most unwavering comrade in my continuing struggles against the imperialist ruling circles at Rutherford B. Hayes Elementary School, and their running dog lackeys, was the sexy and irrepressible Connie Lassiter, the cutest and most popular girl at school. She had surprised me by agreeing, when I finally worked up the courage to ask her, to go as my date to the graduation dance, and I was, for weeks, happier than I'd ever been in my life, except perhaps for the time a few years earlier when I'd gotten Reggie Jackson's autograph at Rickwood Field, when Jackson played for Birmingham's minor league club, before he was called up to the majors.

Connie wasn't cute and popular in the bland consensus-politics way cute and popular girls would, in a few years, be cute and popular in high school. She was beautiful and glamorous and funny as hell and cheeky and irreverent. And smart—unlike most of the girls at school, or the boys, she read books (and not just *Flowers for Algernon*). We were best friends, Connie and I were, always together, united in our determination, having learned the expression in a short study of Voltaire that we'd conducted together, to *ecraser l'infame* at Rutherford B. Hayes Elementary School (and you can only imagine the level of *l'infame* prevalent at Rutherford B. Hayes Elementary School), but moving, in the process, I believed, towards becoming more than just best friends. I was shy, though, and a little traumatized by my sad quasi-amatory experiences with the Vanessa Von Triers and Cheri Chamberlains of years gone by, and, for this reason, slow to make my move.

But the greater hindrance to my realizing my dreams of a more intimate relationship with Connie Lassiter began a few weeks before the dance, when it became clear to me that Connie's outlook on life, her personality, and her priorities were changing. She'd grown, during this period, less and less interested in revolution for the hell of it, and more and more interested in making out with high school boys, especially jocks, apolitical invariably, or even downright reactionary; their politics didn't seem to matter to Connie. She started acting all girly to get these greasers interested in her, and she started hiding how smart she was. Pretty soon she was dating a high school junior called Dirk, who wore long sideburns (I couldn't grow sideburns then, no matter how hard I tried), and a sneer (I couldn't grow a sneer then, either, but I was learning). Dirk played guitar in a band. He was on the football team. He rode a motorcycle. His name was "Dirk."

The night before the dance, Connie called me on the telephone to break off our engagement. She wanted to go stag to the dance. She'd save a dance for me, but she wanted to go stag to the dance, because she wanted to dance with lots of boys. That's the way Connie wanted it, and I shouldn't be so possessive, she told me; in fact, I was being kind of a male chauvinist, and she was surprised. Connie was a different Connie, and everything had changed. We came to the dance separately, and we danced together just once, awkwardly, and everything had changed.

A few weeks after the dance, I went to Washington. Connie's family was poor, and she couldn't afford to go on the class trip to the nation's capital, the trip that threw together all the relatively well-heeled eighth-graders from across the city[2] (for me a kind of consolation prize following the heartbreak of the eighth-grade dance), but Cecily-Anne Bondurant, a popular girl from Sydney Lanier Elementary School—popular in a bland consensus politics kind of way—went on the trip. I didn't even like her, but I kept trying to get her to like me, getting off some very witty remarks at the Smithsonian Institution, at the Ford Theater, at the Bureau of Engraving and Printing, and at the White House, all with the idea of impressing her. Why did I want to impress her? She didn't laugh at any of my jokes, although many other

---

[2] I had a picture of Angela Davis on my wall, but my "dawning consciousness" of race hadn't dawned enough for me to notice that there were no black children on the trip.

eligible eighth graders did, and even some of the chaperones, and she'd never even heard of Abbie Hoffman or Angela Davis. She had a nice figure, though, voluptuous in the va-va-va-voom mode, but she had no charm, no elegance, no glamour, the opposite of Connie, the opposite of Tallulah, but the boys at Sydney Lanier evidently found her fascinating. Va-va-va-voom figures will do that for a girl. I evidently found her fascinating, too, but the whole time I was trying to impress her, I was secretly hating her, and hating myself.

It was in the suite that Cecily-Anne shared with several other girls on the thirteenth floor of the Harrington Hotel, even though they didn't, for superstitious reasons, call it the thirteenth floor, that ten or fifteen boys and girls gathered for a game of spin the bottle the last evening of the trip, as a way to unwind after climbing to the top of the Washington monument earlier that day, and trooping up and down the halls of the Pentagon (where Connie and I, when Connie believed she was going on the trip, had planned some guerilla actions, including an attempt at levitation *a la* Allen Ginsberg). When Cecily-Anne spun the bottle and the bottle stopped spinning and it pointed toward me, my heart started racing and my muscles tightened and I could barely stand when Cecily-Anne and I were called upon by the congregation to go to one of the bedrooms for our seven minutes of heaven. When we closed the door, I stood very close to my would-be partner in forbidden adolescent concupiscence, preparing to pucker up. I flinched, though, and shuddered, when Cecily-Anne looked directly at my eyes (as directly, that is, as she was capable of looking at anything) and uttered coldly, in a bland monotone (except for the last syllable, upon which she raised her pitch slightly), "I won't kiss *you*," and, at that moment, I hated myself for desiring her all the more, for longing to kiss her, and caress her, even though she despised me, and, finding it very, very difficult to get out the words, I reassured her I wouldn't press my advantage, even though, according to Hoyle, I was due an embrace. After a pause of a moment or two, I asked her, fighting back my tears, if she would please wait out the time remaining of our seven minutes, sitting on separate beds, of course, before returning to the orgy proper. Cecily-Anne, who could afford a token of magnanimity, agreed.

~

"Do you want me to tell you what Tallulah says about you? Do you want me to tell you? You'd better have another drink," my concerned friend and fellow graduate student, Azhar al-Shidyaq, said to me, one evening eighteen years or so after the humiliation on the thirteenth floor of the Harrington Hotel, even though they didn't, for superstitious reasons, call it the thirteenth floor. We were drinking brandies at Chez Gaston Monescu, and I was crying my love for Tallulah McIlhenny into my fancy crystal snifter.

"Tallulah says she can count on two people to ring her every day, two people, every day: *you*...and her mother."

I shrank for a moment and then pulled myself together.

"She says you're needy. Girls don't like needy." [A beat.] "You have to take control. I can tell you how to take control. I can tell you how to get Tallulah in bed, but you have to follow my advice."

I didn't have any game—I'd been a flop with chicks since 1966—but Madame Ruth had a plan.

Equally brilliant and almost as beautiful as Tallulah, Azhar was an Alexandrian, of diverse Egyptian, Assyrian, Etruscan, Mycenaean, and Atlantean heritage, and another Biermann Fellow, from two years before, specializing in post-postcolonial discourse. He had broken the hearts of countless girls, and, ecumenical in his affections, countless boys, and he had a reputation for being a bit of a popinjay and a flibbertigibbet. He was known in the department as the *Lufthunde*, or "hovering dog," an allusion to the fantastical ethereal hound in the Kafka story called "Investigations of a Dog." I referred to him, privately, as "a sigh in dancing pumps and silk stockings," an allusion to Heinrich Heine's famous sobriquet for Vincenzo Bellini—but I liked Azhar and defended him when attacks were made, and attacks *were* made; he was not universally liked. (I usually kept quiet, though, when feminists made the attacks, as they often did, because I was studying to be a feminist; also, the feminists in Contemporary Critical and Cultural Studies were *hot*, and I very much wanted to move in their circle.) Like Tallulah, Azhar had befriended me early on that first semester, and had been very kind to me, had even, upon his return from a trip he'd taken with Tallulah to Mississippi, brought me a bough of blossoming crape myrtle, along with the charming observation I have quoted many times over the years that southern accents are "three-dimensional" (Azhar was fascinated with southerners; I was never sure how fascinated he had been with Tallulah, or if she had ever been fascinated with him, and I never asked), and he had a plan to help me win Tallulah over to my way of thinking—a plan that involved using, in some way I couldn't quite dope out, the philosophy, or whatever it is you call it, of the French theorists Gilles Deleuze and Félix Guattari. Azhar, apparently, wanted me, in a kind of applied "nomadology," to "deterritorialize" Tallulah, indeed to "actualize," in a "plane of immanence," her "empty body without organs," which, he elaborated, quoting the big guns, flowed "in all directions, by free intensities or nomadic singularities, by mad or transitory particles"—how or why, or what any of this meant, I couldn't understand. I was hopelessly at sea when it came to Deleuze and Guattari, and, of course, women, and countless other things, but I couldn't even fake a bluff when the conversation turned, as it did more and more that year, to the thousand plateaus of those particular two French darlings.

Continuing his advice to the lovelorn, Miss Lonelyhearts lectured his pupil: "You've got to stop thinking you're going to get Tallulah to like you by being a 'man in feminism' [a sneering reference to the title of a book Tallulah had given me in support of my feminist studies]. You've got to stop sucking up to the feminists in the department. You're acting like an Orpheus seeking quarter from the Bacchantes. They'll tear you to shreds. There'll be nothing left of you except a head floating down the Milwaukee River, singing the verses of 'People's Parties.' Yes, I know about 'People's Parties.' [Another beat.] Women, even feminists—women, especially feminists—don't want to fuck feminists, unless the feminists are lesbians. Women, even feminists—women, especially feminists—want to fuck men. And you've made a perfect woman of yourself. Now listen to my advice. Deleuze says..."

Hip to everybody's tricks, including Azhar's plan to use theory to make a man out of me, Tallulah wasn't so much into Deleuze and Guattari in those days; she often teased Azhar by asking the waiter for an order of Deleuze and Guacamole when the party swung to one of the very good Mexican restaurants on the city's South Side.

One evening, though, the party swung to the North Shore for clams casino, steak Diane, gratin dauphinois, and floating island, at the soigné residence of near-celebrity and Contemporary Critical and Cultural Studies seminarian, Claire Dupray, a Milwaukee native who'd lived in New York for several years, and had been friends with David Johansen, or Richard Hell, or Tom Verlaine, or somebody like that, and had, thus, many fascinating stories to tell of CBGB and the Mudd Club and all the decadence and glamour.

That evening, at table, I was hardly any more charming or witty than I ever was, though, by then, late in that epochal first semester, I'd begun to relax a bit, and I was feeling slightly less socially constrained, able to thrust a little, and even, to some degree, to parry. I hadn't, moreover, in any way that might attract the interest of women, altered my appearance, besides combing my hair and putting on a turtleneck. Nevertheless, that candlelit evening, a wild evening outdoors, with wind blowing falling snow in whirlwinds and eddies before throwing it into piling drifts (and drifting piles), on that wild candlelit evening I was beginning to perceive, or, as I thought at the time, imagine, a change in the way Tallulah looked at me, a change that suggested that she, you know, *liked* me. And I also imagined that Claire was looking at me differently, as well, when she peremptorily took my hand, as if to beat out a rival, when the time came late in the evening to dance an ironic cha cha.

As the evening wore on, and the guests began to express concern about getting home before the storm made drunk driving difficult, I had not been able to figure out how to capitalize on my strange new status as a desirable bachelor. I wasn't even sure that it was anything other than in my head. As everyone was saying their goodnights and making for their rides home, I tried to claim crouching space in the Compact Pussycat, but was overtaken by a swarm of swains and maidens who also lived in Tallulah's neighborhood, and who beat me to my punch. When I caught Tallulah's eye for a second, I thought I saw a hint of disappointment in it, an unspoken epitaph for a moment that had passed. Or was I imagining this, as well? Letting go the dream, I slid into an empty seat in a car driven by another seminarian who lived nearby, a gray sedan, boxy, and equipped with safety features that the Compact Pussycat lacked. I sighed.

When I was let off at the building that housed my sad, shag-carpeted efficiency, I invited another passenger in the gray sedan up for a drink, a passenger called Arthur Redding. Arthur was the other Biermann Fellow that year. He was a tall Texan, only he wasn't a Texan, he was a tall Ohioan, which didn't scan as well; he'd only lived in Texas long enough to take an M.A. there, but everyone kept calling him a Texan, anyway, a tall Texan, because he was tall, almost as tall as Tallulah. (Tallulah was a tall Louisianan.) Arthur and I shared a small office reserved for Biermann Fellows, an office with a splendid view of the lake, on the ninth floor of Tamblyn Hall, a sterile promontory built in the alienating architectural style known as campus brutalism that seemed always to house the Schools of Arts and Letters, and, later, the Schools of Education, at each of the countless non-elite urban universities that I attended for so many years—the Humanities Building at the University of Alabama at Birmingham, where I had taken my B.A., and almost an M.A.; Tamblyn Hall, and, later, Comstock Hall at Milwaukee State; and, finally, the nadir of campus brutalism, or its zenith, depending on the depravity of your architectural predilections, the North Academic Center (the NAC, or as I called it, the 'NAM) at the otherwise charmingly gothic revival City College. It was by smoking cigarettes in our office on the ninth floor of Tamblyn Hall, in the days when one smoked cigarettes in offices, talking books and politics, in the days when one talked books and politics, and going out for a beer afterwards, in the days when one went out for a beer afterwards, that Arthur and I became friends.

Arthur and I had shared a taxi ride to the departmental Halloween party with Tallulah earlier in the season. He was dressed as Hamlet, but with his doublet braced. Tallulah wore the sequined gown, sash, tiara, and architectonically tall bouffant of Miss Mississippi of 1963. She looked fabulous. I was dressed in a hired cow costume. It's hard to dance in a hired cow costume.

I was getting nowhere fast with Tallulah that night, but fast, and my heart was falling out of my how now brown cow. Arthur, who had been my confidante in *l'affaire* Tallulah from the beginning, had managed to convince me, for a moment, that there were other beauty queens in the sea, and, having ditched my cow's head, I danced with Lizzie Borden, the Whore of Babylon, Mata Hari, and Little Red Riding Hood, even making a date with Little Red, at Arthur's urging, but as I danced I closed my eyes and dreamed of Miss Mississippi of 1963. Arthur, seeing how badly I had it for Tallulah, went the day after the dance to speak with her on my behalf, to plead my case, but he was too gallant to reveal very much of the conversation that had passed between them. He didn't have to, of course. I knew.

As we drank Jack Daniel's from highball glasses, because I

didn't have any old fashioned glasses, I told Arthur about the feeling I'd had at the party at Claire's, the feeling that Tallulah was looking at me in a new way, the feeling she was flirting with me. Arthur said he hadn't noticed anything, but wouldn't discount the possibility. Just then we were startled by the sound of something hitting the window. And, before we could get up from our chairs, we heard the sound again. When we opened the curtains and looked out into the parking lot, we saw Tallulah McIlhenny throwing snowballs. When she saw that she'd gotten our attention, she pointed toward the front of the building, gesturing to be let in. The front door was locked, and there were no doorbells or intercoms, and there were no cell phones back then. I went down to let her in.

It wasn't more than twenty minutes following Tallulah's arrival before Arthur understood that he had to leave. I didn't understand it myself, but immediately upon Arthur's departure, Tallulah and I were on the bed, undressing each other. They were feminists, these Contemporary Critical and Cultural Studies girls were, but they seemed in those days to outfit themselves in the garments and accessories from history that symbolize the oppression of women—they bound their feet in tight little half-boots with a thousand buckles and trussed up their torsos in elaborate lingerie that suggested whalebone corsets (but sexy whalebone corsets). After some struggle, Tallulah managed to get her shoes off unaided, but I was intent on removing her complicated underwear myself. I never got all of it off, but succeeded, after some effort, in getting enough of it off to...

A half-hour or so later, Tallulah took her clothes and shoes with her into the bathroom. When she emerged, she was dressed and reaching for her hat, coat, and gloves. I had assumed she'd stay the night with me, that I'd cook breakfast the next morning and then we'd spend the day together. I wanted to cuddle.

Of course I begged her to stay. She was polite but firm. I begged her some more. On her way out she gave me a kiss and said goodnight. It was clear from the way she said it, from the tone in her voice and the way she looked at me, that the thing that had just happened would not happen again, that there would be no, you know, *relationship*. I should have known that, though; I shouldn't have misunderstood.

After she left, I put a record on the phonograph in my sad, shag-carpeted efficiency, but this time I played it loud, and I didn't care what time the tool and die man had to get up the next morning.

What the hell is a "tool and die" man anyway?

The record I put on the phonograph was by the Smiths, and the song I played was called, "Last Night I Dreamt That Somebody Loved Me."

In the meanwhile the semester was nearing its end and the thirty-page seminar papers were coming due, and in my own attempt to deconstruct the famous opposition between the public and the private, and desperate for any material with which to pad the ten or fifteen "scholarly" pages per course I was actually capable of producing, I found myself, as the clock ticked the deadline down, disclosing undisclosed margins with a vengeance, in the process conflating my frustrations as a lover and a scholar, and tucking my heartache (along with my certain knowledge that I was a fraud) into the interstices of the papers I somehow managed to turn in, without taking any incompletes.

One yellowing still-extent seminar paper is preserved in the Blackwell Archive; entitled "'Enter Segismundo, Clothed in Skins': The Feral as a Discourse of Modernity," it serves as a (pretentious and juvenile) model of conflating frustrations and tucking one's heartache (and sense of fraudulence) in the interstices. Inspired by a quick glance at Carl Schorske's essay "Politics and Patricide in Freud's *Interpretation of Dreams*," along with an actual reading of Pedro Calderon de la Barca's seventeenth-century play *Life is a Dream* (a second-hand copy of which I had recently purchased at a thrift shop, and had picked up distractedly while procrastinating getting down to work on the papers coming due) and a few case histories of Freud, which, along with the Schorske, had actually been assigned, and a recent late night viewing of a late, late showing on UHF Channel 58 of *The Third Man* (with poor reception, lots of snow, and problems with the vertical hold), the paper, finished minutes before the deadline struck for slipping it under the professor's office door after discovering there was no more room in his mailbox, begins with an exasperatingly self-referential disquisition on the colon that separates the two clauses in the title of the paper, and segues to the scenery-chewing entrance, at the public/private deconstruction site, of my younger, "scholarly" self:

Note the punctuation puncturing the title: that (spastic) colon, those two dots, one piled on top of the other, (primal) scene and sign (in mathematics) of peremptory, benign ratiocination. Basilio, King of Poland: "You know...that the science I most study and esteem is subtle mathematics, by which I steal from time" (Calderon 96).

Those two dots collaborate to subordinate Calderon's poetic license to the scholarly license to carry a gun, a sub-title dis-entitling a title. They collaborate to subordinate Eros to Thanatos, I find myself tempted to say. "Here the nursemaid supervenes, a cold shadow driving away what I loved" (Benjamin, "Berlin" 4). And,

He [the Wolf-Man]...began to play with his member in his Nanya's [the nursemaid's] presence, and this, like so many other instances in which children do not conceal their onanism, must be regarded as an attempt at seduction. His Nanya disillusioned

> him; she made a serious face, and explained
> that that wasn't good: children who did
> that, she added, got a "wound" in the
> place. (Freud, Three Case Histories 207)

Enter me—hirsute me, Mommy-Daddy-me, clothed in
hair shirt—an hysteric on the analyst's couch, a
schizophrenic out for a walk, Holly Martins
(Harry Lime) at the Prater on the Riesenrad. (But
I anticipate the "argument.")

After several more pages of this sort of thing, and the sketchy development of something like a thesis, the narrative is interrupted by the italicized words of a fictionalized Carl Schorske (except the passage is underlined, because I was typing it on a typewriter), acting as my critic and analyst, who takes it upon himself to disclose some further undisclosed margins in my text. Schorske writes, in a clever—I'll admit I thought at the time—portmanteau of his own words and those of mine that I had packed in his nib:

> Imagine St. Augustine weaving his Confessions
> into The City of God, or Rousseau integrating his
> Confessions as a subliminal plot into The Origins
> of Inequality: such is the procedure of Blackwell
> in "'Enter Segismundo, Clothed in Skins': The Fe-
> ral as a Discourse of Modernity."
> His alleged "diffidence" notwithstanding,
> Blackwell, like the Wolf-Man with whom he rather
> self-indulgently identifies ("Enter me—hirsute[3]
> me," emphasis mine), indeed plays with his member
> in his nursemaid's presence—in an attempt, also
> like the Wolf-Man's, at seduction ("Enter me—hir-
> sute me," emphasis mine). The "wound" he fears?

---

[3] I had very long hair and wore a bushy beard at the time of writing.

Bad marks.

Ostensibly an exploration of "the feral as a discourse of modernity," "Enter Segismundo" is best understood as a rather transparent allegory documenting Blackwell's anxieties and feelings of inadequacy vis-à-vis a disquieting apprehension of the increasing unlikelihood that he will succeed in the profession he's chosen for himself—which he irrationally associates with violence ("the scholarly license to carry a gun") and with the Death Instinct ("they [the two dots that together form the colon conventionally used in academic discourse to join the title and subtitle of a scholarly article] collaborate to subordinate Eros to Thanatos").

The manifest content of Blackwell's "excursus" is less easy to discern, and must be reconstructed from largely illegible notes.

Plainly obsessed with substitution, Blackwell apparently seeks to play out all the possibilities implicit in the Oedipal triad (which, in deference to the fashionable Deleuze and Guattari, the French darlings all the seminarians in the Contemporary Critical and Cultural Studies program are reading this year, he calls "Mommy-Daddy-Me"), as articulated in an intertextual space of his own weird devising, an intertextual space that includes the following "signifiers," or dramatis personae:

- Dr. Sigmund Freud, the Father of Psycho-Analysis
- The Wolf-Man, storied analysand
- Segismundo, protagonist of Calderon's Life is a Dream (significantly, "Segismundo" is cognate with "Sigmund": the name of the Father)

- Basilio, Segismundo's father, the King of Poland, with whom Segismundo is locked in Oedipal conflict
- Walter Benjamin, a walker in the city
- Nanya, the Wolf-Man's nursemaid
- Walter Benjamin's unnamed nursemaid
- Clotaldo, Segismundo's nursemaid (sort of)
- "I," a grammatical fiction
- "me," hirsute in hair shirt
- "Blackwell"
- Carl E. Schorske, American cultural historian
- Holly Martins, played by Joseph Cotton in The Third Man, innocent abroad and "hack writer who drinks too much and falls in love with girls"
- Harry Lime, Holly Martins' "friend," beyond good and evil, charmer, played by Orson Welles
- Karo, a beautiful young woman Blackwell met in Vienna who had a buzz cut and wore leopard skin pants and combat boots

"I longed to take a stroll through the Prater, a schizophrenic out for a walk," Blackwell muses, before he encounters all of his personae.

He continues, "I'd spent a few weeks in Vienna, in the early nineteen-eighties, mainly in the company of a beautiful young woman with a buzz cut who wore leopard skin pants and combat boots, and who took strange drugs I'd never heard of and strange, blurry photographs she exhibited in strange, blurry galleries.

"Her name was Karo, and she showed me the city, or at least its demimonde. She thought I was pretty square, but she seemed to like me anyway, at least as a companion. I could never convince her to go to bed with me—having been a flop with chicks since 1966—even though I'd assumed punk rock girls were easy.

"I'd met her at a cinema on the Ringstrasse where The Third Man was playing. I don't think she'd ever read Freud. 'My name,' I told her, 'is Holly Martins, a hack writer who drinks too much and falls in love with girls.'

"My name is Chip Blackwell, a hack writer who drinks too much and falls in love with girls. The abyssal world of academia in which I find myself struggling today reminds me of post-war Vienna, fascinating, shifting, shadowy; and everything looking like it has just rained…"

(My professor returned the essay unmarked, having written on its cover page, "Exit the professor, shaven…An interesting performance, though of course I find myself agreeing with Schorske's assessment.")

ॐ

I often thought of myself as an innocent abroad, or, I suppose more accurately, a chucklehead abroad, whether in Vienna or in the Program in Contemporary Critical and Cultural Studies, but at the same time I always felt guilty—I was a guilty innocent abroad—as if I'd committed a crime I couldn't remember; I was, moreover, a criminal/student who had never really gotten my lessons, who'd faked my way through charm school, leaving along the way a few scattered interesting performances. I'd always admitted that I was a dilettante, of course (which is why I had majored in English in the first place, not knowing then that English, that "literary studies," was a profession…that it was a career…that it was *serious*, thinking instead that it was a haven for dilettantes, which it is, of course, but there are dilettantes and there are dilettantes). Fumbling all over the place, with a forged passport smile, attempting to fake my way through the free-floating signifiers and abyssal aporias of French theory, I felt sometimes a little less like Holly Martins, and more like that not-so-innocent-abroad, Tom Ripley, from *The Talented Mr. Ripley*, a "rediscovered" novel all the seminarians were reading that year. Dressed in Dickie Greenleaf's clothes (or, I suppose, Azhar al-Shidyaq's), with Dickie's (Azhar's) passport in my pocketbook after I'd bopped him over the head with an oar, always a Freddie-Miles-knocking-on-the-door away from being found out (and there were a couple of Freddies in the department), I, unlike Ripley, *was* found out, and sooner rather than later, before anyone had to be murdered, approximately a quarter of the way through my first semester.

I scored a few small successes very early that first semester, when assignments consisted of weekly one to two page responses, before the thirty-page seminar papers came due, and before my professors had come to understand that my initial silence in class would prove to be run of the play. (Once, in a sad jest on the departmental role I'd assumed, the role of shrinking violet, I included the following line from Rene Char as an epigraph to one of my one to two page responses: "No bird has the heart to sing in a thicket of questions.") I was not a long-distance runner; I had my forte in the fifty-yard dash. And because the fellowship required no teaching the first year, or any other duties, for that matter, I had the leisure to spend up to ten hours at a go burnishing my brittle little well-wrought urns.

What was it Nabokov said? "You can always count on a murderer for a fancy prose style."

Eventually, though, the thirty-page seminar papers came due. Wrought up and near-prostrate as the deadlines approached, brittle myself by then, Blanche Dubois sending someone down to the student union to buy her a lemon Coke with chipped ice, I could rally only enough trenchancy to throw together slap-dash cut-and-paste jobs. Time-consuming in their own right, because I was still hunting and pecking my papers out on a beat-up old Smith-Corona, these mingle-mangles of past performances were, to a small degree, and then only partially, admired for the "verve penetrating the curlicues of fatigue, once you get past the easier ironies," as one professor had noted in the margins of one of them, before chastening me for reheating the soup (and larding the thing with a comic bit from one of the sample essays I had sent up to Contemporary Critical and Cultural Studies when applying for the Biermann), for trying to fake my way through Lacan, and for fading in and out of MLA Stylebook style, like a poor player who can't keep up the foreign accent called for in the script.

I would refine my slapdash technique, though, five or six years later, when, after reinventing myself as a youth worker, as an "education director," I made another go at earning an advanced degree, this time successfully, after two failures in a row, in the (frankly, much easier) Social and Cultural Contexts for Education department at Milwaukee State, where a small enclave of aging radicals who had once, in the heyday, hosted gun-toting Black Panthers as revolutionaries-in-residence, and were settling now into their emeritus years, provided "grassroots educators" from the community a forum in which to take a master's degree, sometimes to get a better spot at the non-profits where they worked, but more often just to get together with other grassroots educators and exchange ideas (or, perhaps, as in my case, to prove they could earn an advanced degree).

There were no free floating signifiers of French theory in the less rigorous Social and Cultural Contexts for Education program, and when I tried to float them, I was met with some (usually tolerant) resistance from my professors, and blank stares from the grassroots educators. If I thought I was too dumb for Contemporary Critical and Cultural Studies, I sometimes (guiltily) felt I was too smart for Social and Cultural Contexts for Education, but I liked the students and I liked the teachers. By the time I came to pursue a graduate degree in the teacher's training course at the City College of New York—where approximately seventy years earlier, Trotskyists and Stalinists, taking their lunch in separate alcoves of the dining hall in the cramped basement of Shephard Hall, had once loudly and aggressively argued, across the corridor, the finer points of the popular front, the Moscow trials, and the Soviet-Nazi Nonaggression Pact, but where, by the time I attended the school, education majors, not a very lively bunch, and all of the same tendency, because everyone wanted, above all, to be "on the same page," quietly and respectfully discussed the relative merits of summative versus formative assessment, hunkering over Frappacinos™ near the Starbucks® cart by the escalators that never worked, in the mezzanine (Bunker One, I called it) at the North Academic Center—I'd grown perhaps too smug in my conviction that I was too fancy for normal school, but it was at City College that I wrote the last of my mingle-mangles, or, I should say, the last mingle-mangle I would write for college credit.

Whether pursuing advanced degrees in literary studies, or critical and cultural studies, or social and cultural contexts, or in English education, at any of the non-elite urban universities where I tended to take my tuition, I had always really only wanted be a writer, but I lacked self-confidence and didn't know how to get started. I had taken classes, and pursued advanced degrees, at least until I started pursuing the partially-subsidized degree in English Education at the City College of New York, my first experience going to school for practical, mercenary, or career reasons (and for me "practical," "mercenary," and "career" all meant the same thing), solely because I needed writing prompts, as much as my own students needed them, and I needed deadlines, even if they did cause me fainting fits. Hanging fire against growing up and punching a clock or filling out a timesheet, or, even more scary, trying to figure out how to make a living as a writer, I had taken nine years to finish my bachelor's degree, signing up for any class I was interested in, paying no attention to prerequisites or degree requirements, taking half a year off to travel in Europe, and at least another two or three, if you add it all up, of just kind of lying in bed in my underwear smoking cigarettes, dropping classes when my hypos got the upper hand of me, as they often did (I had always suffered a frequently debilitating color wheel of depression—blue funks, brown studies, and mean reds), and ultimately graduating with more credits than I needed to graduate. When I graduated, I went into one, and then another, graduate school, where I hung fire for another four years. And, compensating for a kind of hereditary accidie combined, when I finally got to work, with an incapacity for sustained argument, I developed and refined my slap-dash mingle-mangles, building them more and more around the composition books I'd filled with pithy sayings and assorted *bon mots* that I had always collected, stringing them together, either by quoting them directly as epigraphs, or by deploying them in the body of my essays, in the form of machine gun sprays of literary (and sub-literary) allusion.

I had always scrawled down any potential epigraph, any writerly bit of business, any "beautiful language" (as the "literacy coaches" in the English Language Arts department at the gothic revival ghost ship docked in Inwood called it), that instructed or delighted, from any book I was reading, any film I saw, or any song I heard, in the beginning onto scraps of paper that I stuffed in various pockets of the blue jeans, denim jackets, and flannel shirts I wore (those were the days before the Moleskines, and the blazers and Oxfords and khakis) and later in the Macguffin I carried in my pocket. Compounding, or attenuating, my weakness for the quotable quote was a generational preference for the "fractured fairy tale," the *MAD* magazine parody, and the *Classics Illustrated* adaptation to the real thing. I liked it funny, and I liked it funny in a half an hour, and then something else funny. That's the way I wanted to write. I wanted it funny, but I wanted some heartbreak in it, too, like in Francois Truffaut's *Shoot the Piano Player*. Truffaut had said about the movie that his goal was to make women laugh and men cry (or maybe he said it the other way around, but I like it better the way I said it). That's what I had in mind in December of 2004, when, starving to become, I cobbled together my multi-genre triptych, in partial fulfillment of the requirements for a master's degree in English education at the City College of New York, and that's what I had in mind two months shy of four years later, when, still starving, I began the struggle to cobble together a multi-genre memoir, with neither triptych nor memoir necessarily altogether truthful in every single detail, but still somehow, I believed, something like the *emmis*.

I mean, you know, up to a point:

TRIPTYCH: STARVING TO BECOME

The following multi-genre triptych, submitted in partial fulfillment of requirements for Professor Herman Jarvis's "Teaching Writing" course at the City College of New York, explores some ramifications, implications, and side effects that resulted when I came to New York City to be a schoolteacher. Genres employed include (annotated) statement of purpose, invitation, and standardized test...

I. ANNOTATED STATEMENT OF PURPOSE

Fourteen years ago, unsatisfied with graduate studies in English *I lost my Biermann Fellowship and had to drop out of the Contemporary Critical and Cultural Studies program. I lost the fellowship because it was discovered I hadn't completed my M.A. at UAB. I hadn't completed the M.A. because I'd failed my comprehensive examinations* and having second thoughts about pursuing an academic career in a diminishing market *It was more than having second thoughts: I knew I'd never finish my Ph.D. because the program coordinators would insist on a qualifying examination and a dissertation and a dissertation defense and some evidence—any evidence—that I was or ever could be a scholar.* All of this was moot anyway, of course, because I *had lost my funding* I accepted a short-term position as a community teacher at the Lourdes Valdez Education Center, an alternative high school located in an economically-distressed (and crime, drug, and gang-besieged) central city neighborhood in Milwaukee, Wisconsin. *No other career choices were available to me; it was either Lourdes Valdez or keep working at the Chili Bowl Restaurant, where my wife, girlfriend then, had gotten me a job. As far as crime, drug, and gang-besieged-ness goes, I'm sexing things up here, trying to make myself sound heroic and self-sacrificing, a (white) dogooder risking my life rushing nobly into the "central city" to rescue poor little (black and brown) children from anomie and urban blight. Also, the neighborhood, while iffy, wasn't really "besieged," not exactly* When I reported to work at Lourdes Valdez *Lourdes Valdez, the school's founder, by the way, had been assassinated on the steps of the school (which of course had a different name at the time), two weeks after it opened (well, maybe the neighborhood was, after all, a little besieged), by former Young Lord, and rival for city funding, Salvador Velazquez; this happened a few years before I started working there. Velazquez is now serving a life sentence at the federal penitentiary in Green Bay. Students of mine, confusing the principal of the school, Fernando Velazquez, with Salvador Velazquez, assumed that Fernando Velazquez had gunned down Lourdes Valdez in order to secure his position as principal. Not an unreasonable assumption if one takes the long view of history, or the short view* I had no previous teaching experience other than a year and a half as a graduate teaching assistant at the University of Alabama at Birmingham *I gave all of my students "A's," and sometimes, if I didn't like them so much, "B's." I was accused of diluting standards by the director of composition and rhetoric, who each semester published a mimeographed list— those were the days of mimeograph machines—of the "easy graders." I thought I was hot shit giving away all those "A's," an anarchist abolishing the money system, but I wonder now just how bad a teacher was*

I? I was well-liked by my students, though, which is all I really cared about where I taught freshman composition and developmental writing courses. *Actually, I only taught composition classes. I thought the Teaching Fellows would appreciate my having experience teaching "developmental" students. "Developmental" is a euphemism for "remedial," which is itself a euphemism for something else* I had taken no education classes in college *I was too fancy to take education classes at college* and no on-the-job training was offered at Lourdes Valdez. *Not entirely true. Martin O'Brien, a veteran teacher in alternative schools who had gotten me the job at Lourdes Valdez, taught me as many of the tricks of the trade as I was willing or able to learn.*

Deciding to swim rather than sink *See item 2, "Standardized Test," below* I plunged head-first into the work. *I also started drinking heavily at this time, plunging head-first into bottles of J&B, Jameson, and Jack Daniel's* Despite flailing around a bit at first, and gasping for air sometimes *lots of flailing, lots of gasping* I registered several solid accomplishments *look out, here it comes*: while teaching English, social studies, math, and science, I developed a *blah blah blah*, helped my students start a *blah blah blah*, and research and compile a *blah blah blah (I started all of these blah blah blahs, but didn't finish any of them).*

As often happens in the kind of narrative I am now relating, my short-term position at Lourdes Valdez, initially intended as a stop-gap measure while I assessed my career goals, expanded to two years. *I was stuck, and couldn't do any better; I had no "career goals" to "assess"* The experience—difficult, challenging, frustrating, heartbreaking, deeply rewarding, and personally fulfilling—really did change my life. *I threw up every morning before I went to work, and started drinking every day when I got home, which I suppose was a change* Fourteen years later, I still earn my living providing educational support for *blah blah blah euphemism* and *blah blah blah platitude.*

For the past twelve years I have worked in the field of community education at three nonprofit youth-serving agencies. I served for seven years as Education Director at the Hogarth Street YMCA, where I *blah blah blahed* and *blah blah blahed...*

I then served for three years as *fancy made-up title* at CSS Children and Family Centers, formerly Children's Settlement Service. At CSS *I blah blah blahed*, secured *blah blah blahs*, helped disadvantaged *blah blah blahs blah blah blah*, and designed effective *blah blah blahs give me the fellowship.*

I am currently employed as Director of *Important Sounding Blah Blah Blah* at the Ranald and Lilias Fairbairn Kidz Clubhouse, which shares a building and program space with a public school, the Devereux P. Woodruff Year Round School (K-8). The Fairbairn Clubhouse and the Woodruff School collaborate to provide a variety of cultural, educational, and recreational programs for children and families who reside in Milwaukee's low-income Woodruff Park neighborhood. For the past three years I have worked closely with school staff *See item 5, "Standardized Test," below* to provide programs that *blah blah blah, blah blah blah,* and *blah blah blah.*

These very successful programs, which now serve as a national model for other Kidz Clubhouses pursuing partnerships with public schools *Gross hyperbole: Visitors from two or three Kidz Clubhouses located in a neighboring state were given a tour of the facilities and I gave them a little talk about the things I was doing and got some scattered applause* include, among other *blah blah blahs*, a reading skills program that increased student reading skills by an average of *blah blah blah* per *blah blah blah*, as measured by *blah blah blah: i.e., cooking the books, putting a thumb on the scale, "creaming" participation (Note: "creaming" is social service jargon for serving a select client base in order to achieve desired results), etc.*

Despite my longstanding commitment to the field of community education, I have reached a point in my career in which classroom teaching as a certified teacher in an urban public school is what is most appealing to me. *(Most appalling to me!) The thing that was really most appealing to me was moving to New York. But then, on the other hand, I really did sort of believe, at the time, that I wanted to be a public schoolteacher, that I really could be a public schoolteacher, a good one, even, or I think I did. I must have known I'd be miserable teaching in a public school, that I would be awful at it, and very unhappy trying, but I decided to roll the dice anyway. I was feeling lucky. I was feeling hopeful* I have examined alternative certification programs in Milwaukee, and decided they aren't for me. *Because I wanted to move to New York; it's bad enough being a public schoolteacher in New York City, but no way would I have wanted to be a public schoolteacher in Milwaukee, Wisconsin. For one thing, I would have had to take a cut in pay...* On a recent trip to New York, a city I love and visit often and have always wanted to live in, I saw a subway ad for the New York City Teaching Fellowship, did some research, thought a lot about it, and decided to apply.

My desire to teach in a New York City public school is carefully-considered, sincere, and enthusiastic. *Not very carefully considered, possibly sincere, and I am not by temperament enthusiastic* I believe I can apply my experience in community education to ensure high academic *blah blah blah* for my students in a high-needs school. *Could I really have ever believed that?*

I don't know...

II. INVITATION

(Written to members of my Fellow Advisory Group, 8CC3, with whom I had completed my "pre-service training," and to my Fellow Advisor, Sebastian)

Dear 8CC3 and Sebastian,

Hello. Is anybody out there? Does anyone else miss the lazy, hazy, crazy days of summer, our halcyon salad days, when we were young and beautiful (well, you guys were young and beautiful), champing at the bit, full of beans, untried, idealistic firebrands, the world our oyster, our whole lives ahead of us, full of promise, before things got dark and bureaucratic and early to bed and early to rise, and we started saying things to kids that we promised our now-forgotten childhood selves we would never say when we grew up? Or maybe it's just me. *(Note: It was just me.)*

Anyway I miss you all, and invite you to brunch this Saturday morning at Kate's Joint, 4th Street and Avenue B, circa 11:30 a.m. It's a vegetarian diner, casual and large enough to accommodate as many of us as can make it. They don't serve oysters, but you can get salads or beans and braised halcyon, or, better, the brunch special for $8.95—omelets, tofu scrambles, etc., and coffee, tea, Bloody Marys, Mimosas, etc. I eat there almost every Saturday morning and order the tofu version of the Kate Benedict with vegan Hollandaise sauce. Then I linger over bottomless cups of coffee, but they don't have espressos or lattes, which is kind of a drag, asking my tired, depressed middle-aged self why in hell I had to go and do some fool thing like jot down the NYCTF web address Thanksgiving before last while riding the 1 train (or was it the 9 train?) to Lincoln Center to see an opera on an innocent little holiday I took in New York just because my mother-in-law was coming to Milwaukee for a visit.

Or, sometimes at Kate's I mark student essays, and laugh in delight at some of the wonderful things my students write, things like the following; written by Amaryllis Suarez, age 11:

> Recently, I made a coat of arms for myself. On this coat of arms I wrote about my motto. I wrote about what I'm starving to become, and about the people I admire. When you read this you will find out why my motto is my motto. Why I'm starving to become what I'm starving to become. And why I admire the people I admire. Read on and all your questions will be answered. You will find out a little more about me. it will be a journey through part of my life. Even my future. You will find out fasenating things about me. I'll make shore that I make it interesting. My life is a mission, not yet finnished, but just starting. When you read this you will feel like your in my

shoes. As I said you will go on a journey through my past and soon to be future. So enjoy yourself while you read this essay. And know I proceed. Read on. Read till the end. Read and imagen. Read and experience. Read and learn. Read part of my life. Read and love it. Read and enjoy!

And read and enjoy I did.

(I also read and enjoyed, on a sadder note, lingering on the same occasion at my table at Kate's Joint, another student memoir, this one written by Amaryllis's classmate, Juan Diego Solos, about when he was a boy in the Dominican Republic, and his grandmother gave his puppies away. I believe that the concluding sentences of Juan Diego's essay contain, in thirty-five elegant syllables, all the sadness of the world, "The man in the overalls put my puppies in a cage in the back of his truck. He drove away. I knew then that I would never have a good life.")

Whatever you're starving to become (and whether or not you're having a good life—but I hope you are), you can take the F train to 2nd Avenue, the N/R/W to 8th Street, the Green Line to Astor Place or Bleecker Street, or probably some other trains I haven't thought of to some other stations I also haven't thought of, if you want to meet me for brunch. No need to RSVP but RSVP if you so desire. As I said, I go to Kate's Joint every Saturday anyway. Oh yeah, I forgot to tell you about the non-dairy cheesecake. It's very good.

Love and Kisses,
Charles

III. STANDARDIZED TEST

1. When Charles Blackwell accepted a short-term position as a community teacher at the Lourdes Valdez Education Center, he did so because

    A. he felt a strong urge to help children in need

    B. he thought people would respect him if he did something important and high-minded like teach in a "hard-to-staff," "high-needs" school

    C. he was desperate and had no other choices

    D. he had seen too many movies like *Blackboard Jungle* and *To Sir With Love*

2. "Deciding to swim rather than sink, I plunged head-first into the work..." is an example of

    A. a cliché

    B. self-aggrandizement

    C. alliteration

    D. all of the above, and, moreover, that's a pretty easy decision—to swim rather than sink

3. When Blackwell left his job at Hogarth Street after working there for seven years he

    A. took a $7,000 a year pay cut

    B. felt guilty for abandoning the children he knew

    C. had high hopes for his new job at CSS

    D. stole a TV and some office supplies

4. When Blackwell taught adult education classes at Hogarth Street, he

    A. rationalized his low success rate by arguing that he worked with adults with the lowest skills and the greatest problems, the ones who "fell through the cracks" at larger institutions staffed by trained professionals

    B. sometimes falsified official reports so students who had missed class could keep their welfare benefits or avoid breaking the terms of their parole and go back to jail

    C. learned a lot about the lives poor people live

    D. enjoyed many pleasurable hours of warm camaraderie

5. Examples of how Blackwell worked closely with school staff to provide programs that increase the academic skills and enhance the self-esteem of students when he worked at the Fairbairn Kidz Clubhouse include

    A. shouting matches with school staff

    B. misrepresenting numbers of students served in reports he wrote to funders

    C. sucking up to staff members he didn't really like

    D. covering for incompetent teachers who were his allies

GO TO THE FOLLOWING PAGE

6. How did Blackwell pay his tuition while pursuing his Master of Science in Social and Cultural Contexts for Education?

    A. His employers paid it

    B. Student loans

    C. Tuition is free in a democratic society

    D. Cash advances from his credit card

7. Why did Blackwell apply for and accept a position as a New York City Teaching Fellow?

    A. He wanted summers off

    B. He wanted to move to New York City

    C. He did it as a lark

    D. He thought he might be a good teacher

8. Why does Blackwell miss the summer pre-service training?

    A. The weather was nice

    B. He spent a lot of time with interesting and attractive young people

    C. He ate a lot of beans and salad

    D. He hadn't yet realized that he had made a terrible mistake that would make him very unhappy and fill him with regret

9. What role did Blackwell's mother-in-law play in his becoming a New York City Teaching Fellow?

    A. She suggested he apply

    B. She came for a visit to Milwaukee and, to avoid seeing her, Blackwell took a week-long vacation in New York, where he saw an ad for the Fellows

    C. She created the New York City Teaching Fellows because she was concerned about the shortage of schoolteachers in New York City

    D. None of the above

10. Blackwell is starving to become

    A. A teacher

    B. A writer

    C. Somebody else

    D. A grown man

STOP

Sad, Slight, Useless Things

The beauty of the world which is so soon to perish, has two edges,
one of laughter, one of anguish, cutting the heart asunder.

Virginia Woolf

On June 10, 2004, approximately nine months after writing my
"Why I Want to Be a New York City Public Schoolteacher in a
Thousand Words or Less" essay, and six months before annotating it, I wrote myself a letter, which is to say an e-mail, that consisted of a clearing out of Milwaukee and heading to New York
to-do list. It also included an inventory of household possessions
to be moved to a self-storage facility in Clinton, New Jersey,
where they would be stored until my wife and I could secure an
apartment in Manhattan. Any item that didn't make the list
would have to go. This was before I was "Charles" Blackwell.
This was before I was "Mr." Blackwell. This was when I was *Chip*
Blackwell. This was when everyone I knew, even children—especially children!—called me "Chip," and nobody, child or
adult, called me "Charles," and especially not "Mr. Blackwell,"
except maybe telemarketers and headwaiters.

I had a week or so earlier introduced myself as Charles Blackwell, when I clutched a student carved and graffitied desk at the
job fair at B---- and R---- High School in Harlem, New York City,
but I was Chip Blackwell on June 10, 2004, when I wrote myself
a letter, sitting at my own desk in Milwaukee, Wisconsin, at a
time when I could still afford enough floor space to

accommodate a desk, which was situated in my study, painted brown (as a joke, in homage to the brown studies into which I tended to drift), at a time when I could still afford a separate study (and before my brown studies—and blue funks and mean reds—had come to require medical intervention), on the second floor of a modest frame house on Newhall Street, situated in the Lake Bluff district of Milwaukee, near the bike trail, in a friendly, progressive-leaning almost bourgeois enclave of bungalows and frame houses and old Volvo station wagons from the decade before. The modest frame house, front-gabled, sporting a charming gambrel roof, was built in 1905, in the then-popular Dutch Colonial Revival style. Perched on a small hill overlooking several pretty craftsman bungalows built twenty years later, when tastes had changed, the house had been purchased three years earlier, with an FHA loan and $5,000 down.

A lifetime after that purchase, and that housing market, when early every weekday morning, very early every weekday morning, as I frog-marched myself from the penultimate stop of the A train, along broad and roiling Upper Broadway, past the *bodegas* and *botanicas*, past Sal's House of Mofongo and La Reina del Chicharrón, to the ghost ship docked in Inwood where I attempted to ply my new trade as "facilitator" of English Language Arts, I paused most days for a minute or two at 4881 Broadway, to gaze ruefully at the Dyckman House, an original Dutch Colonial, side-gabled, sporting a charming gambrel roof, built in 1784, and in need of restoration, the last remaining house from that period left on Manhattan Island, situated a few blocks from the craggy outcropping of the island's bedrock, called Manhattan schist, where Peter Minuit is said to have come to such favorable terms with representatives of the Metoac band of Lenape Indians known as the "Carnarsee."

As I gazed at the *echt* Dutch Colonial in Manhattan, I thought about the ersatz I'd left behind in Milwaukee. Sometimes as I gazed, on very early mornings of my fourth, and final, year of teaching, when everything had gone to shit, feeling remorseful, feeling bereft, I found myself crying—crying for what I had lost, and for what I had thrown away, crying for the mess I'd made of things. And, once, resting peacefully on one of the benches in front of the landmark, where Dominican pensioners sat playing dominoes from morning till dusk, when they could find a spot not fouled by pigeons, a most-likely imaginary and sadder-but-wiser Carnarsee, adorned in beads and holding a leather pouch, noticed my tears and handed me a handkerchief from his small bag of trinkets. I marveled at how much time there was for gallantry uptown. And I wondered if I could be forgiven my racist sentimentality in conjuring another image of the noble savage.

The Dutch Colonial revival on Newhall Street, in Milwaukee, Wisconsin, where, on June 10, 2004, I wrote myself a letter, had itself been stuffed with trinkets, gathered on the cheap and second-hand, worth more than twenty-four dollars, but possibly not much more, and maybe even less, if the original figure of lore is adjusted for inflation; these were the traces, remnants, and souvenirs that my wife and I had amassed during the previous fourteen years of our marriage, the traces, remnants, and souvenirs soon to be discarded, as moving day approached, and the yard sales began, and the trips to the Goodwill, and the trips to the city dump. Because my wife—whose name was Caroline Schultz, whose name remains Caroline Schultz—and I were collectors, and had each separately, and as one, always felt a parvenu's nostalgia for somebody else's past, which is to say, a nostalgia for the beauty of the world, we had, over the years, devised for ourselves a pleasing and, in its way, orderly replica of the world we so desired, with each item collected representing a discrete entrée into the beauty we coveted.

While the basement, attic, and closets of the Dutch Colonial Revival archived a succession of our shifting decorative vogues—Pre-Raphaelite, Vienna Secession, Analytic Cubist, Imagist, Vorticist, De Stijl, Black Mountain, neo-geo—the living quarters were gluey with furnishings, fixtures, and furniture, as well as assorted gewgaws, gimcracks, whim-whams, and bibelots, that exemplified our most recently acquired aesthetic, a style later identified as "mid-century modern." There was plenty of mid-century in the basement, as well, of course, keeping lost passions company—for every finger bowl, lampshade, or toaster on display or at the ready in the house proper, ten or twelve were waiting patiently downstairs to serve, whenever Caroline or I should get a whim. Weekly trips to the flea markets, thrift shops, swap meets, and yard sales of Milwaukee and the outlying areas, and quick swoops down the alleys and past the front stoops of Lake Bluff, kept the inventory hopping. Occasionally, we might slip an item in the donation bin at one of the thrift shops, or possibly haul something out to the curb, to create a sense of ebb and flow, and maintain the fiction that our compulsion to hoard—I mean collect—was under control, but the tide tended always to err on the flow side.

As we prepared for the move to New York, though, we slowly, and imperceptibly, came to view all our souvenirs, all the traces, remnants, and orthographic projections of our earlier life, as so much impedimenta and marine debris, a collection of anthropogenic artifacts to be auctioned off, donated to tax-deductible charity organizations, recycled, thrown overboard, sloughed off so we could charge up our new life, and cram ourselves, and any inventory we could salvage, into the six hundred or so square feet we would be able to afford in Manhattan. And later, ensconced in six hundred or so square feet on West 76th Street, still house proud, we adopted, of necessity, a somewhat more minimalist approach to home decoration, influenced or perhaps justified by a slogan of Anatole France's that I had found collected in the dashing and heroic Bruce Chatwin's paean to the nomadic life, *The Songlines*: "It is good to collect things, but it is better to go on walks." We started donating pieces we had no room for to a nearby thrift store, and taking long walks in Central Park.

One day, backsliding, I was in the store looking to buy something, and I noticed an aquamarine molded-plastic chair, with black piping and metal legs, that we had dropped off a week earlier. The chair that we had bought for $6 on "Half-Price Saturday" at the Value Village on Dr. Martin Luther King, Jr., Memorial Drive in Milwaukee was being offered for sale at the Housing Works Thrift Store on Columbus Avenue in New York City for $90.

I stood in the shop, transfixed, for a long period of time, gazing at the chair, and at the price tag, thinking about the value of things—use, exchange, and sentimental—and, my heart aching, I remembered the miles and miles of irrecoverable sacrificial swath divested back in Milwaukee, the beauty of the world that Caroline and I had collected by hand, and with love, the beauty we had relinquished, let go of, as one, in the end, lets go of life; and then I thought about the beauty of the life itself we'd left behind, gotten rid of, along with the treasures we'd collected, believing that something was wanting, that there was a hole in our lives that could be filled only by moving to New York. I remembered how our life in Milwaukee, built piece by piece, over fourteen years, in the beginning with scant resources, and against some adversity, had come to seem insupportable, disposable, tainted even, when weighed against an irrepressible flutter we felt in our hearts when we closed our eyes and pictured in our minds the spires and the wonder, "the green light" and "the orgiastic future," that were waiting for us on the eastern seaboard.

The move to New York City would serve as fulfillment of the dreams of both our youths, dreams long held dormant and then shaken awake by a placard in a subway car. New York was the fulfillment of our dreams, and we would always love it— blindly, intemperately—but as each day passed it became clearer and clearer to us that the life we'd left behind in Milwaukee, touched though it had been with sadness and care we could scarcely remember, would remain forever the *Saturnia regna* of our years together, and what was lost could never be regained; this our hearts knew, but couldn't accept, before the first year we'd spent in New York had passed.

And in that first year, fumbling in the brightness of our new life, tucked into our beautiful and crowded six hundred or so square feet of the Upper West Side, we began to dream a different dream, a recurring dream of eternal return, when, late of an evening, unable to sleep, one or the other of us would happen to fall upon a souvenir of our old life, a *memento mori* signifying "Chip and Caroline," lying on the beach at eternal ebb tide, correlating loss, a relic that I likened in my mind to the "old white china doorknobs" salvaged in the "wake of refuse" in Robert Lowell's beautiful and elegiac poem, "Waking Early Sunday Morning": "sad, / slight useless things to calm the mad," and we began to enumerate for each other, in the whispers of a childhood sleepover, the ten thousand objective correlatives we had thrown into the sea, invoking the magical names of all the old white china doorknobs we'd lost or abandoned in our lives (feeling, of course, at that late date, remorse for everything but the truth, and thus no compunction to be necessarily altogether truthful in every single detail concerning the precise extent of our holdings): the thousand-place servings of china, for instance, in Caroline's favorite patterns: Blue Ridge Apple, Dixie Dogwood, and, especially, Ballerina Ware—in gray, chartreuse, deep red, and yellow; as many servings, and more, of stemware—crystal, beaded, fluted, and lead; of silverware—sterling, Britannia, stainless, and Sheffield plate... *I had first come across Lowell's poem, had first been moved by the image of the old white china doorknobs, when, as a teenager, I had stayed up all night reading* The Armies of the Night, *in which several stanzas are quoted, vowing early the next morning, when I closed the book, to become a writer, a nonfiction novelist or a poet, I wasn't sure which, because of Mailer or Lowell, I wasn't sure whom, forgetting my vow almost as soon as I'd made it, as I would later forget so many other vows...*the *batterie de cuisine*, that included, but was not limited to, stockpots, soup pots, *sauciers*, steamers, chef's pans, crêpe pans, paella pans, cake pans, loaf pans, Bundt pans, *gratins*, *bains marie*, soufflé dishes, madeleine molds, etc....*The vow to become a writer had been made in the same bedroom where three years earlier I'd hung my "Free Angela" poster, to the horror and incomprehension of my parents, and that I'd decorated with various other fading accoutrements of the by-then atomizing counter-culture, and where I'd cried myself to sleep when Connie Lassiter called to break our date to the eighth-grade dance...*the window treatments: curtains, drapes, shutters, sheers, blinds, tie-backs, shades (roller, Roman, and pleated), and valences (balloon, ascot, scarf, and swag)...*The bedroom that was located in the upper level of my family's mid-century modern split-level house, except it wasn't a split-level, my mother insisted, but I always called it a split-level anyway, a house built to my parents' specifications, and appointed, following countless leafings through the home and garden magazines, with 1960s low-pile fern green carpeting throughout the living room, dining room, and bedrooms, except for my brother's room, which was carpeted in incarnadine red (my brother and I had been given a choice in floor covering and window treatment when the house was built and the rooms furnished; because I was at that earlier date a dedicated traditionalist in interior design, I had chosen an Early American print for my curtains, Liberty Bells and churches, the Trinitarian spires of Robert Lowell's New England, while my younger brother, an avant-gardist in predilection, daringly selected a Piet Mondrian pattern of black and white checks to set off his deep red carpet)...*the wall hangings: oil paintings, cave paintings, watercolors, acrylics, encaustics, enamels, and gouaches; drawings and sketches in graphite, Conté, charcoal, pastel, pen-and-ink, and silverpoint; woodcuts, linocuts, drypoints, mezzotints, aquatints, etchings, engravings, lithographs, transfers, and *giclée*...*The split-level's kitchen, appointed with avocado-colored range, refrigerator, and dishwasher, opened, via French doors, onto a breakfast nook with bay windows overlooking a redwood deck, equipped with gas-powered barbecue grill, that rose high on the sloped lot, shadowing the septic tank below, a deck from which, many years later, my sad teenage self and desultory shifting alliances of other sad teenage boys gathered in the ruins of the by-then broken home where teenage drinking was, if not explicitly* *suffered, largely overlooked, and threw our empty beer bottles into the wooded back lot—I closing my eyes and saying a silent prayer with each toss—a deck that would eventually rot to the point at which it became dangerous to tread upon it, or to climb its steep stairs...*the porcelain and ceramics: Sancai, celadon, earthenware, jasper ware, slipware, Arita ware, Bottinger, Wedgewood, Jun ware, Delftware, fine white semivitrous, Belleek, studio pottery, majolica, terracotta, and Raku-yaki...*And downstairs, in the den, the mid-century modern split-level house had been carpeted in orange shag, paneled in faux knotty pine, and furnished with a pool table, a gas-jet fire place, and a bar (though not the customary "wet bar," so prized by the more advanced* arrivistes *in the neighborhood, since my parents weren't drinkers, then, when they furnished the house, not yet, except for my mother's occasional Beefeater martini or my father's Tom Collins or whiskey sour, taken usually only on vacation, in a restaurant in Panama City Beach, Florida, or Gatlinburg, Tennessee, and the bottle of chilled Lancer's Imported Rosé served at Christmas dinner, and they couldn't, in those early times, foresee the day they might come to appreciate the convenience of running water near the bar)...*the vases, ewers, urns, and amphorae of all sizes, colors, shapes, and materials, to hold the fresh cut flowers I brought home every few days—poppies, anemones, ranunculus, mountain lilies, pentas, bluebottles, nasturtiums, sweet peas, lisianthus, cosmos, cleomes, and various *orchidaceae*, including, but not limited to, Vanda, Dendrobium, Cymbidium, and Cattleya...*Under the staircase leading down to the den lay a water feature with a spitting cherub fountain powered by a hidden electrical pump, and in an underused corner sat an out-of-tune piano that no one could play anyway, painted yellow and "antiqued" with gray specks of splattered paint...*the bric-a-brac, curios, *objects d'art*, and kickshaws: snuff boxes, horse brasses, portrait miniatures, figurines in *blanc de Chine*, singing bird boxes, Colima dogs, clockwork automata, netsuke, Fabergé eggs...*Adjacent to the den, forming the other half of the "full basement" prized by all aspirants to the American dream, lay the equally-prized two-car garage where my father parked his*

*Oldsmobile, a loose and jangly behemoth of an oversized sedan be-
queathed, in time, to my younger brother, when he assumed his own
driving privileges, after my father, by then steering a second-hand
Chevrolet Caprice through the "Traces," "Circles," and "Lanes" of the
"Gardens" "Manors," and "Estates" sprawling in the former hinterlands of the rusting city, had moved out of the split-level, and into an
apartment complex with swimming pool, "club house," and game
room, one of many such apartment complexes blooming in the subdivi-
sions, in an era of multiplying divorces, that had been built, as part of
some unstated five-year plan aimed at adapting the architectural infrastructure of the suburbs to fit the changing mores of the middle classes,
and to accommodate—among the varying and shifting formations of
all the other remnants and lees of so many newly-decimated "nuclear"
families—the concerned fathers-in-exile who wanted to be close to their
children, the ones who were careful to make the distinction, so their
children understood, that it wasn't them their fathers were leaving, it
was their mothers, and that their relationship, the relationship between
the fathers-in-exile and the children left in their mothers' care, would
continue as it was before, because everything would be managed and
everybody would be reasonable...*a Sevres vase bearing Napoleon's
portrait, a sphinx dedicated to Sesostris, a pyx, a Republican sa-
ber, a medieval hackbut, an Indian chibook, curious pistols, dis-
guised weapons, porcelain tureens, Dresden plates, translucent
cups from China, comfit-boxes belonging to feudal times, a
carved ivory ship speeding full sail on the back of a motionless
tortoise, green and golden slippers from the seraglio, a Moorish
yataghan, a Tartar idol[4]...*The two-car garage where my mother
parked her two-door Monte Carlo, and a few years later, when I could
beat a by-then raging and embattled parent to a parking space, I parked
my own new-hatched AMC Hornet, the bright orange Christmas present I'd received the Christmas after my sixteenth birthday, in consolation for the MG Midget my mother had decided was too dangerous
for me...*a soldier's tobacco pouch, a priest's ciborium, plumes

---

[4] I will admit I have lifted this list of items, and the two that follow, from *The Wild
Ass's Skin*, by Honoré de Balzac.

that once adorned a throne, a mummy swathed in black bandages, an Etruscan vase, salt-cellars from Benvenuto Cellini's
workshop, a cameo depicting the conquests of Alexander, a
matchbox depicting the massacres of Pizarro, a suit of Milanese
armor, a sleeping child modeled in wax, the cotton garment of a
Tahitian maid, myriad sea-shells and madrepores..."Raging"
and "embattled" parents because they were divorcing and taking their
time doing so, seeming to savor each body blow because they'd never
divorced each other before and didn't know how to do it, and who were,
at the same time, to greater and lesser degrees of sincerity, admitting
certain scruples, that they'd soon learn to overcome, concerning the effects of divorce on sensitive children...a precious missal in manu-
script, adorned with arabesques in gold and blue, a tomahawk
from Illinois, a Cherokee scalping-knife, votive shields, pano-
plies, carved shrines and figures, an ebony table carved after
Jean Goujon's designs, precious caskets, and a priceless vase of
antique porphyry carved round about with pictures of the most
grotesquely wanton of Roman divinities...My parents were the
son and daughter of coal miners who died in their early sixties, the coal
miners, not the parents, one during, and the other after the divorce, of
black lung disease and other complications of working themselves to
death, coal miners married to two different kinds of coal miners' wives:
one grandmother, Mimi, on the spear side, the grandmother I loved,
gentle and kind, substitute teacher at Sumiton High School and founding member of the Jasper Women's Literary Society, who, in the early
days of the Great Society, had taught Head Start classes to black children, the first black children that I, in my segregated childhood, had
ever met, and the only ones I would know, until, many years later, I
began my career as a youth worker in Milwaukee, Wisconsin, a grandmother who once defied a policeman in Washington D.C. by wading in
a fountain in solidarity with some hippies protesting the war in Vietnam...the stamps, hinge-mounted, though such mountings are
risky, in albums, binders, and supplements: Penny Blacks and
Penny Reds, Treskilling Yellows, British Guiana 1c magentas,
Mauritius "Post Offices," Inverted Jennies, Basel Doves, Perot

Provisionals, Finland Zeppelins "1830," Gronchi Rosas, Scinde Dawks, General Balbo triptychs, etc....*The other, distaff, grandmother, a heavily-armed neurasthenic fishwife, and seething racist, who dipped snuff and called Mimi a "nigger-lover" and sat on her porch and shot cardinals out of trees with a pistol because she said they were unlucky, who wrung the necks of chickens purchased cheaply from old black women whom she seemed to believe tenanted on her land, and then chopped the chickens' heads off with an axe...*the books, displayed in large cases of satinwood, rosewood, and mahogany: hardcover books, softcover books, trade paperbacks, clay tablets, scrolls, codices, volumen, illuminated manuscripts, a Gutenberg Bible, a First Folio, a Ben Hur 1860, Third Edition, with a duplicated line on page 116, a Chevalier Audubon 1840, the Sarajevo Haggadah, etc....*The raging and embattled divorcing son and daughter of over-worked coal miners, one dead, the other dying, and coal miners' wives, one kind, one cruel, had contracted to have the split-level built before the raging began, and the battles commenced, and the colliers had wheezed their last breaths, on a wooded two-acre lot located at the pastoral (and alliterative) address of 100 Willow Way, where my mother had planted several, but not one hundred, willow trees (as she'd joked, saying she would), the only trees in the front lawn not later uprooted and thrown upon the roof of the split-level by one of the retributive Biblical tornadoes that every spring level thousands upon thousands of split-levels all over the south, both "New" and unreconstructed...*in the garage: traps, gigs, landaus, phaetons, flies, broughams, fiacres, barouches, equipages, victorias, cabriolets, tilburies, four-in-hands, char-a-bancs, dogcarts, diligences, troikas, and chariots...*The split-level, spared the wrath of God, situated in a near-suburb of Birmingham, Alabama, called Killough Springs Forest, had been built in an era of generally-rising prosperity to replace the two-bedroom ranch where the coal miner's son and the coal miner's daughter, accountant and homemaker, had made their first home, a wattle and daub affair, lacking a full basement and two-car garage, subtended, instead, with a dirt-floored crawl space, and annexed with a carport accommodating only one car, a carport with an absurdly* *pitched roof that swooped down, like a curtsey, almost to the lawn, a roof that my brother and I could climb with little effort, using an adjacent fence post as a platform, squirreling up the asphalt tiles, and then jumping off, laughing hilariously as we tumbled, earth-bound, into our father's long and limber arms, outstretched and waiting below*...back in the house: *escritoires, Cheverets,* trestle desks, *chabudai,* breakfronts, dining tables, coffee tables, davenports, loveseats, *chaises longue, fauteuils, bergères,* club chairs, bistro chairs, Morris chairs, Eames chairs, *zaisus, icpalli, cathedrae apostolorum,* etc....*A ranch house with carport occupying a half-acre corner lot at 401 Wedgeworth Drive, in a less prestigious subdivision known as Roebuck Lawn Estates, the first, and for some, the next but last alighting place of the newly-arrived and striving immigrants to the suburban pastoral who, like fellow Alabamian Hank Williams, their necks red, and their drawls three-dimensional, had left their homes on the rural route, but for generally more sober (and prosaic) purposes, the ranch house that had come to seem, to the whole family, in the effervescent always-expanding bright green affluence of the nineteen sixties, before the heartaches began, and the divorces, and the stagflation, plant closings, and oil embargoes, as too small and déclassé, and thus to be sold off and abandoned for a brighter, greener future*...and the closets (closets!), wardrobes, chifforobes, armoires, chests of drawers, and steamer trunks filled to overflowing with vintage clothing and accessories: with chlamys, himations, peplos, chitons, stollas, pallas, palliums, cotes, coathardies, doublets, blaits, stoles, jerkins, maniples, shirtwaists, codpieces, and surcoats...*And much later, the heartaches long since begun, and the oil embargoes come and gone, some seven or eight years after the divorce had been "finalized," and three or four years after my father had remarried and gone to live with his new family in south Florida, the by-then-dilapidated brighter and greener future in Killough Springs Forest had fallen, as per divorce decree, onto the real estate market, a buyer's market, as it always is when it's your turn to sell ("a maggot's market, as it always is when it's your turn to die," one almost writes), and was sold "as is" at a cut-rate price, a "fixer upper," and a "divorce special":*

Offered for Sale, Reasonable Terms: Mid-century modern split-level house, except it isn't really a split-level; three bedrooms; "family" room; wall-to-wall carpeting in fern green and incarnadine red; two and a half baths; large kitchen with avocado-colored appliances, garbage disposal, dishwasher, and breakfast nook; finished basement with fireplace and orange shag carpet; washer/dryer; two-car garage; rotting redwood deck with gas grill; septic tank; two-acre wooded lot littered with empty beer bottles; retributive Biblical tornadoes...

...with evening dresses, cocktail dresses, caftan dresses, slip dresses, shirt dresses, frocks, trapezes, dirndls, chemises, shifts, saris, a-lines, *huipiles*, kimonos, and cheongsams...*Shortly before the house was sold, in financial and emotional arrears, I had moved back home, and, following six or seven apologetic showings leading to the humiliating acceptance of the inevitable "lowball" offer, and, finally, to the sad and solemn exchange of signatures and transfers of titles and property rights that I learned then, for the first time, was called the "closing," I found myself newly-employed as a kind of landreeve, or major domo, coordinating my mother's, and my own, move into a beautiful, if well-lived-in, older apartment in the city, a fortunate fall, I might have said at the time—if the apartment had been meant for me alone, or for me and a girlfriend, or a wife, or a roommate—a fortunate fall from the ticky-tacky of the suburban bright green, a new start east of prefabricated Eden, capacious enough to accommodate an adult man and his mother, with windows opening in three of the four cardinal directions, a "large and airy" "classic six," as the apartment would have been touted in the New York real estate listings, that I'd found for us on the seventh, and top, floor of a once-elegant apartment building situated on Highland Avenue, a winding, and, in parts, still cobble-stoned vestige of the old urbanism planted with hundreds and hundreds of dogwood trees, with magnolias, and with crape myrtle, a main artery of the city's once-fashionable, then decaying, and, at least since the nineteen-sixties, bohemian Southside, lined with block after block of beautiful and wisteria-vined old* *mansions cut up into smaller flats and beautiful old apartment houses fallen into disrepair (their polished oak floors carpeted over and their twelve-foot high—and higher—ceilings preemptively lowered with "acoustical" ceiling tiles)…*with dinner jackets, Nehru jackets, Norfolk jackets, flak jackets; top coats, frock coats, morning coats, evening coats; dress suits, leisure suits, Beatle suits, Nudie suits, safari suits, zoot suits, and suits of armor—in glen plaid, toile de jouy, linen, dress wool, worsted wool, satin, velvet, nankeen, foulard, gabardine, twill, pique, cambric, and chain mail…*A once fashionable, then decaying, and again fashionable, if inevitably "gentrified," "updated," and "gut-renovated" precinct where, before the retreat to my mother's house that I could in truth never call "strategic," I had alternately toiled and wasted the previous several years, rooting in various "quaint" old apartments, dropping in and out of college, moping, brooding, reading, drinking, trying to write poetry, trying to write fiction, trying to paint, trying to get a girlfriend, earning my daily bread as a part-time stock clerk, at a time when stock clerks, part-time or full-time, were called stock boys, at a department store in a terrible shopping mall where I took my lunch at a Hot Sam and an Orange Julius, failing at most everything I touched, but also, in a sense, performing reconnaissance work for my mother's and my later move from the sad, dispiriting comforts of Willow Way into the welcoming "dangers" of the city, a move that would have seemed incomprehensible to our neighbors in Killough Springs Forest, neighbors who feared the city, feared crime waves, feared jive-talkin' African Americans, and feared, above all else, the prospect of encountering any small difficulty finding a place to park their cars, but then neither my mother nor I had had relations with our neighbors since even before the neighbors had first complained, several years before, that the lawn at 100 Willow Way was never mowed, which, in truth, it never was…*with cerements, shrouds, and winding sheets…*And now, which is to say then, having retreated in defeat to my mother's house, the mid-century modern split-level, except it wasn't a split-level, cankering, by then, and listing in its wooded lot, preparing to prepare for the move to the large and airy classic six on Highland Avenue, I stood heart-deep* *in the ruins of the brighter, greener future at Willow Way, my feet resting in a more primal wake of refuse than the later one at Newhall and Hampshire that would break my heart again, but only in retrospect, when I looked back in anguish from 76th and Amsterdam, but now, which is to say then, because now is always then, choked in sadness and dust, I surveyed the immense and intractable wreckage that formed a kind of palimpsestic regolith massed on the house's crumbling floors: stacked up, piled on, and tamped down, it documented a near half-century's catamnesis of cuts, abrasions, lacerations, and open wounds, of recoveries, remissions, relapses, fresh starts, and normal wear and tear; a searing near half-century's tragicomic afterschool special* opéra bouffe *of mock-heroic rising and bathetic falling action: the triumphs, reversals, and catastrophes; the climaxes and anticlimaxes of my parents' lives (several, cleaving, and torn asunder) and of their children's lives (nascent, burgeoning, and stalled); all the sad, slight useless things that remained of my brother's and my childhood, and the sad, slight useless things that remained of the obscure and partly rural prologue to that childhood...*

Papilionaceous

Though we think our thoughts are ours by choice, and our ills a mere consequence of our own recklessly unhealthy life, it may well be that, just as papilionaceous plants produce a seed of a certain shape, our family hands down to us the ideas that keep us alive, as well as the illness that will cause our death.

Marcel Proust

The fading snapshot, for instance, that I found nesting near the bottom of a discontinued chest of drawers rotting in a corner of the two-car garage too crammed by then with the sweepings and offscourings of the good life to park even one car; a three-by-five glossy, its scalloped edges curling at the corners, portraying my mother, Dora High School homecoming queen, class of 1950-something, kneeling demurely on the forty yard line, draped in a calf-length wide-swing felt skirt and wrapped against the late autumn chill in a dark woolen sweater, a string of faux pearls arced across her neck, her lady-gloved index finger extended to hold a pigskin to the ground as if for kick-off. A bit of pale calf peeks through the folds of her skirts as she gazes longingly at posterity through a pair of tortoise shell cat eye glasses, while my father, my mother's curly-haired dreamboat, tall, dark, and handsome, six feet two, slouches awkwardly in the background, all boxed up in a by-then out-of-fashion square-shouldered double-breasted suit coat that he'd soon trade in for the flight jumpers and dress blues of an Air Force radio operator and staff sergeant, and later for the chinos and argyles of a big man on campus, and, upon graduation, for the gray flannels of a 1950s junior executive.

Or, buried deeper in the same drawer in the two car junk-garage, another photograph of my father, in different aspect, taken a few years before the homecoming game, his near snarl softened by the baby fat that still pudged his delicate face, the baby fat he'd eventually lose, and bequeath to me (I kept mine for nearly fifty years), looking insolent (sort of), my father, with no helmet in sight. Suited semi-menacingly in a leather bombardier's jacket, incongruent dress shirt and tie, and heavy dungarees rolled in large cuffs, he leans one of his worn boots into the kickstand of the two-stroke motorbike he'd purchased with money earned pumping "rabbit gas" at the Mutual station in Argo (or was it Flat Top?), "rabbit gas" Mimi called it because of the cut-rate oil company's memorable proprietary emblazonment, a red rabbit courant on a field of white, fading on its rusting tin oval by the time I came to see it, but still luring bargain-seeking motorists off Old Highway 78, and amusing my brother and me, trained as we'd been by television to laugh at any old-fashioned-looking deviation from the streamlined name-brand standards, crests, and chevrons of the forward-thinking modern corporations, the photograph I would present as Exhibit A in the many briefs I'd file over the years, arguing before an implacable judge—my mother—that yes I could have a go-cart because Daddy had had a motorcycle when he was fourteen.

Strewn, too, in the immense and intractable wreckage massed on the crumbling floor of the house on Willow Way—stacked up, piled on, and tamped down—lay the relics my father left behind when he moved out of the house, leaving my mother, not my brother and me.

His old college yearbook, for example, the *Entre Nous*, which so many years earlier had fascinated me with its serene evocation of charming campus idylls—sweaters, smiles, and glee clubs, and somebody going out for junior varsity something or other; the yearbook that made me long to go to college for the rest of my life, which, in fact, I almost did.

The Agfa Isolette 120mm medium format folding rangefinder with f3.5 75mm Apotar lens, in its brown leather carrying case, that my father had bought in Germany, when he was stationed there during the Korean War, occupying the country and contributing his bit to the *Wirtschaftwunder*, and where he'd also bought Mimi, along with a set of Meissen dinnerware in the famous "Blue Onion" pattern (never used, but always on display, along with her collection of miniature pitchers, in a dainty cherrywood hutch in a corner of the dining room), a glass-domed clock with heavy brass escapements, weights, and pendulum, a clock I loved when I was a child, and talked Mimi into giving me one Sunday visit, though she knew I wouldn't take care of it, which of course I didn't, breaking the dome within the year, and, shortly thereafter, losing the pendulum—losing the momentum—and then, in a sustained gesture of self-loathing, keeping the broken clock on display as a kind of mortification of the soul for almost forty years, until I finally found the heart to dispose of it in the latter days of closing out inventory in Milwaukee, Wisconsin.

The remains of my father's short-lived bowling career: his bowling ball, sheathed in its by-then moldering beige and burgundy leather carrying case, the ball that I could never grasp when I was a child, except with two hands, because it was so heavy and because the holes for the middle, thumb, and forefingers had been drilled so peremptorily far apart; the gaudy pair of patchwork bowling shoes, size 11, also in beige and burgundy, and also moldering, too big for my feet, or for those of anybody else in the family, shoes too big for anybody in the world for all I knew; the trophy with the perfect plastic Anglo-Saxon bowler (captured for all time smiling and in mid-throw, with no plans, it seemed, ever to release the ball), that had been awarded to my father, for meritorious bowling, in the days before I could remember, when my father bowled in a league, a member of the American Cast Iron Pipe Company office team;

his shiny indigo-blue cotton/polyester blend team shirt, also too big for me, but I wore it anyway—"ironically"—when I was a teenager, the shirt with "Wayne Blackwell" stitched in gold curlicue script above a bowling pin emblazoned with the company's logo—converging rays of an uppercase "A" joined with a stylized cross-section of pipe in the middle—and resting below the logo the acronym by which the company was known, "ACIPCO" (pronounced "uh-sip-co" by the white employees and "uh-sippy-co" by the black—employees who, when ill or injured, stared blankly at each other across a wide linoleum-floored aisle in the segregated waiting room of the ACIPCO infirmary, where I, like so many other dependent children, black and white, had my tonsils and my adenoids taken out when I was six, anesthetized with ether pumped under a blanket).

The golf clubs and golf shoes because at some point in the early sixties the executives at ACIPCO had foresworn bowling for golf, and my father, consequently, was going to take up golf, too, but something happened, and the game was never taken up; though on rare outings to the driving range, with my brother and me in tow (on the occasions we'd been able to plead our father there), he could sometimes be seen, three or five wood in hand, the index finger of his left hand delicately intertwined in the pinky of his right, and his left thumb cradled in the hollow of his right palm, the grip he'd learned from Ben Hogan's *Five Lessons: The Modern Fundamentals of Golf*, the Bible, or I guess more like the *Pilgrim's Progress*, of suburban duffers everywhere, and the grip he taught his boys, as he chopped half-heartedly—with no follow-through—at the row of dimpled balls egged in their tiny tees; a nice set of clubs that I, who never had much of a follow-through either, would, sometimes, after my father had left for Florida to start his new life, leaving the clubs to me by default, toss into the hatchback of my Hornet and haul to the driving range to swing sadly and commemoratively at my own bucket of balls.

A four horsepower Mercury outboard motor and other by-then-rusting implements of the sea-faring life, except it was a lake and not a sea: battery-powered trolling motors; rods, reels, nets, and creels; and tackle boxes crammed with disorganized piles of hooks, line, corks and bobbers, and colorful plastic fili-gree lures: weed bugs, purple wrigglers, dingbats, torpedoes, and hellzapoppins—but the only fishing trip I can remember is the one to Lake Purdy when I snagged a hook in my brother's head, a result of poor casting that caused much enmity with the frequently put-upon, and often banged up, Benjamin of the family.

The same Benjamin whose finger I once slammed in a car door as I was let off for school (this was before my brother started school), an accident that occurred when the younger son scrambled to climb into the front seat that I seemed always, based on some unspoken and mistaken interpretation of the laws of primogeniture, to have permanent dibs on, an accident that caused me a long and nervous worried day in the second grade, terrified I'd come home to find a brother missing a finger, my anxiety abated only when my teacher, Miss Russell—who towards the end of the day noticed my agitation, and reassured me, when I confessed my fear to her, that my brother's digit was surely still attached—took me to the office so I could call home and get an update on my brother's condition, which, as it turned out, was stable, his hand whole and almost ready to ball into a fist.

Miss Russell, a long, cool redhead, with freckles, and very sexy, a proto-Tallulah McIlhenny, with a beehive hairdo worn without irony, who earlier that year, to supplement her income, the income of a grade school teacher in the state of Alabama in the year 1965, had sold the family a set of World Book Encyclo-pedias, a set that I, by the time I entered high school, had read almost in its entirety, but randomly, and rarely reading any arti-cle all the way through, learning then to prefer knowing a little bit about a lot of things to knowing a lot about any one thing.

An electric guitar, because my father, with the help of *Mel*

Bay's Complete Chet Atkins Guitar Method, was going to learn how to play the electric guitar, but never did; a beautiful burnished Gibson solid body with sunburst finish that I used to hold and strum, as I "played along" with, and lip-synced, acid rock of the late sixties, but, like my father, who was more interested in learning how to play country music (or more precisely, I guess, "countrypolitan" music, because he didn't much care for the "hillbilly" stuff), I also never learned to play: it was a big country-western looking guitar that looked to me, at the time, all wrong, that looked to me like short hair and straight-legged pants and Okies from Muskogee because what I really wanted was a long-haired, bell-bottomed, love-beaded, fringe-vested Haight-Ashbury Fender Stratocaster that I too would never learn to play.

The language tapes—French, Italian, and Spanish—because my father was going to learn a foreign language, but never did, just as I, too, was going to learn a foreign language—French, Italian, or Spanish—but never did.

My father's "360-sound" stereophonic hi-fidelity long-playing records—Chet Atkins, Jim Reeves, Los Indios Tabajares, Acker Bilk, The Ames Brothers, "Sing Along with Mitch," and Claudine Longet (my dad sort of had a thing for Claudine Longet)—still cohabitating, in the little brass-plated cart on wheels sitting next to the Danish modern stereo console, with my mother's records (they never divvied them up, the way you're supposed to do when you break up with somebody): Robert Goulet, Tom Jones, Engelbert Humperdinck, the soundtracks of *South Pacific, Camelot,* and *My Fair Lady.*

And, from an earlier era, the 45s, and even a few 78s, that I used to play over and over when I was very young on my child's portable plastic record player: "She Wore A Yellow Ribbon," "Flowers on the Wall," "Sixteen Tons," "*Auf Wiedersehen*, Sweetheart," "King of the Road," "Twisting USA," Stan Freberg's "St. George and the Dragonet" b/w "Little Blue Riding Hood," and the Four Lads crooning their unforgettable, if, in retrospect "orientalist," evocation of moonlit nights on the Bosporus of long ago: "Istanbul, Not Constantinople."

And in other piles of debris, stacked parallel to the remains of things my father had left behind, lay the remains of things my father had given to me, things I didn't deserve or take care of, things I didn't even use, because I was lazy and ungrateful and dilatory and had no follow-through and didn't deserve nice things because I didn't take care of them, as Mimi had learned (and forgiven), my irresponsibility instantiated most emblematically (and expensively) by the orange AMC Hornet that had long since thrown a rod and been junked because I never changed the oil, not once, because I didn't know you were supposed to change it, and I wouldn't have known how to change it even if I'd known you were supposed to, and I probably still wouldn't have changed it anyway; and further instantiated, albeit less expensively, though still emblematically, by the also long-gone East German-made SLR I'd asked for (I was fascinated by things from behind the Iron Curtain) after I'd spent an afternoon studying a copy of Robert Frank's *The Americans* (a recent purchase of *Exile on Main Street* had whet an appetite) and some picture books of Walker Evans and Diane Arbus that were also on hand, at the beautiful cluttered old-fashioned Smith and Hardwick Bookshop located downtown, on Twentieth Street, accordion-filed in a tight fit between Joy Young's Chop Suey House and the Bon Ton Hatters, with books stacked everywhere in the beautiful tiny narrow shop, even on the stairs of the heavy wrought-iron staircase leading up to the mezzanine where, propping my feet on the railing, I sat in a folding director's chair flipping through the oversized books, deciding I wanted to be a photographer and would need, therefore, the sleek little number I was reading about in the "Cameras of the DDR" spread of a recent issue of *Popular Photography* magazine that was also at hand—a 35-millimeter Praktica LLC with 50mm f1.8 lens (manufactured in Dresden), the f-stops, shutter speeds, and depths of field of which I soon gave up trying to cope with, once the camera was mine, before exposing even one roll of film, the camera I later pawned to pay the rent on one of my "quaint" apartments, and then never redeemed, a month before I also pawned, to pay the next month's rent, and, again, never redeemed, the nickel-plated high school trumpet I'd almost learned to play, the trumpet that had kept me out of gym—had gotten me a deferment—when I settled on the band as a less militaristic alternative to physical education than the ROTC, though as a band member I was also required to march, and to wear a uniform— but a smart, slightly comical-looking Sgt. Pepper uniform, with sash, cummerbund, epaulets, and shako decorated with a bright orange plume.

And also still extant and on the premises, neither junked (yet) nor pawned: the darkroom equipment my father had bought for me when he bought me the camera—the trays, chemicals, tongs, red light bulb, and enlarger that I had never tried to learn to use, though I read the instruction manual over and over, along with all the other books in the little library of teach-yourself-photography I'd assembled.

The microscope I'd peered through once or twice many years before, knowing not what I looked at, or why I was looking, or bothering to try to learn, but the instrument that looked impressive on my desk, sitting next to my typewriter and stock ticker and crystal ball and fake human skull and phrenology bust.

The telescope I used early on, when I first got it, and was, for an evening, amazed to see the craters of the moon magnified so clearly through its lenses, and telephoned my best friend, Harry Stahl, to tell him about my discovery; Harry Stahl, who stuttered and was excitable and was very small, the object, in fact, of the third-grade schoolyard chant "Harry Stahl / was so small / a cat could eat him / hat and all," who, stuttering and excited (and small), hung up his phone and came running to my house because he'd misheard what I had told him, thinking I'd said I could see "the Invaders" on the moon; the Invaders, a cadre of cunning, if invariably foiled, extraterrestrials enjoying, for a season, their own network television show, produced by Quinn Martin (with three acts and an epilogue), advance scouts from a dying planet (aren't they all?), located, presumably, somewhere in a quadrant of the universe lying forlorn behind an intergalactic Iron Curtain, aliens who'd learned to assume human form (except they couldn't get their pinkies to point the right way—a small, and to my mind, at the time, poignant defect that, besides making teatime difficult, was forever blowing their otherwise flawless cover), intrepid and merciless (if poignant and forlorn) extraterrestrials bent on colonizing the earth and destroying humankind because they had to eat, too, Harry and I allowed, philosophically, feeling kind of sorry for their poor little deformed fingers.

The rusting ten-speed English racer, a Nishiki Olympiad with Shimano derailleur gears and center-pull caliper brakes, the comparative advantage over side-pull I would never admit that I didn't really understand, as I would later never admit that I didn't really understand the comparative advantage of, say, the full-hilt, carbon steel blade of the 10-inch Henkel's chef's knife I'd later have to have over the half-hilt (?) stainless blade of the inferior brand, or other similar comparative advantages that would lead me to spend much more money over the years than was probably necessary, just ask my wife, as my dad had spent much more money over the years than was probably necessary, just ask my mother, or any of my father's other wives, but my brakes had to pull from the center or they wouldn't pull at all, the bike that I actually rode, and kept polished and lubricated for a few years because it was, during this time, my principal mode of transportation, primarily for the two and a half mile journey to the Huffman branch of the Birmingham Public Library, where I was coming to spend a great deal of my time, and where on one visit I spent the day reading a clunky library-bound copy of Voltaire's *Candide* (how I loved the smell of library books!) because I'd read about the "philosophical tale" in the "Age of Enlightenment" section of the child's history of the world my parents had given me a few years before, and I was struck by Voltaire's motto—"*Ecrasez l'infame!*"—and tried to make it my own, though I would finally, late in the game, admit in despair that *l'infame* is ultimately too intractable an interest, with too powerful a lobby, to *ecrasez* definitively—the first book that, it sounds corny to say, "changed my life"; the library where I also read William Faulkner and Thomas Wolfe and John Dos Passos and James T. Farrell (along with Tennessee Williams and Eugene O'Neil and Arthur Miller and William Inge and Edward Albee because, after seeing a television production of David Rabe's *Sticks and Bones*, the third ambition of my life was to be a playwright—the second had been to be a newspaper reporter, inspired by a viewing of *His Girl Friday* on the late, late show; and my first had been to write and draw for *MAD* magazine…the desire to be a photographer came a little later), and where I listened with headphones to *The Rite of Spring* and *Prelude to the Afternoon of a Faun* and *Bluebeard's Castle* and *Rhapsody in Blue* and Duke Ellington and Charlie Parker and Dizzy Gillespie and Miles Davis and Thelonious Monk, and looked at art books (Matisse, Miro, and Stuart Davis were my first favorite artists and I imitated their colorful curls, curves, and swirls in construction paper cut-outs) and decided that my favorite author would be John Steinbeck, until a smart and sexy girl called Angie (another redhead, but just a friend) suggested I read *The Sun Also Rises*, and I longed, as I closed the book, to say to somebody someday, after I'd achieved disillusionment, "Isn't it pretty to think so?" or "It's awfully easy to be hard-boiled about everything in the daytime, but at night it's another thing"; the flat-roofed New Frontier mini-Bauhaus Huffman branch of the Birmingham Public Library that was my refuge and sanctuary until, a few years later, the orange Hornet provided me with the means to weave my way through the several lanes of the newly-constructed Interstate highway leading downtown to the central library, in the days before the main collection was relocated to the inevitable post-brutalist (but just as brutal) postmodern shopping mall on stilts (monolithic duck or decorated shed—I never understood the distinction), with escalators and atria, and temperature-controlled tinted windows that couldn't be opened, assembled in the early eighties across the street from the original lavish and pre-war civic-minded neo-classical building, left miraculously un-demolished in an era of remorseless demolition, reassigned as a research library to house the dusty bloody burden of southern history collection, a fantastic and inviting temple the main reading room of which was decorated with strange and fabulous murals depicting strange and fabulous figures real and imaginary—or both—that represented various world civilizations and historical epochs: John Smith and Pocahontas, Shahryar and Shahrazad, Confucius, Isis and Ramses II, Lancelot, Celimene and Alceste, Faust and Marguerite, Bellerophon and Pegasus, King David, Krishna and Radha, Dante and Virgil, Otohime and Urashima Tarō, Saadi, Igor Svatoslavic, Sigurd and Brynhild, and Don Quixote, charming murals the maintenance for which I generously helped subsidize through massive fees paid over the years for books returned late, always late, once so late, and with fees so high, that a deputy sheriff appeared at my doorstep with a warrant for my arrest, a warrant that led to a court appearance and a relatively stern admonition from an otherwise kindly judge, who looked like a hanging judge, at first glance, and who, upon learning I had finally paid my late fees, and that my record was otherwise clean, suspended the municipal fines, and extracted from me a frightened and stammering promise to be a more responsible library patron in future.

And even deeper in the Blackwell family archives, stacked in the moldy basement utility room positioned directly beneath the front porch, lay the slide projector and trays of color transparencies that captured, among other fading Ektachrome phantasms of yesteryear, a very young me and an even younger younger brother, both of us suntanned, chic, and in dark sunglasses, two Italians tricked out in matching white terrycloth jackets with our collars turned up, checked Bermuda shorts, and saltwater sandals, each of us wearing a carved bone tiki idol on a leather thong around our neck, and putting a colored golf ball though a dinosaur's mouth at the Goofy Golf in Panama City Beach, Florida, putting another ball between a windmill's gyrating wooden blades, and yet another over the baby alligators swimming anachronistically in a medieval castle's moat (or did I dream the alligators?).

My brother and me squeezing through Fat Man's Squeeze in one of the sandstone outcroppings of Rock City, on the top of Lookout Mountain, near Chattanooga, Tennessee, swinging giddily on the Swinging Bridge, defying everybody's busybody parents' advice not to look down into the chasm below, and, in further slides, mugging for the camera, feigning vertigo, as we stand close by the edge of Lover's Leap, the celebrated promontory from which so many years earlier the legendary and beautiful Cherokee maiden Nacoochee leapt to her death upon learning that her lover, a young brave of an unnamed rival tribe (the Cap-u-lets, my mother joked), had, as the price for loving her, been thrown over the ledge—it's expensive loving a girl from another tribe.

My brother and me trying to build a snowman out of the annual Birmingham one inch of snow that closed schools and shut down highways, our father struggling in the background to attach chains to the tires of the Galaxie 500 that would crash a year later, fracturing my skull, gashing my father's head, cutting and bruising my mother's knees, and giving my brother a concussion, in a four car collision at the same intersection on the Huffman-Tarrant Road where a few years earlier the Ku Klux Klan had castrated a black man to teach a lesson to the civil rights movement, but I didn't know anything about that.

After the wreck my father purchased the safest car he could afford, a 1964 Rambler Classic 770 station wagon, equipped with seat belts, safety glass, and a padded dash to protect the young family from the dangers of the road...

The same Rambler that my nervous mother would later use

to teach me how to drive, my learner's permit in my pocket and my mother on the front seat to my right, as I swerved to avoid hitting a porcupine in the road, and that had, for a few years, when it was my mother's car, been parked in the two-car garage of the mid-century modern split-level, next to my father's second-hand two-door Fairlane, with its tiny atavistic fins, reaching back longingly to "the tranquillized *Fifties*" (as Robert Lowell called them), before all hell broke loose, two vestiges of the wattle and daub past, stop-gap rolling stock deployed in the interval of depleted cash-flow following the closing on the house on Willow Way, until, cash and credit flowing again, they were superannuated by the Oldsmobile and the Monte Carlo, and after another interval, by the sweepings and offscourings (superannuating all the superannuations of before), that by then filled the garage:

The Alexandrian ruins of a child's long-ago library, for instance, the books caking together in their listing little row of whitewashed bookcases lined up against the cinderblock wall: *The Cheeky Kittens, The Bingety-Bangety School Bus, Teddy Bear of Bumpkin Hollow, The Happy Hollisters, Stuart Little, Winnie the Pooh, Charlotte's Web, Tom Sawyer, Pippi Longstocking, Treasure Island, Twenty Thousand Leagues Under the Sea, The Swiss Family Robinson, The Legend of Sleepy Hollow, The Jungle Book, Alice's Adventures in Wonderland*, etc.

A child's art gallery of withered Kleenex flowers, chipped tile mosaics, crumbling cigar boxes decorated with macaroni, and the remains of other Vacation Bible School arts and crafts projects constructed of pipe cleaners, popsicle sticks, sugar cubes, Quaker Oats boxes, plaster of Paris, toilet paper tubes, wood, leather, construction paper, Ivory soap, and papier-mâché.

A child's arsenal of plastic weapons, stockpiled, as an effective deterrent, to maintain the balance of power among the children in the neighborhood: cap guns, water pistols, BB guns, sawed-off shotgun, knife, bludgeon, box of dumdum shells, crossbows, tridents, quarter staffs, mauls, blackjacks, Tommy guns, Winchester 73s, machine pistols, hand grenades, bazoo-kas, flamethrowers, napalm jelly.

Stacks and stacks of early childhood wax: "Gossamer Wump," "The Poky Little Puppy," "Let Your Conscience be Your Guide," "Little Shirley Beans," "Puff the Magic Dragon," "Little White Duck," "Frosty the Snowman," "Angus McFergus McTavish Dundee," "Merrily We Roll Along," "Whoopie Ti Yi Yo, Get Along Little Dogies."

Later 45s that my brother and I bought for ourselves with our own money, "Touch Me," "Crimson and Clover," "Lady Ma-donna," "Lonely Days, " "These Eyes," "25 or 6 to 4," "Spinning Wheel," "Midnight Confessions," "Lady Willpower," "Time of the Season," "Morning Girl," "You Showed Me" (b/w "Buzz Saw"), "In The Ghetto," "Jump into the Fire," "The Snake."

Starter LPs, Christmas presents and birthday presents, in-cluding my complete set of Monkees records—*The Monkees, More of the Monkees, Headquarters, Pisces, Aquarius, Capricorn & Jones Ltd., The Birds, The Bees & The Monkees, Head, Instant Re-play*—and my brother's near-complete collection of Elvis Presley soundtracks—*Speedway, Clambake, Viva Las Vegas, Blue Hawaii, Kid Galahad, Fun in Acapulco, Harem Scarum, Kissin' Cousins, Roustabout, Spin Out, Speedway, Double Trouble, Easy Come, Easy Go,* and *Girls, Girls, Girls*.

Later collections of acid, glam, and "classic" rock, with a small *soupçon* of soul and funk and R&B, in various evolving formats: LPs, eight track tapes, and cassettes, the records scratched be-yond usability, the eight tracks and cassettes oozing out in un-spooled piles: *Sticky Fingers, Exile on Main Street, Electric Warrior, Eat a Peach, Superfly, Hunky Dory, Madman Across the Water, Thick as a Brick, Dark Side of the Moon, Harvest, Transformer, Innervisions, Imagine, There's a Riot Going On, There Goes Rhymin' Simon, Who's Next, Nilsson Schmilsson*.

Another kind of rock collection—the igneous, sedimentary, and metamorphic kind—with specimens labeled and epoxied to a bit of particle board, and pinned with a ribbon reading,

"Honorable Mention, L.M. Smith Elementary School Science Fair, 1967," except my father had assembled the collection, purchasing the rocks from a nearby quarry and gluing them to the particle board, while I wrote and attached the labels, just as my father would later, out of pity, write the speech advocating liberty and other American virtues that I would deliver as my own when my sad attempts at writing the speech myself had failed, in a competition sponsored by the Rotary Club, Lions, Civitans, Kiwanis, Optimists—one of those—where I took third prize among three finalists (the charitable view is that the fathers of the other two contestants were more accomplished propagandists for the American Way).

The black lights and fluorescent paints of my brother's and my psychedelic early adolescence, and incense, incense burners, scented candles—vetiver, patchouli, and sandalwood—love beads, bongo drums, swinging medallions, Tarot cards, I Ching hexagrams, lava lamps, fringed vests, strobe lights, sandals, iron-on peace symbols, denim jackets, head bands, tie-dyes, dayglo posters.

Model cars: Corvette Stingrays, Porsche 911s, Jaguar XKEs, Shelby Cobras, Ferrari 250 GTOs, Aston Martin DB4 GT Zagatos, Mercedes-Benz 300SLs (with gull wing doors that opened on plastic hinges), Lotus Elans, dune buggies, drag racers, and hot rods, smelling of airplane glue that I had been careful not to sniff inadvertently when I glued the pre-cut plastic parts together, having been warned against the dangers of hallucinogenic drugs by Sonny and Cher, wearing bellbottoms, love-beads, and matching fringe vests, in a 16mm film that I myself, a card-carrying member of the Bell and Howell Audio Visual Club, had projected on a pull-down screen for the moral and hygienic edification of the sixth-grade.

A bi-wheeled motor pool, lined up like the ascent of man, marching proudly up to my beautiful Nishiki Olympiad, starting with my old 3-speed Sears Spyder Bike, with its high-rise handlebars, tiger-print banana seat, and sissy bar, brought over in a truck from the carport at Wedgeworth Drive, and deployed only for a month or two before being replaced, as part of my family's general rise in status, another sign of its upward mobility, by my new mod-a-go-go 5-speed Raleigh Chopper, imported from the U.K., also equipped with high-rise handlebars and sissy bar, but significantly "tuff-er" looking, and definitively "boss-er," with frame-mounted T-bar gear shifter, sprung black leather seat with backrest, differently-sized front and rear wheels, with knobby thread on the rear wheel and bobbed mudguards on the front.

An assortment of potentially toxic non-biodegradable later-to-be-vintage collectible plastic Hasbro, Mattel, Wham-O, Ohio Art, etc.—Super Balls, Silly Putty, Etch A Sketches, Hot Wheels, Creepy Crawlers, Rat Fink charms, Duncan Yo-Yos, gyroscopes, G.I. Joes, Slinkies, Hula Hoops, Mr. Potato Heads, GAF View Masters, Legos, Play Doh, Frisbees, Lite Brites, Mouse Traps, Rock 'Em Sock 'Em Robots.

And from an earlier, pre-industrial, pre-plastic era in the development of Blackwell *Ludens,* an old toy chest filled with old-fashioned toys made of wood, fabric, rubber, and tin—stuffed animals, blocks, spinning wheels, whistles, fifes, erector sets, toy pianos, toy soldiers, tinker toys, whirligigs, jack-in-the-boxes, pick-up sticks, pogo sticks, gee-haw whimmy diddles, rocking horses, stilts, tops, cups and balls, Lincoln Logs, jacks, rubber duckies, quoits, Jacob's ladders, battledores and shuttlecocks, trundling hoops and rolling sticks.

Grocery sacks from the A&P stuffed with gags, magic tricks, and novelty items, purchased on periodic field trips to novelty stores downtown or ordered from the back pages of comic books: x-ray specs, play puff cigarettes, bald wigs, onion gum, joy buzzers, whoopee cushions, itching powder, snakes in nut cans, stick-on scars, phony hickeys, plastic bugs stuck in ice, clattering teeth, fake arm casts, dribble glasses, two-headed quarters, plastic hillbilly teeth, Van Dyke beards, Fu Manchu mustaches, invisible ink, fake vomit, fake doo-doo, fake blood, nails thru the finger, arrows thru the head.

And finally, because my brother and I were boys of mystery and preferred to go in disguise: vaudeville trunks filled with costumes, props, wigs, greasepaint, and makeup towels; with masquerades and bedizenment for all occasions, but mainly cheesy synthetically-spun TV-inspired *bal masque*: first and second Darrinses, J. Maynard Krebbses, My Favorite Martians, Arnold Ziffels, Bat Mastersons, My Mother the Cars...

And, our specialty, paired suitings: Batman's cape, cowl, and utility belt, worn by me; Robin's eye mask, cape, and jumpsuit, worn by my brother: Dick Grayson (Robin) was, of course, Bruce Wayne's (Batman's) ward, and I was forever, cruelly, suggesting to my brother, a blond in a family of brunettes, that he was adopted, or that he was the milkman's son—and we had a milkman in those days.

Daniel Boone's frontier suit (basically Fess Parker's slightly re-tooled old Davy Crockett outfit) with coonskin cap, bowie knife, boots, and plastic musket, worn and carried by me, and, worn and carried by my brother, the fringed leather Indian suit, headdress, tomahawk, bow and arrows, moccasins, and leather pouch full of trinkets worn and carried by Mingo, Dan'l's opera-singing, Oxford-educated, friendly-Indian Indian guide, played by Ed Ames, of the Ames brothers, my father's favorite singing group.

Complete sets of Green Hornet crime-fighting attire: the Green Hornet's trilby hat, white shirt with standard collar, striped tie, topcoat, wool trousers, mask, white scarf, black leather gloves, black loafers, "Hornet Sting," "Hornet gun," and transmitter gold pocket watch, worn and carried by me; and the Hornet's friendly Japanese/Filipino/Chinese/Korean (the ethnicity of the inscrutable factotum changed several times during the show's long run on radio and television) manservant Kato's chauffeur's hat and ten-button chauffeur's jacket, black cuffless trousers, mask, black leather gloves, throwing darts, and nunchucks (worn and carried by my brother).

But our favorite costumes, costumes we have never changed out of: our "Man from U.N.C.L.E." Special Agent counterspy outfits (there was, after all, a cold war on): suave and unflappable Napoleon Solo for me and resourceful, friendly-Russian Ilya Kuriyakin for my brother, outfits that included, besides the obvious black turtlenecks and official credentials of the United Network Command for Law Enforcement, such necessary appurtenances as false Van Dyke and goatee beards, dark sunglasses, cardboard attaché cases, tan vinyl imitation Burberry trench coats with secret pockets useful for concealing the stocks of the trade: nerve spray cameras, exploding cap-grenades, fake lighter/cigarette case communicators, cap-blasting Berettas that convert to rifles with attachable scopes, stocks, silencers, and launcher barrels; and later, in my case: Moleskine notebook, subway map, MetroCard, *Time Out New York*, grade book, lesson plan, student essays to correct, and green pens (because red ink, you will learn in Chapter Thirteen, hurt the children's feelings).

A Miscanthus Bud

As Caroline and I lay curled in the darkness of our dream of eternal return, sweating out a sickness of regret, a debauch of seller's remorse, incanting the magical names of all our old lost touchstones and abandoned idols, the magical occult names of all the fragments of the world's beauty and anguish we could remember the names for, we would finally, counting our losses instead of sheep, drift off into sleep. And as we drifted, an aspect of ourselves usually turned inward, beyond sleep, a chthonic third eye we shared, would sometimes catch, in a corner of itself, a vision of our spirits rising to the ceiling and looking back down upon our two sleeping bodies below, observing from their new vantage point, in the succession of a dream, three ghostly film sequences projected onto the astral plane by a phantom pudgy-faced boy of eleven, his Bell and Howell Audio Visual Club membership card tucked in the back pocket of his flare-legged pants, the pants that would within two years stitch out further, to the horror of all the adults he knew, into "elephant bells": the flickering image, first, of two children tucked in matching red flannel devil pajamas, their teeth brushed clean and their faces scrubbed pink, solemnly bleating their prayers at bedtime — "God bless the turquoise ottoman, God bless the Fabergé egg..."; and then, emerging from the movie-magic dissolve of an all-but-forgotten Hollywood auteur later to be resurrected at the Film Forum or Anthology Film Archives, two tousled film noir lovers, nervous and post-coital, reclining in the darkened bed of a black-and-white B movie, their clothes rumpled, their hair mussed, each of them keeping, for the sake of the Legion of Decency, one modest foot touching the floor, and each blowing, from an unfiltered cigarette, an upward rising stream of imaginary smoke rings through the slats of Venetian blinds, one billowing ring growing and then dissipating for each item forfeited; and finally, in the baroque flourish of an iris wipe from the earlier silent and sepia era of film history, two scrofulous and bewhiskered old speculators would appear, archetypes of the century before the century that had just passed, gesturing wildly, and reading aloud from exaggeratedly long-scrolled ship's manifests and bills of lading of vessels gone down at sea, their faces mouthing the words that were flashing in fast-cut title cards,

Or, in a second iris wipe from an alternate ending of a lost reel, two bully, though still red-faced, capitalists, indefatigable and unsentimental, reading from their scrolls and cutting their losses, vowing to indemnify the next cargo, if there is a next cargo, or to find a less risky venture for future investment, if there is a future investment, but, at any rate, never flagging.

Caroline and I, though: we flagged. Sentimental, fatigable, exhausted in spirit and capital, we flagged.

Just then one of myriad ghost sounds of the city would rise to rouse us from our autoscopic reverie, and, thus wakened, our souls would suddenly seize up, sputter, and slide back into our bodies: a newsboy crying, "Read all about it"; the blasts and counterblasts of raging car horns; a slaughter on Tenth Avenue; crowds cheering a returning hero's ticker-tape parade; church bells pealing a celebrity wedding at the Little Church around the Corner; or knelling a gangster's funeral; a Gershwin tune tinkling on a grand piano across an air shaft; a pair of bouncing dice tumbling a hard eight the easy way or seven come eleven baby needs a new pair of shoes; dead end kids playing stickball in slang shouting, "So's your old man"; a flush-faced red-headed red-whiskered beat cop beating his nightstick on the pavement or opening a fire hydrant on a hot summer's day; a freshly-fleeced and mickey-finned drunken tenor stumbling from the suicides of McGurk's, crooning "Mother Machree" in unevenly modulating keys; a hoisted safe wrested free of its moorings crashing to the sidewalk, just missing a slinky shady flimflam dealer of three-card monte, temporarily between suckers, twitching nervously and cradling the "little lady" he will invite passersby to keep their eye on, as a fat sweating short-order cook fries an egg sunnyside up that sizzles on the sidewalk.

Even as it called us from our dream, though, and back into our bodies, "New York" itself would seize, sputter, and slide, as it had always seized, sputtered, and slid, back into *its* body, fading, as it would always fade, into a dream itself, into a dream *of* itself, into the dream it had always been and the dream it will always remain.

Caroline and I, though, rubbed our eyes and climbed out of bed. We put on our robes and our slippers and drip-brewed a big black pot of Old Government Java or, more likely, by then—at that point in the development of our consumer consciences—something "fair trade." Falling into a more sober reverie than the other one, the one from which we'd been awakened, we'd reminisce for hours about the pleasures we'd enjoyed accumulating the now discarded things of our old life, tabling, for the while, the sorrows ("bracketing" them I might have said back in seminary days), two scarred and blustery old campaigners, reunited, handicapping the weather with the shrapnel in our knees, fighting again all the battles we'd fought before, the battles we'd lost and the battles we'd won, time-traveling veterans of foreign wars on bucket shop reunion tours of Guadalcanal, Normandy, Verdun, Wounded Knee, Gettysburg, Waterloo, Agincourt, Shrewsbury, Hastings, Zama, Marathon, surveying with misty eyes the now tranquil fields we'd fought them in, drinking deeply again all the heady draughts of war we'd drunk together in our seedtime amassing the booty of spoils and the plunder of swag we'd pinched, pillaged, and purloined, marauding and ransacking the flea markets, thrift shops, jumble sales, yard sales, rummage sales, garage sales, and estate sales; all the rag-and-bone shops of our hearts, in and around Milwaukee, and in the other corners of the state, and in Illinois, Iowa, Minnesota, and the upper peninsula of Michigan—trading posts we torched before moving on, leaving salted earth and Carthaginian peaces behind us—two stupid happy commodity fetishists; not really the reivers and freebooters described above, though; that was just a joke; we were really more like a nation of shopkeepers or a gentle Tasaday of "hunterers" (as I liked to joke) and gatherers, or else we were theatrical property managers moonlighting as casting agents not so much looking over as auditioning each potential bibelot, each potential "crash tinkle tinkle" (stagehand slang, I recently learned, for when something breaks), discussing (out of item's earshot) whether to accept purchase or decline...

"Gee, you'd look cute with a lorgnette."

"Wow, an original iron lung from 1947—an Emerson, with negative-pressure ventilation!"

"Oh my god, is that an orgone box?"

"Do you think we should we buy this magic donkey skin?"

[We bought the magic donkey skin.]

...admiring, on the ride home, each purchase after it had been made, talking it up, hypothesizing a romantic provenance, inventing a picturesque history, and, getting the thing home at last, petting it, admiring it again, and, stagehands ourselves, trying it out in different settings as if decorating a set or (more like) blocking a scene in a play (a play in which the props were the actors).

We drank our coffee and remembered things for a long time, matching story for story the just-right lamp for the just-right table, the shrewd haggling, the brilliant purchases, the diabolically *bon marchés*; but then, after several rounds of such cheerful fanfaronade, I paused and, once again—I flagged. Lowering my head and my tone of voice, I quoted with a sigh—portentously (pretentiously!)—a pretty confession of Flaubert's I'd read "a million years ago, in the nineties" (as my old friend Azhar al-Shidyaq, quoting Beckett, titled a novel he published, overseas, a few years before Caroline and I moved to New York), a confession cited by Walter Benjamin in an essay so often cited itself—by overwrought graduate students of a sensitive nature (me)—entitled "On the Concept of History," but also known as "Theses on the Philosophy of History": "*Peu de gens devineront combien il a fallu être triste pour ressusciter Carthage.*"[5]

Caroline gently corrected my badly pronounced and Southern-drawled French, and, though she privately questioned the precise applicability of Flaubert's candid declaration of afflatus, as stated, though it was poignant and elegantly phrased, to the particular case at hand (you can't beat Flaubert for elegant phrases, though, whether or not they apply to any particular case at hand), she too lowered her head, and we sat silent for several minutes, two grandes dames, until Caroline interrupted this melancholy pause (which was edging on the lugubrious) by joking, in perfectly-pitched Laroussian French, that an angel of history had passed.

The angel of history she had in mind, of course, was *Der Engel*

---

[5] "Few will be able to guess how sad one had to be to resuscitate Carthage."

der Geschichte that Benjamin evokes with such poignancy in a passage from another of the theses, the angel that perceives history not as a chain of events, as we foolish mortals do, with our false consciousness and limited perspective and whatnot, but as a "single catastrophe which keeps piling wreckage and hurls it in front of his feet." "The angel," Benjamin continues, "would like to stay, awaken the dead, and make whole what has been smashed. But a storm is blowing in from Paradise; it has got caught in his wings with such a violence that the angel can no longer close them. The storm irresistibly propels him into the future to which his back is turned, while the pile of debris before him grows skyward."

And though irresistibly propelled into the future (but how could we have known then that there was a future, or that there'd ever been one before?), the two of us sat sad and heartsick, trailing to the floor in vintage dressing gowns, sipping expensive cups of egalitarian brew and gazing nervously at the wreckage of the past, at the crash tinkle tinkle, for a long time, until we remembered together another angel that in another past had passed before the wrecking ball, and falling upon each other in renewed laughter we shouted out in one voice, slightly asynchronous, of Hawksian overlapping dialogue (you can't beat Howard Hawks for slightly asynchronous overlapping dialogue), but the overlapping dialogue seemed to echo like in a movie where somebody has been drugged and is slowly losing consciousness: "Do you remember the time that the time that the time that the *do you remember the time that the angel* that the angel that the angel on Oakland Avenue on Oakland Avenue *on Oakland Avenue* do you remember the time remember the time remember the time remember the time..." Voices trail off; image dissolves; camera zooms out. Distorted voice-over in an echo chamber is heard stage-whispering off-stage:

It was Halloween, and it was 1989. Communism was falling everywhere (except in China, where the tanks kept rolling over everything and history wouldn't go away like the neo-cons said it was going to) and, on the home front, universities up and down the eastern seaboard were establishing Madonna studies programs. I had just dropped out of graduate school, but hadn't found my "true vocation," yet—that is, I'd quit the police department but hadn't got myself a steady job. This was shortly after Caroline and I had met, before we got married, but we had already moved in together. These were in-between days, but not, as I remember them now, incapacitating and Brian Wilson-ish, like the in-between days that would come later, and pullulate into weeks and months and years and galaxies of Internet-enabled hypochondria, self-canceling folies du doute, *agonizing reappraisals, and deep-tissue prostration; these were greener in-between days—brief, young, and tender—and I was playing, for a few months, at waiting tables (a job I would later tell people reminded me of the teaching profession, but without the apron, with the pad and pencil, though! or more precisely, the marbled "conferencing" notebook into which I scribbled the data I'd been mandated to collect and logged my "interventions," sidling from table to table, like a tummler at a Catskills resort schmoozing the customers, or a waiter taking orders at a restaurant: "Hi, my name is Mr. Blackwell, and I'll be your facilitator of learning this marking period; today's specials are 'targeted instruction for struggling readers,' 'activating prior learning,' and for dessert, 'fix-up strategies for reading comprehension'") at the Chili Bowl Restaurant, a fun and kitschy neo-dive (now defunct) that had once been written up by the famous food ironists Jane and Michael Stern for* Holiday *magazine in a review that the restaurant's owner had had laminated and posted on the door, a review in which the (also now-defunct, but, being grown up about everything, still collaborating) couple praised, among other things, the "masculine aroma of cumin greeting customers as they walk through the door," a job Caroline—my girlfriend then—who was already working there (we met, in fact, at the Chili Bowl, but I'm getting ahead of myself...) had arranged for me. There hadn't been many customers that evening, and Caroline and I were hanging out with a few friends of ours, drinking, as we often did, rounds of beers supplied, without his knowledge, by the conveniently absentee proprietor, an amiable chap, most likely in cups of his own, like everyone else in Milwaukee, who (we told ourselves) probably wouldn't have minded the larceny, and who certainly never noticed it.*

We were sitting in a booth near the window, cracking jokes and providing color commentary as the carnival of costumed souls cake-walked by. Just as the conversation was passing from dangling stage to full-blown lull, a sweet, pale, attenuated-looking little girl, all got up in angel gear—wings, halo, harp, wand (do angels have wands?), the whole bit—glided by, solemn and sad, smiling wanly, as if in replay of a secret martyrdom that no one else would ever know about. Moved by the spectacle, I took it in for an hour or two of frozen time that was in reality only half a beat, and quipped, in my customarily badly pro-nounced and southern-drawled French, "Un ange passe..."

The memory of this incident—that would soon compound with interest into an ever-more embellished anecdote we'd keep in our repertoire for years, even though it never got any laughs, except from each other—served to fortify our courage, and we rallied for some moments. Then, as our laughter subsided, we remembered—again together—something else that also gave us cheer, something that gave us an approximation of hope, of con-tinuity (and continuity with our old life had come, for us—by then—to equal hope). We remembered that through an accident of real estate the capital, yes, but not all of the colonial outposts of the Carthaginian Republic (The Carolingian Empire, we— Charles and Caroline—called it, before it fell) had been sacked after all; the quondam holdings that we—Trojan women, ululant in bereavement—had been mourning had not been confined to Milwaukee/Carthage/Aachen/Troy, and, for this reason, they weren't all quondam; we'd left an umbrella behind—an old masher's trick—to recall us back to Wisconsin's venereal soil.

Our bounty, we reminded each other, our republic, our em-pire, still extended [extends today!] 250 miles southwest from the shores of Lake Michigan to Vernon County, located near the Mississippi River, in the so-called "driftless area" of Wisconsin, the portion of the state that the retreating glaciers of the Pleisto-cene epoch had not pock-marked with the kettles, eskers, and moraines typical of the alternately flat and rolling landscape around Milwaukee, a region of ridges and hollows and trout streams where Caroline and I had many years before purchased eighteen acres of land, acreage we hadn't, in our frenzy of divestment, been able to sell, though foolishly we'd tried, a hill wooded with walnut, pine, hemlock, oak, ash, hackberry, shagbark, maple, and aspen, with a small building site hacked out of a stand of sumacs that had grown in the clearing of an original, and later abandoned, building site of a previous owner, where we had hauled and parked a 15-foot camper trailer, also midcentury modern, and also still in our (legal) possession, if a thousand miles away, a 1967 Aristocrat Land Commander, with green and white Colorado license plates (the kind with the snow-capped mountains), appointed with an avocado-colored range and refrigerator, faux knotty-pine wallpaper, and orange shag carpet. I had nicknamed the Land Commander the "Banana Hut," in honor of the shack the disciples of seventeenth-century haiku poet Matsuo Bashō built for their master across the river from the court at Edo, in rustic Fukagawa, where the reclusive Bashō wished to retire from public life. Bashō, who was born Matsuo Kinsaku, named the cottage, and himself, after a banana tree (芭蕉, or *bashō*) his students had planted near the hut. Of course, Bashō's hut ultimately burned down, and apparently he wasn't entirely happy with the building site, judging from a poem he wrote just after moving in, but I adored Bashō and called my trailer the Banana Hut, anyway:

> by my new banana plant
>   the first sign of something I loathe —
> a miscanthus bud![6]

The Banana Hut had been purchased from an elderly retired couple, crabbing out their last days in a mid-century modern

---

[6] Translation by Mokoto Ueda.

ranch box, with carport and satellite dish, erected sometime in the 1950s, the box and carport, not the dish, on an eave overhanging the Mississippi River, not far from the Army Corps of Engineers lock and dam, where, hiking one snowy afternoon, Caroline and I once counted thirty-three bald eagles half-napping in trees. Nearby, a horse was tied to a railing, its rider's footprints trailing into an adjacent wood. I thought of a poem by the eighteenth-century haiku poet, Yosa Buson:

> A tethered horse,
>   snow
> in both stirrups[7]

I had jury-rigged a bookcase in the trailer from a frail upper berth meant for a child, but Caroline and I had no children. I stocked the bookshelf where the child would have slept with Bashō and Buson, and with Kobayashi Issa (1763-1828), whose poem,

> Don't worry spiders,
> I keep house
>   casually[8]

would become the motto of the Banana Hut; I also stocked the berth with the *Shih Ching*, and the T'ang Dynasty poets Tu Fu, Li Po, Po Chu-I, and Wang Wei, and with several other poets, including James Wright, whose poem "Lying in a Hammock at William Duffy's Farm in Pine Island, Minnesota" had inspired me to rig a hammock outside the Banana Hut, and to renounce— for each weekend's visit, at least—all purposeful activity in the city:

> Over my head, I see the bronze butterfly,
> Asleep on the black trunk,

---

[7] Translation by Robert Hass.
[8] Ibid.

Blowing like a leaf in green shadow.
Down the ravine behind the empty house,
The cowbells follow one another
Into the distances of the afternoon.
To my right,
In a field of sunlight between two pines,
The droppings of last year's horses
Blaze up into golden stones.
I lean back, as the evening darkens and comes on.
A chicken hawk floats over, looking for home.
I have wasted my life.

Many years later, crouching in yet another student carved and graf-fitied desk aboard the ghost ship docked in Upper Manhattan, trapped like the boy in the barbershop in the poem by Philip Levine, another touchstone author on the Banana Hut bookshelf—"You've gotten in through the transom / and you can't get out / till Monday morning or, worse / till the cops come / [t]hat six-year-old red face / calling for mama / is yours; it won't help you / because your case / is closed forever, hope-less..."—except in my case (closed forever, hopeless), trapped in a never-ending series of "professional developments"—I would often fall into another reverie, the freeze-framed image of my late-forties-year-old red face calling for mama, dissolving, or iris-wiped, into a fog-filtered daydream of hammocks floating among bronze butterflies, black trunks, green shadows, and golden stones. On the "real" side of the daydream, to the right of me and to the left, battered and exhausted teachers learned the new jargon and most-up-to-date best practices, receiving their (data-driven) instruction and taking their (research-based) cate-chism from inevitably less-seasoned, but decidedly more ambitious for-mer colleagues who'd said goodbye forever to the thankless toil and limited earning potential of classroom teaching (but who could, of course, "reach so many more" students in their new roles as adminis-trators), lesser links, until they made captain, or regional sales man-ager, in the administrative Great Chain of Being, temporary Bodhisattvas of the bureaucracy, disseminating, salesman-like, various vials of patent-medicine satori, peddled by an array of for-profit ven-dors called "Comprehensive School Reform Providers," with generic supermarket names like "Success for All®," "Accelerated Schools Plus™," and "America's Choice®," that had been quickly incorpo-rated in the waxing years of the first administration of the second George Bush, to ensure that No Child would ever be Left Behind again, Bodhisattvas with a career path, pursuing night courses in "adminis-trative leadership," fundamentalists of a kind, imbued with a literal be-lief in the scriptural inerrancy of the teachings of a mysterious eminence called Lucy Calkins, and the divine revelations of the Teach-ers College of Columbia University, where Calkins, an apparent oracle of the burgeoning and lucrative spiritual practice called "balanced lit-eracy" (or was it "the workshop model"? I could never remember the doctrinal distinctions) held court, journeyman illuminati, with their own partial purchase on the key to all mythologies, who, like "made men" of the mafia, had proven their fealty to the sacred solemn shibbo-lethic cause of "school reform" by making their first contract hit, a let-ter in the file, say, or an "unsatisfactory" rating, for one of the weaker prey, a first- or second-year acolyte who had neglected, perhaps, coun-ter to the doctrines of the workshop model (or was it balanced literacy?), to write her "agenda," "teaching point" or "standard(s) addressed" on the chalkboard, or who has—in a willful and morbid reversion to the benighted days of the discredited "chalk and talk" method of instruction that had failed to educate so many generations of scholars—held the floor for more than ten consecutive minutes without eliciting any "no-ticings," "wonderings," "text-to-self connections," "text-to-world connections," or "text-to-text connections" from the "emergent read-ers" in her classroom, or had held the floor without inviting her stu-dents to "turn and talk" (under the new dispensation, students were always being cordially invited to do things they didn't want to do; they did of course want to talk, but not about any lesson at hand), thereby committing the most egregious error of them all: direct instruction, a deviational tendency smacking even more nostalgically of "chalk and talk," and therefore expressly forbidden in the "student-centered class-room," thus bleeding time (which is money) away from the students' "independent work period," preempting the "data-gathering" "interventions" and "ongoing assessment" of teacher-student "conferencing" and the "closing meeting share"; battered and exhausted teachers, ingénues and burnt-out cases, and all the stops along the way, some gossiping, some morose, some punch drunk and slap happy, some detached and stoical, some openly resentful, hostile even (me, for instance), others silently fuming or simply wary, and still others, the mature ones—the professionals—the ones who knew how to pick their spots (or who had acquired a mortgage in one of the greener arcadias lying across the George Washington Bridge), the ones who, at some earlier or later phase of their careers, had come, "proactively," to understand a few of the sunnier uses of adversity, how to make lemonade out of cherry pits and how to turn frowns and half-empty glasses upside down, and who, like recovering alcoholics—which many of them were, of course, the ones who weren't still practicing the austere rigors of the discipline—had been granted, by a Power greater than themselves, the serenity to accept the things they could not change, the courage to change the things they could, and the wisdom to know the difference: "We've all been here before / we took our turn / under the electric storm / of the vibrator / and stiffened our wills to meet / the close clippers / and heard the true blade mowing / back and forth / on a strip of dead skin / and we stopped crying..." But I had never stopped crying, had never known, nor sought, serenity (or, god knows, wisdom), and as I watched the true blade mow in one malfunctioning PowerPoint presentation after another, more clicking, swooshing phantom projections on the astral plane, in animated bullet point upon animated bullet point, in **Cooper Black** *typeset, in* Elephant, *in* **Franklin Gothic Demi**, *in* Lucida Console, *in* Perpetua, *in* Playbill, *in* Goudy Stout, *in* **Rockwell Extra Bold**, *in* Verdana, *and in* **Wide Latin**, *ascending, spinning, zooming, bouncing, pinwheeling, and boomeranging the finer points of "flexible grouping," "differentiating instruction," "zones of proximal development," and "scaffolding schema," I often thought of these lines from another poem of Wright's, entitled "A Prayer to Escape from the Market Place": "I want to lie down under a tree / This is the only duty that is not death,"*

and I longed to lie in my hammock again, sipping lapsang souchong
from an earthenware mug, writing in my diary, my heart soothed with
evening birdsong, a hundred million light years away...

&

A hundred million light years away, less three hundred and
sixty four days, and nine-hundred and ninety-nine thousand
miles, on the last trip I would make to Vernon County, a week
or so before boarding my long one-way flight to La Guardia Airport, I cleared out the contents of the Banana Hut for good *I was*
still "Chip" — then — but only just barely, having already begun hard-
ening my heart to the old joy, even as I swam one last time in the small
cold lake at Jersey Valley, where the West Fork of the Kickapoo River,
never wild but always winding, is dammed, and as I climbed for the
last time to the summit of Wildcat Mountain to watch the sunset, sur-
prising, on my way up, a flock of wild turkeys that upon hearing my
footfall ran out ahead of me, scurrying up the hill, in ascending order
of height... I started my demolition job with the library...*I'm pack-*
*ing my library: Yes I am...*spending an hour or so dusting off the
by-then musty volumes and carefully packing each volume, and
all attendant memories, annotations, digressions, and margina-
lia, all reflections and illuminations, into corrugated boxes I'd
brought with me from Milwaukee, boxes that were labeled, in
big block letters,

DISPOSIBLE VAGINAL SPECULUMS

that I'd acquired from a nurse I knew at a drop-in clinic, later
"de-funded," that was housed, for a brief time, in a small office
with a makeshift examination room pitched in a narrow alcove
off a wide hallway, with skylights and potted plants (the hallway not the examination room) — sort of like an atrium at a mall
or an airport, that functioned as a kind of no-man's-land,

separating the always feuding, but, for funding purposes, con-tractually "partnered," Ranald and Lilias Fairbairn Kidz Club-house (my employer for the three years prior to my move to New York) and the Devereux P. Woodruff Year Round School (K-8), a public school that had, in the first weeks of my employ-ment at Fairbairn, appended the phrase "year-round" to its offi-cial designation when its teachers voted, astonishingly (to me; to no one else, but to me), in a near-unanimous decision, to forgo the only perquisite that teachers, as far as I knew, had ever been able to call their own—summers off: the only reason, frankly, that I could think of to become a teacher in the first place (as I would later, upon taking up the trade, scandalize my more ear-nest colleagues by repeatedly fulminating) except, perhaps, to impress strangers you meet on an airplane ("Oh, you're a teacher; that must be *very* rewarding! Society really owes you a debt of gratitude. By the way, though, I support legislation to link your rate of pay, and continued employment, to student achievement as measured by standardized test scores. Oh, and I'd very much like to bust your union"), or, of course, for the opportunity to relocate to New York City.

In coming to their near-unanimous decision, the teachers had, I imagined, been strongly encouraged by their own Great Chain of Being, but maybe not, maybe it was their own idea (I have always been amazed at how it is that people get their own ideas). "Year-round schooling" was a "cost-effective" nostrum, popular among the mandarins and technocrats flourishing in the upper echelons of the profession; it *sounded* like "reform," but required no greater cash outlay than the traditional calendar it was replac-ing—an agricultural vestige, it was said, based on older rhythms of the planting season and associated political economies, long-since antiquated by various industrial and post-industrial revo-lutions, and thus rife for modernization, rife for "reform." It was certainly cheaper than implementing the only educational nos-trum sounding like reform that ever (for obvious self-interested reasons) made sense to me, a nostrum that would remain forever, it seemed, nothing more than a slogan and rallying cry for the *Re-thinking Schools* crowd: "smaller class size"—a slogan that the architects had built into the recently-constructed physical plant of Devereux P. Woodruff Year Round School (K-8) by designing classrooms meant to house fifteen students, even though they might have guessed that the classrooms would wind up housing the usual thirty to thirty-five when the school opened.[9] Teachers weren't, as far as I could tell, allowed a vote on class size.

The two worthy, if often quarreling, institutions shared program space and "missions" (everything and everybody had a "mission," or at least a "mission statement"; and then later a "vision" and an "impact statement") to serve the at-risk youth of the city's socioeconomically-challenged Woodruff Park neighborhood, a neighborhood that had made the national news a year or so before I tendered my resignation at Fairbairn, when fifteen of its at-risk, socioeconomically-challenged youth, ages ten to nineteen, beat a thirty-six year old man to death with baseball bats, shovels, broom handles, tree limbs, a folding chair, a plastic milk crate, and a rake. None of the boys had been students at the school or members of the clubhouse, staff at both institutions were relieved to learn. I was accused of being "cynical," though, by some of my colleagues, when I speculated, the day after the crime, that the "fundraising executives" who formed the upper echelon of the "development team" at the new and of course very fancy and expensively-constructed Kidz

---

[9] I did hear, from sources in the school administration, that it wasn't true the rooms were designed for fifteen students; that the story was a kind of urban folktale promulgated by a handful of malcontents. An unrepentant malcontent since early adolescence, I tended to believe the tale. Even if untrue, the number of students in the classrooms, regardless of the number of students they were designed to hold, was too large for any activity other than crowd control, or so it seemed to me (but the last thing I want to do in this somewhat fictionalized memoir of mine is weigh in on education debates, except, of course, to mock and sneer). Of course, the dedicated teachers at the school, notwithstanding the high population density in their classrooms, carried on doing their best anyway, as dedicated teachers will.

Clubhouses of Greater Milwaukee administrative headquarters, officially called the Henshall Möller Center for Administration, Training, Development, and Excellence, referred to simply as "Möller" by the working class at the clubs, but which I "cynically" dubbed "Moloch," had by then sniffed out an opportunity and were already discussing ways to make capital of the story—by pasting, for instance, some of the more prurient details of the horror into the "Describe the needs of your target population" sections of the various proposals for funding they would submit that year (just as I would later make capital of the story in my "somewhat fictionalized memoir," to help me score some easy points—some easier ironies—at the expense of yet another Great Chain of Being). I wasn't surprised to find my cynicism vindicated when the President/C.E.O. cited the outrage in an appeal for funding delivered to a ballroom full of power-lunching—or was it prayer-breakfasting?—business executives/prospective donors, not two days later.

I can't remember now whose fundraising executives, the clubhouse's or the school system's, submitted the proposal that had originally funded the clinic, or which worthy institution had been "de-funded." Each of these worthy institutions, like all worthy institutions, took its turn having its budget bled. Though, to staunch the bleeding, no one in the upper echelon of any Great Chain that I could remember the name of had ever been required to sacrifice his or her job when the ink started flowing red, as it invariably did toward the final quarter of every fiscal year (I had learned many years earlier to spend down any "discretional" allocations I might have argued into my budget by the third week of October, when the spending freeze was traditionally announced). No, those smarmy glad-handing self-aggrandizing careerists (my pet name for them) generally fell—if on their pilgrim's progress to career self-actualization they stayed long enough at any one station of the cross or on any one rung of the career ladder to fall (or to be found out)—either to moral turpitude or *coup d'etat*, but always with a "golden parachute" to tide them over until they'd completed the "pursuit of new career opportunities" upon which they had embarked; pursuits cited in preemptive press releases—tweaked, cut, and pasted from previously prepared boilerplate carefully worded for damage-control, written in advance like *New York Times* obituaries for elder statesmen and grandes dames, or reckless heart-throbs, pop stars, and latter-day method actors on their way to dying young—to explain their sudden absence from executive suite; new career opportunities that seemed always to await them, teleologically, the way heaven awaits good children in counting rhymes, or "Millionaire Estates" awaits canny players of The Game of Life.

As the latest step in my own pilgrim's progress to career self-actualization, I had, a week or two prior to acquiring the boxes labeled "DISPOSABLE SPECULUMS," handed my bosses at the Fairbairn Kidz Clubhouse a carefully-crafted, and cliché-ridden, letter of resignation, in which I expressed gratitude for the "opportunity to serve" and begged to be relieved of my duties, citing a desire to pursue new career opportunities of my own with the New York City public school system (career opportunities that would turn out, in my case, to be more *eschato*logical than *teleo*logical). I had written several such letters over the years, and would write one more before suffering the nervous breakdown, but they don't call it a nervous breakdown anymore, that eventuated in my subsequent retirement from active life across the river from the court at Manhattan, in rustic Brooklyn, where, sequestered, now, and having an extended lie-down, I cut my losses, lick my wounds, fret over my health, and dictate my memoirs, but, again, I anticipate—and digress...

Back in Vernon County *on the last trip to the Banana Hut I would make before boarding my long one-way flight to La Guardia Airport,* after taping the bottom flaps shut, I carefully packed the boxes labeled "DISPOSABLE VAGINAL SPECULUMS" with the dusted off contents of the now-emptied bookshelf. Then, after sealing them, I loaded the boxes into the rear compartment of my little green station wagon, a 1995 Ford Escort that everyone thought was blue, but it was green. (I would, within a couple of weeks, surrender this car, which I called "the Green Flivver," along with the keys, pink slip, owner's manual, and a windshield wiper that had fallen off, to a young friend of mine to whom I'd sold the car because where I was going I wouldn't need a car; where I was going I'd take "the train," not the subway, but "the train.")

I packed most of the rest my rural provisionment into the remaining boxes I'd brought along, and packed the boxes, along with the implements and tools that wouldn't fit in boxes, into the Green Flivver's rear hatch. I swept the Banana Hut's floor one last time, wiped down all surfaces, battened down the hatches, and locked the door for the last time (promising myself I'd keep the key to the trailer on my key ring to remind myself, whenever I locked or unlocked a door, of all the things I used to love, all the things I used to treasure), then I drove away, knowing one day I'd regret it, or not knowing one day I'd regret it, fighting back tears I wasn't sure I knew why I was crying, and heading out for Viroqua, the county seat, and U.S. 14, a winding, climbing, dipping two-lane blacktop that would take me to Madison, where I would have to transfer to the flat monotonous tractor trailer and recreational vehicle hogged Interstate highway that would take me the rest of the way into Milwaukee—all told, a four and a half hour drive.

As I sat brooding over my cups of coffee on the Upper Side West, trying to talk French and absorb my sense of regret into a new expression of life, I remembered all of the supplies that made up the rural provisionment I had stashed away in the Banana Hut; I remembered where each tool or implement had been stowed; and I could almost remember on which particular weekend trip I'd purchased which item at the Andersen Agri-Supply Center in Viroqua, an old-fashioned hardware/feedstore/lumberyard/general mercantile that was making a brave last stand against the Wal-Mart "Discount Store" that was metastasizing, amongst the corn, sunflower, and tobacco fields spanning the stretch of U.S. Highway 14 between Viroqua and Westby, into a Wall-Mart "Supercenter." (Once, while taking my breakfast at The Olde Norwegian Café, in downtown Westby, I was reminded of August Bebel's remark that "anti-Semitism is the socialism of fools" when I over-heard a farmer offer a woman I assumed to be the farmer's wife an insightful and carefully reasoned analysis of the devastation Wal-Mart wreaks on rural America, and then, as a punch line, credit the dodgy business practices he'd been describing, business practices pioneered by Sam Walton—a Presbyterian, by the way—to (wait for it)"Jew-thinking." As I sat in astonishment, I was also reminded of something Karl Marx, another famous Jew-thinker, wrote in "The Communist Manifesto": "The bourgeoisie has subjected the country to the rule of the towns. It has created enormous cities, has greatly increased the urban population as compared with the rural, and has thus rescued a considerable part of the population from the idiocy of rural life.")

These tools, implements, and other gear, all of which, except for a pair of binoculars, would be sacrificed in the burnings to come, had all been stashed in the trailer's small closet and in its even smaller half bath, with its tiny shower stall and toilet, a shower stall and toilet Caroline and I couldn't use anyway because we'd never dug a well or put in a septic tank. We drew our water from a pipe in the side of a hill in the nearby village of Avalanche, out of which flowed pure water, cool and clear, from an underground spring, and hauled it back in jugs to the Banana Hut. We took bucket showers behind the trailer, and, like the bear, relieved ourselves in the woods (but unlike the bear we buried our solid waste in widely dispersed cat holes located at least 200 feet from water, trails, and camp—because we'd read a pamphlet about it). We'd never dug a well because we didn't know how to dig a well and later because we'd been influenced by a stanza of T'ang poet Tu Fu's "Six Quatrains," and, more particularly, by an annotation written by the poem's translator, J. P. Seaton—"…the stanza as a whole suggests not just the futility of what we call 'purposeful' or 'constructive' human effort, but its immorality, its disharmony with the Tao, as well":

Sink a well, plait a rope of palm leaves,
Break bamboo, make pipe for drains:
Little boat comes tangled in halyards,
Narrow ways bind tight the hamlets.[10]

We didn't even know if we were close enough to the water table to dig a well at all, because we were in such a hurry to buy up the property, a bargain at $10,000, we were told, by our real estate representative, the kindly Lowell E. Whittier—who seemed more New England than Middle West, in name, if not demeanor—and so worried we'd queer the deal that we hadn't insisted on the customary perk test before making our offer. (We later learned that a perk test doesn't have anything to do with digging a well, but rather with putting in a septic tank; we thought at the time, though, that it had to do with digging a well, but, at any rate, we wouldn't have cared if the land "perked" or not because we didn't want to put in a septic tank; we wanted to build an outhouse with a crescent moon carved above the door and keep some old Sears Roebuck catalogues on the floor, or Monkey Ward, to use for toilet paper.)

No bank would give us a loan to buy the land since we weren't planning to reside on the property, so we raised the ten thousand on cash advances from credit cards. When the time came to conclude the deal, I had to write the draft three times because I was so nervous making out a check for such a large amount that I kept scribbling *"one* thousand and 00 dollars" instead of "ten thousand and 00 dollars."

We loved the ridges and hollows of Vernon County, especially the secluded, morning-misty hollows. We didn't crave vistas. We wanted to entangle ourselves in the beauty the cravers of vistas were admiring from their high rises. We had encamped at the foot of our hill, the hollow of our ridge, only to scale the slope of a late summer evening to look up and take in the

---

[10] *Bright Moon, Perching Bird: Poems by Li Po and Tu Fu*, translated from the Chinese by J. P. Seaton and James Cryer.

spectacular meteor showers of August, and to try and learn the names of the constellations in the clear country sky, where, unlike in the city, with its distracting halogen radiance, you could bathe in the pure and mysterious white light of the Milky Way. We also loved going on long walks in the winding, climbing, and descending country roads, following old Indian and fur-trapper's and farmer's trails, and barely perceptible deer trails, and blazing our own trails, identifying and sketching and photographing wildflowers along the way, researching their folklore and pharmacology. As we hiked we scanned the ground for the elusive blue monkshood, and surveyed the sky and trees for the even more elusive pileated woodpecker, for the ivory-billed woodpecker, for the passenger pigeon, for the Carolina parakeet. We collected bird's nests and lichen-bark and exoskeletons and sloughed mylodon skins and intercostal clavicles for temporary exhibitions that we took turns curating in a makeshift natural history museum we'd laid out in a corner of the Banana Hut.

We didn't own a car yet, that first year after we bought the hill in Vernon County, so every Friday evening (if we felt ambitious) or Saturday morning (more realistically) we made our way, on foot, to the rental counter of a car dealer near where we lived, queuing up to rent the cheapest subcompact available so we could get to our rural retreat and press our extinct flowers in memory books, stalk our *rarae aves*, dig for dinosaur bones, and entangle ourselves in the beauty of the pure and mysterious white light of the cosmos. (We hadn't acquired the Banana Hut yet, then; we camped, that first summer, in a tent we pitched in the overgrown building site, amongst the mayapples, trillium, trout lilies, jack-in-the-pulpits, and wild columbine fruiting and wilting in the rustling sumac stand.) Just as we would later make a point of being proud of not eating meat and of not owning a television set, we had spent the several years before we bought the land making a point of being proud of not owning a car—a car we couldn't have afforded anyway.

We had further made a point of being proud of living close

enough to the Hogarth Street YMCA, where I was employed as coordinator of educational programs when we bought the land, and, before that, to the other youth centers and alternative schools where I learned my trade—in surroundings that, to naïve suburbanites, might approximate something like "the 'hood"—for me to walk to work. If pressed, though, we would have had to admit that we lived in one of the more predominately white and middle class enclaves within the largely poor, working class, and "minority" neighborhood served by Hogarth Street—a neighborhood, like Woodruff Park, that seemed (to invading and indigenous do-gooders alike), because of its demographic preponderance of poorer and darker-skinned residents, to be abjectly and axiomatically in want of "strategically-planned" not-for-profit "community-based organizations" and "youth-serving agencies," organized, philanthropically (though they'd never use that word), to meet the needs of residents constituted, in somewhat militaristic language, as "target populations" in grant proposals and other appeals for public and private support. ("The compulsion to do good," Ivan Illich once wrote, and I once quoted in a grant proposal that, curiously enough, didn't get funded, "is an innate American trait. Only North Americans seem to believe that they always should, may, and actually can choose somebody with whom to share their blessings. Ultimately this attitude leads to bombing people into the acceptance of gifts.")

Since dropping out of the Contemporary Critical and Cultural Studies program (and trading in my dilettantish academic would-be Marxist theory for "praxis" —such was my conceit, anyway; and "praxis" was a word I might actually have used to apply to my case circa 1990—but I hope with some sense of irony), I had, of course, organized *myself* to meet the needs of various target populations as well, to bomb them into the acceptance of my gifts, seeking and gaining employment in three successive youth-serving agencies (and resigning, usually rather self-importantly, from each one over some trampled "principle"

or another—once even taking a proud $7,000 per annum pay cut
for the privilege of the sacrifice—and, moreover, planning for
what promised to be an impecunious dotage by scrupulously resigning six months to a year before becoming vested in the
agency's retirement plan). I was, in my way, though, "doing well
by doing good"—of course not nearly as well as my bosses
(whom, as the careful reader will have already surmised, I bit-
terly resented), but nevertheless better than I'd ever done before,
and better than I'd ever believed I would ever deserve to do. For
this reason my cheeks burned with self-reproach when I sneeringly, if accurately, pointed out a dirty little open secret about
the hand that fed me: While none of the more up-to-date and
better funded charities of the day used the word "charity," or
any of its derivations, any longer, having been instructed—a
"lesson learned"—that charities don't "empower," the charitable infrastructure of the *idealistic* community-based youth-serving non-profits (one sought employment at such organizations,
in the days when one sought employment, at a website called
"*idealist*.org") that so strategically empowered communities,
was almost always, with, sometimes, the non-binding auxiliary
assistance of "community input," governed by white people,
(and, in some instances, *staffed* mainly by white people), while
the population targeted for their largesse, for all their earnest
and technocratic "strategic planning," was invariably black and
brown.

Specifically, these charities seemed always to be superin-
tended, on the "volunteer" level, by white boards of directors
(exceptions admitted), whose members—so willing to share
their blessings—lived outside the neighborhood (for the most
part, *way* outside the neighborhood—*way, way* outside the
neighborhood), and, on the careerist, by predominately white
Great Chains of Being (who tended also to live outside the neighborhood), styling themselves, with much pomp and jargon, as
"Leadership Teams."

Again, exceptions to these generalizations must be admitted;

in the celestial sphere of leadership, second-tier posts, such as Operations Director or Director of Human Resources, were sometimes filled by "articulate" men, and occasionally women, of color ("Articulate" was of course the highest praise predominately white search committees, yielding to pressure to diversify, could lavish on "qualified" black applicants; it was a kind of code word signifying "not loud and disagreeable like the others," or perhaps "light-skinned...with no Negro dialect," or "bright and clean and good-looking"; "qualified" was the other shibboleth evoked by search committees to explain to critics that they'd have hired more African Americans if it hadn't so happened that every time they posted an opening for an executive position so many charming white people with such *better* qualifications hadn't so kindly made themselves available to serve); and in the sublunary, and less well-compensated reaches, where youth serving agencies actually stand a chance of serving youth, the captaincy of the local clubs or branches ("colonial outposts," I called them or, sometimes, "strategic hamlets") had largely been set aside for similarly articulate and qualified men, and occasionally women, of color.

The (largely socioeconomically distressed) neighborhood where I lived and worked was served by several charities (except they didn't call themselves charities), three of which were willing to share their blessings with me, to provide me, that is, with employment opportunities when I so kindly made myself available to serve (and to provide me also, I would learn later, with something like a purpose in life): the Lourdes Valdez Education Center, which was the "MPS Partnership" school where, following my brief interlude waiting tables, I had gone to work when I said goodbye to the abyssal aporias of the Contemporary Critical and Cultural Studies program, and where I would later boast, in the written portion of my earnest, and, in retrospect, touching, even tender effort to gain a position "building equity" by "invest[ing] in 1.1 million futures" in New York City, that I had opted heroically to swim rather than sink (and where, tapping a different cliché from the endless reservoir, I would, fuddling up my four elements, boast as well, in separate venues, that I'd no less heroically also submitted myself to a baptism by fire); the Hogarth Street Youth Center (later born again as—re-christened, re-branded—the Hogarth Street YMCA); and the Children's Settlement Service, which later re-branded itself as CSS Family Centers, pluralized even though there was only one such center, dropping altogether any mention of the phrase "Children's Settlement Service," an old-fashioned sounding name that had been its handle since its founding in the early nineteen-hundreds, as a settlement house for recently-arrived immigrants, and in so dropping, leaving itself open to the charge, to the "easier irony," that "CSS" stood, literally, for noth-ing—though in later promotional material, the development team, perhaps mindful of this vulnerability, started slipping in, parenthetically, the explanatory phrase "formerly Children's Settlement Service" to soften the new brand.

CSS Family Centers was, of course, a much older youth-serv-ing agency whose services the Hogarth Street Youth Center, founded in 1990, was careful, for funding purposes, not to "du-plicate" (if you want to get funded you'd better learn not to du-plicate anybody's services—funders, who like to see efficient approaches to "problem-solving" get particularly worked up about that one), and it is where I went to work two weeks after I delivered one of my carefully-crafted letters of resignation to the latest qualified and articulate man of color (an earlier such twice-gifted mortal had been quietly assumed a few months before into one of the celestial spheres of upper management) that the YMCA had posted as branch executive (that's what they called the chief—"branch executive") of its wholly-owned subsidi-ary/colonial outpost, located on Hogarth Street (though when I went to work there, it was still just plain "Hogarth Street Youth Center"; this was five years before the hostile takeover and sub-sequent appendage of the seemingly-benign tetragrammaton that would later irk me so—coming, as it did, to represent for me a kind of suburban white bread cult of banality imposing its bland, condescending monoculture on all it touched).

The (largely socioeconomically distressed) neighborhood (with pockets of affluence nestling among the various target populations) served by these worthy institutions where my wife and I so generously shared *our* blessings and made a point of being proud to lay our hats, was known to its white residents, and to its more affluent black and Puerto Rican residents, as "Hogarth Hills," and had, since the early seventies, positioned itself as a funkier, more multicultural Brooklyn-like alternative to the costlier, and whiter, *haute bourgeois* (sort of) Manhattan on the other side of the Euclid Street and Division Avenue bridges. The neighborhood, which served as a kind of buffer zone between the central city and more fashionable quarters, and was thus a step up for some and a ho-bohemian "step down" for others (but just right for certain counter-cultural Goldilockses that I admired, and envied, who'd distinguished themselves in the food co-op or fought off greedy developers and insurance redliners) was called "Lake Bluff" by its less affluent black and Puerto Rican residents, who seemed not to have been let in on the designs certain white hipsters and activists had for the neighborhood that had been theirs since they found it abandoned, thirty years earlier, by the white "ethnics" who originally settled there. The two names for the same neighborhood occasionally caused confusion for white residents and more affluent black and Puerto Rican residents, who employed the designation "Lake Bluff" to refer to the *much more* affluent, and *overwhelmingly* white neighborhood of bungalows and frame houses and Birkenstocks (and duplexes and mansions) across the Milwaukee River.

Lake Bluff, of course, was the neighborhood that Caroline and I, in our third concession to the institutional practices of the possessing classes whose ranks we seemed to be joining (our first concession was getting married), would skulk our way to when we found our annual income (and, more importantly, "creditworthiness") increasing.

This rise in standard of living that ultimately provided us with the financial wherewithal for the move to Lake Bluff—as well as the expansion to Vernon County—was due, it must be noted, to an accident of strategic planning that had occurred a few years earlier when the at-the-time deep-pocketed YMCA of Greater Milwaukee, the organization that irked me so, a going concern, then,[11] that operated (as I, though not only I, used, "cynically," to say) a string of successful health clubs located in the green (which is to say white, though their books were in the black) arcadias surrounding the city, finding itself anxious to expand its holdings in the central city as a means of bolstering its tax exempt status, perpetually challenged by Greater Milwaukee's other, explicitly *for*-profit health clubs, assimilated the struggling Hogarth Street Youth Center (which was near to closing its doors due to lack of funds) into its "assets" column, as a kind of loss leader, after first sending over a couple of suits from Mergers and Acquisitions to case the joint. (They looked like Mormon missionaries, or Amway salesmen, these representatives of the YMCA "movement," as they called it, blandly ecumenical Christian soldiers soft-pedaling Jesus—in favor, it would subsequently appear to me, of Dale Carnegie and Dr. Stephen R. Covey—a strategic "de-emphasis" that I suspected had been the result of market research.[12])

A condition of the sale, insisted upon by the youth center's original (and straightforwardly secular) proprietors, was that the new management retain the current program staff, many of whom would have been ineligible for employment at the Y, because they had criminal records and/or had never been to college. Once all the arcane complications of "salary grade" had been calculated and recalibrated by the wizards in Human Resources, the tetragrammaton shared its blessings generously,

---

[11] They subsequently went bankrupt.

[12] Don't know how this fits in with Jesus, soft-peddled or not, but the Y closed the Hogarth Street branch in 2008.

bestowing preferment and conferring upon me the title of "Program Director," along with all rights and privileges of the office. "Exempt" and salaried, I found the contents of my pay envelope increasing by approximately $10,000 a year, setting the stage for further increases when I later signed on with the Fairbairn Kidz Clubhouse, following a three-year interregnum at CSS—during which time I took the "principled" cut in pay I had made such a point of being proud of.

It was approximately five years after buying the land in Vernon County, and four years after buying the Green Flivver (our second concession to—what was it?—"the institutional practices of the possessing classes"), that we learned that somebody would give *us* (the undeserving lower-middle class, stepping up from "voluntary poor") a mortgage (a mortgage that was just one step up from "sub-prime," but a mortgage, nevertheless). This is when we made our move.

We hired three mustachioed silent-movie movers—big burly "white ethnics" from the city's South Side—to load up the largest moving van in their fleet and make several trips across the river, hauling ton after ton of the mid-century's hell's own amount of beauty and anguish that Caroline and I had collected up to that point (at the end of the move, taking their hats off and holding them over their hearts, the movers testified with awe that never, in all their years in the business, had they moved as much gear as they moved that day), a collection soon to be multiplied (as God had once commanded of those whom he had created in his image), and then ritually sacrificed like a son upon an altar (as God had also—unreasonably in my view; I thought so even as a child, *especially* as a child!—commanded of one of the more prominent multiplicands of his original injunction), and later grieved over so remorsefully that I had to write a book about it, all so we could set up shop in our almost-bourgeois modest frame house, front-gabled, sporting a charming gambrel roof, and scandalizing, in the process, many of our former neighbors and left-leaning friends (and, to some degree, our own consciences).

Woodruff Park, incidentally, had no white or middle class pockets—it was all "target population"—and consequently there was never any discussion of our moving there when I went to work at the Kidz Clubhouse.

The Polish Moon, Part One

One discontinued fragment of the beauty of the world shored against ruin in the Dutch Colonial revival towards which Caroline and I would look back on later with such remorse, from two perches in New York City, one in Manhattan, and the other in Brooklyn, a fragment we particularly treasured, and one which would survive the move to New York, was a lithograph depicting a T'ang dynasty boar rooting among some lotuses. The boar was encased in a gilt frame, peeling but elegant, that we'd picked out ourselves from the storeroom at the shop where we bought the lithograph, because it was handsome and because it bore a small inscription that read, "Property of the Whitney Museum, New York City." The shopkeeper told us that he had only a week or so before purchased a consignment of discontinued frames from the museum.

The frame was about the right size to mount Edward Hopper's "Nighthawks at the Diner," and, when gazing upon our treasured peccary, which was hung gallery style in the living room of the Dutch Colonial Revival on Newhall Street, in the midst of a crowded array of other framed pictures arranged in imitation of Gertrude Stein's salon at 27 Rue de Fleurus, a photograph of which I had studied many times as a teenager, dreaming of expatriation, of being a lost generation, I often imagined I could sense an aura of Hopper's painting radiating from the frame, even when I learned, a few months after acquiring the lithograph, when I saw the picture hanging in a gallery of the

Art Institute of Chicago, where I was also reminded that the title of the oil is simply "Nighthawks," not "Nighthawks at the Diner"—which is the title, I remembered later, of an album by Tom Waits—that I'd been mistaken in believing it (the painting, not the album) was part of the Whitney's collection. (I was relieved to learn later on, when I checked it out at their website, that the Whitney actually did own, but rarely exhibited, another painting also instrumental in the development of the dream of New York City that had, for so many years, swirled in my brow: George Tooker's urban paranoiac egg-tempera entitled "Subway 1950." I had first seen reproductions of the two paintings when I was a child, and spent many lonely brooding hours lying on the floor in my bedroom staring at them, meditating on them, taking them in, dreaming of New York City. I also stared, in those days, at another favorite picture of New York—Piet Mondrian's "Broadway Boogie Woogie," a painting also not a part of the collection of the Whitney Museum of American Art, but in the case of "Broadway Boogie Woogie," the omission was because of the artist's foreign birth, a vital statistic that also disqualified the artist from running for president, even though he was well over thirty-five years old when he painted the picture.)

Reading the inscription, "Property of the Whitney Museum, New York City," as I often did, I was reminded of past visits I'd made to the Whitney when in New York, on holiday, or on reconnaissance, in search of Hopper and Tooker, in search of Mondrian, believing, as I did, that "Broadway Boogie Woogie" belonged in the Whitney, since its subject matter was American. *I had as a young man found myself possessed of a similarly irredentist sentiment at the National Portrait Gallery, when, winding down a six-month student's budget "Grand Tour" of Europe in a gloomy midwinter London during the horrible Margaret Thatcher years, I saw a painting of Charles Chaplin hanging there; always the diplomatist,[13] I was prepared, in a propitiatory gesture of transatlantic goodwill, to*

---

[13] I was never a diplomatist.

concede T. S. Eliot, the likeness of whom was hanging nearby, but Charles Chaplin was an American, by god, even if he had been hounded out of the country. I had often wondered, on these visits to the Whitney, where the museum stored its vast reserves of permanent collection not on display at any particular time, the Stuart Davises, Reginald Marshes, Paul Cadmuses, Marsden Hartleys, Albert Pinkham Ryders, George Bellowses, and Charles De-Muths, that were forever being bumped to fill the house with installations and mid-career retrospectives, and, of course, with fretful, long-queued biennial showings of the most up-to-date interrogations and subversions of the male gaze, of racialist narrativity, of hegemonic discourse—name your (phal)logocentric poison. I imagined great Jack Benny vaults buried deep in the chthonian substrata of Manhattan schist, the rough-hewn walls of which shook every time a train roared by in the adjacent tunnels burrowed just below the surface of nearby Park Avenue—a train loaded with commuters having a drink or two in the club car or playing a rubber of bridge, on their way up to their *echt* Dutch colonials in Connecticut, or to an afternoon of adultery in somebody else's *I'd been billeted for my fortnight's stay in London Town in a lower bunk in an over-crowded dormitory room in the basement of an unheated and comically miserablist youth hostel in Gayfere Street, Westminster. At five quid a night, these were the cheapest lodgings I could find, and this in the glory days of the dollar's resurgence overseas, when, for a brief, shining moment, £1 equaled $1 and $1 bought eleven French francs or, in any number of separate transactions, three Deutschmarks, a hundred and seventy pesetas, twenty-three Austrian schillings, ten and a half Danish kroner, four Dutch guilders, and god knows how many millions of Italian lira...*

(Even with such a formidable ally, I was, by the time I got to Gayfere, down to my last few farthings—or crowns or tuppences or ha'pennies or whatever they're called...hardly any brass at all.)

Our own vast reserves of permanent collection, in the early stages of accumulation, had originally been stocked in the cellars and attics of small flats in duplex houses and workingman's cottages (and the occasional bungalow), built, often two to a lot, at the turn of the last century (the duplex houses and working-man's cottages, I mean—the bungalows were built a little later), in the working class neighborhood (and, eventually, students' and artists' quarter) that would later be called Hogarth Hills by some and Lake Bluff by others, that lay across the Milwaukee River from the Dutch Colonial revival we could never have imagined would be ours one day, a Dutch Colonial situated, one to its lot, along with a dilapidated garage, in a neighborhood referred to, sarcastically, as "fashionable Lake Bluff" by the artists, students, and activists tenanted in the upper and lower flats, squats, crash-pads, safe houses, and garrets of Hogarth Hills.

Originally occupied by the families of Polish immigrants attracted by then-plentiful jobs in nearby tanneries and breweries, the duplexes of Hogarth Hills had been built on acreage platted by Germans who had once owned the now-defunct tanneries and breweries, and whose legacy survives today only in the names of the streets (and the abundant corner—and even mid-block—taverns, taps, and *rathskellers*; though production has declined, there's still a lot of beer consumption goes on in Milwaukee, Wisconsin): *Schlegel* Street, for example, where Caroline and I made our first home together, in a tiny space above a so-called "Polish flat," a local name for a type of utilitarian, yet often charming dwelling—unique, as far as I knew, to Milwaukee, and I think maybe Chicago—constructed to accommodate new arrivals by raising the floor of a one-story frame house and building another story out of the basement. *Bremerhaven* Street, where, upon evacuating my sad shag-carpeted efficiency, I had moved, along with my friend and fellow seminarian, the tall Ohioan Arthur Redding, into a fairly large upper flat of a duplex, without a stove, but with a bellowing lout and a screeching harridan from an old two-reeler shouting obscenities at one another and exchanging gunfire downstairs, a fairly large upper flat where we two whining schoolboys (well, I whined), prone, regressively, as well, to mewling (ditto) and to puking (we both of us puked, god knows: there was a lot of drinking went on in the fairly large upper flat of this duplex on Bremerhaven Street), laid our satchels each night, and emptied our pockets of our frogs, slingshots, and grammatologies—but could never get a good night's sleep, or cook any dinner; the two of us bunked at the raucous mead hall on Bremerhaven Street for a few months only, until, facing eviction for disturbing our quarreling neighbors with the unpleasant odors of Arthur's un-neutered cat, Willie, the three of us, Arthur, Willie, and I, accepted Caroline's kind invitation (an invitation not any the less kind for my having played, behind the scenes, a small hand in eliciting it), and moved in with her at her apartment on Schlegel Street—the tiny space above the Polish flat in the house known as the Blue Hotel (for reasons that will be explained directly) that Caroline shared with her cat Silver Moon Baby, and with her roommate, a third, non-feline border, whose identity one is reluctant, for reasons of dramatic effect, to reveal at this point—me into Caroline and Silver Moon's bed, and Arthur and Willie onto the living room floor, until a month or so later Arthur found his own accommodations, and Caroline's original roommate fled the country. And, lastly, our final stop in Hogarth Hills, *Hölderlin* Boulevard, where, following a seven year idyll—or so it came to seem later—above the Polish flat on Schlegel Street, we re-moved to a very cute, and slightly tonier, if even tinier apartment (but, like the apartment on Schlegel Street, with plenty of storage, something they've never heard of in New York City), carved from half an attic in a 1920's bungalow. This was when we changed our scheme of decoration from Vienna Secession to Arts and Crafts, only to abandon the style for Mid-Century Modern when moving to the Dutch Colonial Revival, shortly after we bought the eighteen acres in Vernon County, the Flivver, and the Banana Hut (in that order), four years before we bought the house and dilapidated garage on Newhall Street, and seven years before we pulled up stakes (like glossolalic tent revivalists *en route* to the next Pentecost, or grifting carnies in midnight flight from a county sheriff who has gotten wise), and pitched our mansion in the sacred ground (and prime real estate) that lay atop the hallowed schist of the beckoning and "insular city of the Manhattoes."

...I often thought, in later years, that in its resurgence this revitalized dollar, pulsing with vigor, flexing its beach bully muscles in the money markets of the world, kicking sand in the face of all the other currencies on the strand and making headway against even God's own Yen, that this Charles Atlas dollar, toned and ripped, a muscle man, but a sugar daddy of a muscle man, a great green sugar daddy, must have subsidized many another poor boy of my generation's Grand Tour of Europe; but I wasn't poor; nor was I part of a generation (neither a baby boomer—not really—nor a baby buster, I was born too late, or too early, to be part of a generation); and besides, it sounded funny to say "poor American," unless you were talking about, I don't know, Appalachia or the Ozarks, or an Indian reservation, or, most likely, "the ghetto": busted-up mythopoetic lunar dreamscapes sunk deep in a darkened mire of despair and zip-guns and child-endangering and wife-walloping and razor-toting (and rockabilly bluegrass honky-tonk doo-wop bebop hip hop) that I had heard, when I was a boy, sung in popular song (in "Tobacco Road," for instance, by the Nashville Teens; in "Indian Reservation," by Paul Revere and the Raiders, featuring Mark Lindsay; and in "In the Ghetto," by Elvis Presley), seen portrayed, usually in flames, with the National Guard mobilized, in live remotes on the Huntley-Brinkley Report (the latter dreamscape, that is, which tended, monopolistically, to crowd out the others caucusing and petitioning for redress in my imagination), and would, a little later, gather enough shocking data about to want to start my own war on poverty when I stayed up all night reading The Other America *(for a few teenage years I consumed Michael Harrington like a Eucharist—"The most decent man in America" some liberal or other called Harrington in a blurb on the back of one of his books—the way some of my classmates ate up science fiction or Hermann Hesse or J.R.R. Tolkien), vowing early the next morning, when I closed the book, to become a*

democratic socialist or some other kind of professional do-gooder (I still feel a pang of sorrow when I pass by the Catholic Worker on my way to P.S. 122 or the Anthology Film Archives, even though I always hated the way "faith-based initiatives" had to go and spoil all the fun with Jesus); forlorn and unredeemed barbed-wire dreamscapes where dads never assemble rock collections for their sons or write their speeches for them and nobody ever gets an orange AMC Hornet for his birthday instead of the MG Midget he wanted: busted-up mythopoetic dreamscapes that had begun to haunt my imagination as a boy—like Vietnam and its exploding twisted Harley-Davidson/Peter Fonda/Dennis Hopper simulacrum at the end of the third reel of Easy Rider ("The thornbush," Saint Kakfa reveals, "is an old obstacle in the road. It must catch fire if you want to go further"), a film I had snuck in to see at a critical point in the development of what I was pleased then to call my political consciousness, when it played briefly at the Roebuck Plaza Theater (the film, not my "developing political consciousness," or maybe also my "developing political consciousness"), before it was withdrawn when somebody told some Baptist ministers about it, a holocaustal dreamscape (nightmare, myth, hallucination, revelation), that was, in its way, the other side of the swirling dream of New York haunting my reverie, or a funnyhouse iteration in a discarded broken shard of it, apocalyptic, too, in its deep oneiric contours, calling one back to grindhouse blackout Son of Sam Kitty Genovese days when the Bronx was still burning and the graffiti hadn't been wiped off the subway cars, to the bad old days before the squeegee men had been banished from the city and a caravan of tie-dyed organic hemp tents, lavishly stocked with glistening hand-crafted jeroboams of fair trade nectar, shade-grown ambrosia, and locally-sourced manna from heaven, had been pitched, like love in excrement, upon the neo-Arcadian sheepfolds of the Union Square greenmarket, near the bicycle lane; nightmare dreamscapes that refracted as well a broken shard vision of, and at the same time nightmare escape from, the torn and trellised split-leveled soul of redneck-"aspirational" exurban Birmingham, where, in the Christ-tormented southern-fried kudzu-entangled version of the American sublime, pre-Roe v. Wade fetuses were found, slopped annually in ladies' rooms at

the junior-senior prom, and a boy a year, upon finding out that he was
gay and that the world was bad, shot himself in his beautiful sacrificial
tow-headed head with his daddy's 12-gauge shotgun, or equally acces-
sible .30-06 — Springfield, Enfield, Browning, Winchester, or Reming-
ton…

The space above the Polish flat in the house called the Blue
Hotel that was situated on Schlegel Street sat kitty-cornered
from St. Stanislaus Kostka Church. The church was clad in Milwaukee's famous cream-colored brick, but by the time I came to
know it, the bricks were smudged black with age and soot and
looked less like a golden ladder to heaven than an angel cake
blessed by a priest and dropped in a fire grate. The illuminated
clock in the church's tower, known in the neighborhood as the
"Polish Moon," the clock not the belfry, tic-tocked time in the
irregular accelerating rhythm of a heart going bad, or at least it
seemed to to me, because at one peal the chimes appeared to in-
dicate, for example, that it was two in the afternoon, suggesting
archaic British licensing laws or a T. S. Eliot reference on the ID
section of a comprehensive exam, and at the next, approximately
fifteen minutes later, it was the witching hour, or thereabouts,
changing the mood and putting one in mind of scotch whisky,
cigarettes, and Thelonius Monk, the hands of the clock all herky-
jerky like Warren Beatty and Faye Dunaway dying in staccato
slow-fast time-lapse in the back seat of their car all broke down
on the side of the road in *Bonnie and Clyde* (which had also
played — to long queues, and the usual disapprobation of the
clergy — at the Roebuck Plaza) or else spinning like the wheel of
an upside down Sears Spyder bike from the same era (the era of
the film's release, not the depression the film revisits), with baseball cards clothes-pinned to the spokes to sound like a motorcycle, crashed and abandoned on the side of Five Mile Road in a
ditch full of old car parts and beer cans and spent condoms and
rebel yells and pieces of blown out whitewalls, the scraped up
boy who had lost control and spun out and was thrown over the

handlebars limping home, in bloody near-delirium, to his mother's painful loving swabs of red mercurochrome, a caustic substance surely banned by now, like thalidomide and napalm and DDT and Agent Orange, and so many other ghastly mid-century chemical advances ("this won't hurt," she lies tenderly; but it hurts: love hurts, chemistry hurts, the mid-century hurts), administered in the beige-applianced kitchen (these were Danish modern days, before the inflorescence of avocado and the other scratch and sniff colors of the later sixties and early seventies) reached through the back door that was really a front door (only traveling salesmen used the front door, traveling salesmen and several times a year the Rev. Dr. William "Brother Billy" Grace, pastor at Crestlawn Baptist Church, trying like hell to get the Blackwells, never regular attenders, to come back to church; we'd abandoned our pew pretty much altogether when my mother had gotten huffed up at the prim self-righteous biddies—prim and self-righteous on Sunday mornings, gossipy and adulterous the rest of the week—who had spent a whole Sunday School session bashing the immorality of *Peyton Place*, a television show my mother never missed—and neither did the biddies—mainly, in my mother's case, because Ryan O'Neal was so cute) off the carport of the ranch house in Roebuck Lawn Estates, at about the time of the Tet Offensive, a whole subdivision transformed every day, when Daddy went to work, into an emergency triage of childhood injuries as a nursing pool of sad, fierce, Southern mothers coifed in beehives and slacked in Laura Petrie capris tended to their wounded sons (they were a mishmash of signifiers, these sad, fierce, southern mothers, a little bit Jackie Kennedy, a little bit Lurleen Wallace; trendy yet segregationist)...

But tell the truth—the clock in the belfry of St. Stanislaus wasn't illuminated, and it wasn't known in the neighborhood as the "Polish Moon." The "Polish Moon" is the name for the actually-illuminated four-sided clock of the Allen-Bradley Clock Tower, at the headquarters of Rockwell Automation, located on the South Side (a once "white ethnic" working class city-within-the-city), where it dominates a skyline of steeples and chimney stacks, and shines as a beacon for ships approaching the harbor, delivering whatever raw materials they still deliver, and onloading whatever finished goods they still onload, if they still deliver and onload anything anymore, raw *or* cooked, the economy having been twice, thrice, and as many times more adjusted, corrected, downsized, deregulated, de-industrialized, and then finally gutted in the years that followed the factory's heyday, with one or two anachronistic exceptions—throwbacks to the days of actual production—practically all industry and commerce (except for nail salons, pay-day loans, and tattoo parlors, as well as, of course, various limited liabilities dedicated to "providing content" to the information superhighway, offering large sub-prime mortgages to indigents, and speculating in collateralized debt obligations, credit-default swaps, and other such arcane postmodernist—poststructuralist, even, in their Byzantine obscurantism—financial instruments) having been freighted off, successively, to cheaper and cheaper labor markets overseas. It is the largest four-faced non-chiming tower clock in the world,[14] larger even than Big Ben, the largest chiming four-faced clock in the world,[15] but holding the distinction only as the result of a propitiatory gesture of transatlantic goodwill on the part of Messrs. Allen and Bradley, whose fortune had been built on the bones of South Side "white ethnics," who later made the national news by giving their vote to George Wallace in the 1968 Democratic Primary, proving, once again, that race trumps class every time and the workers of the world just aren't fucking ever going to unite; a fortune that was later augmented with the sale, by Bradley's heirs, of the family business to Rockwell International, providing seed money for the notorious Bradley Foundation, most famous for funding "research" that would demonstrate conclusively the intellectual inferiority of black and

---

[14] Not anymore. There's a bigger one in Mecca, now.
[15] I don't know if the one in Mecca chimes.

150

brown folk (see Charles Murray, *The Bell Curve*) and, thus, the ineffectiveness, in fact the plain foolishness, of liberal "tax and spend policies"—you know, "throwing money at the problem"—meant to alleviate, or at least mitigate, inequality, which, as it turns out, isn't a problem at all, just the law of nature or the will of God. The Polish Moon is usually referred to these days, though, as the "Mexican Moon," because of some demographic changes that have occurred in the neighborhood.

(I first learned that the clock was called the Polish Moon from my friend Azhar al-Shidyaq; Azhar the reader will remember, was my Deleuzian advisor on affairs of the heart in Chapter Three of this narrative; he was also the third man in the apartment on Schlegel Street, as the reader will soon learn, and he had once, over brandy and sodas at Monescu's, told me that he was planning to write a novel or a story or a play about Milwaukee to be called "The Polish Moon," but I have long been out of touch with Azhar and can find no evidence that he ever did, and so I appropriate the title, and offer it as an affectionate homage to an old friend to whom I owe a large debt of gratitude, the nature of which will become clearer as our narrative continues to unfold.)

The church's illuminated clock (except it wasn't illuminated), known in the neighborhood as the "Polish Moon" (except it wasn't known in the neighborhood as the "Polish Moon"), served as our living room clock, knelling each hour's death sentence, as I, having only the year before turned thirty, had begun melodramatically, and prematurely, to intone (the midlife crisis wasn't due for another fifteen or twenty years, and though I was in nearly every other respect a late bloomer—graduating from college late, at twenty-seven, taking a wife late, at thirty-one, landing my first salaried position late, at thirty-three, writing my first book late, at fifty-one, etc.—I was precocious at fearing death. I'd turned thirty the summer before the move to Milwaukee, and then thirty-one upon giving up the ghost at Milwaukee State, and I was feeling—fiercely, achingly—the accumulating brutality of the relentlessly aggregating algorithm, $n+1+1+1\ldots$, the only mathematics, I suspected, that I would ever understand, except for a few parlor tricks Caroline had taught me, so I could, in turn, share my blessings with the at-risk youth of Milwaukee, Wisconsin, and a little later, when I had expanded my practice, with the adults, beaten down and less cocky, who had fallen hard by then into the slough of "pathologies" that at-risk youth are presumed to be at-risk for, and who—in an effort to "better themselves" (and I use this anachronistic phrase only partly ironically), or to meet the conditions of a probation or a parole, or, more and more frequently, to continue to receive any of the diminishing remittances still referred to, nostalgically, in the era of "the end of welfare as we know it," as "public assistance" — would enroll in the GED, pre-GED, and Adult Basic Skills classes that I was, at the time, learning how to teach, not in an effort, in my case, to better an old self, but to cobble together a new one, from a conception that, if not precisely Platonic, had the virtue, at least, of being available.

The name I had fixed on for this new self, this self that would redeem the loss of the other, was "grassroots educator."

And in my capacity as grassroots educator, I was attempting to share with my students the small store of mathematical sleight of hand I had only recently acquired myself, a store they needed more than I ever had, "to break," in the words of a phrase popular in those days, "the cycle of dependency," but I can't remember any of my students ever breaking any cycle of anything that I had ever heard of, and I wonder now if there is a cycle of dependency that anyone anywhere ever breaks, except in the shroud of death (with apologies to Dr. Martin Luther King, Jr., the ultimate "inescapable garment of mutuality" that binds us all together).

"God," as Jean Paul-Marat said, back in *le jour* (*de gloire*), "has always been hard on the poor": in addition to the other burdens they must bear, the poor alone, among the social classes, are called upon to "break the cycle of dependency." I can, in fact, remember only two or three of my students—these were my "success stories," included in reports to funders, a bullet point away from "lessons learned," and two from "describe your target population"—ever passing any of the examinations I was, ostensibly, preparing them for. I remember much more vividly the difficulty my students had, on the verbal side of things, reading for comprehension or even getting through a sentence pronouncing all of the words correctly ("decoding," in current jargon) and knowing their meanings (I forget what this is called: prescience? immortality of the soul?). I remember the monotony of the predictability of the same mistakes ("miscues," in current jargon) made over and over by it felt like every single student I ever pre-tested, during the student intake session, on the Slossen Oral Reading Test: "groove" for "grove," "hungry" for "hunger," "timmed" for "timid," "clammed" for "claimed," "danty" for "dainty," and so forth; and on the math side, the difficulties my students had with basic adding and subtracting. I remember in the place of what might be called, in current jargon, solid achievement, a kind of warm amniotic camaraderie in the classroom, a non-quantifiable beloved community, in miniature, of mutually beneficial race-mixing, a gorgeous mosaic cultivating, in retreat from the world, its own hermetic garden of good humor and gentle raillery and dark laughter and tales of making a way out of no way, a kind of respite, a kind respite, or cleft in the rock of the world, and haven from both market and mean street for the tired and battered and lumpen and "social-capital" poor who, with no content to provide the information superhighway, and only debt to swap, would never break the cycle of dependency (certainly not under my tutelage); a refuge where the dependent congregation of half-lost, half-found black and brown strivers led by a half-lost, half-found white boy, a dependent child myself, also striving, but a privileged striver, a coxcomb striver, could sit at a table laid with the shards and fragments and filtered down artifacts of the great world—with pie charts, picaresques, passages, and parables; with odes, sestinas, villanelles, and periodic tables; with fractals, theorems, axioms, and georgics; with prolegomena, philippics, perorations, and philosophical tales; with confessions, spiritual autobiographies, *cris de coeur*, advertisements for oneself, and *apologias pro vita sua*, etc., etc., etc. —and, under the unqualified instruction of their quack self-taught hillbilly Perfessor, play school together, carefully studying each exhibit, each specimen, turning it round in their hands, holding it up to the light, smelling it, tasting it, subjecting it to heat and to cold, testing its tensile strength and ductility, and in so examining prepare themselves to gain admittance to one or another substrata of the great world that had rejected them and would reject them again—and again and again and again.

Only a small handful of my students ever earned in their lives any kind of equivalency diploma; only a small handful ever answered any of the riddles posed them at any of the gates that remained closed, locked, chained, bolted, barred forever, hung with a hand-lettered sign that said, effectively, that they need not apply, but then I worked with the most vulnerable (and often most venerable) of the *sans culottes* ("God has always been hard on the poor"); that was my excuse; I ministered to the least among them, the least likely to succeed, the most likely to—what did I call it? oh yeah, "fall through the cracks." And fall they did, fall and tumble, tumble and fall, and as they tumbled, as they fell, as they failed, falling and failing, failing and falling, by all objective measure (these were the days before "outcomes" and "logic models" and "accountability," the days before the "reform" of welfare and education and everything else that looked like maybe it had an existence, in part, outside of the market and could be delivered more efficiently, and profitably, by subcontractors of the invisible hand, the days when all the children were left behind and men and women—because there was no, you know, accountability—failed at everything they attempted), I, a blind boy of Alabama, leading the blind, tried to teach the *sans culottes* sans lesson plans, sans do nows, sans aims, objectives, and teaching points, sans qualitative or quantitative analysis, sans formative or summative assessment, sans data-driven instruction, the few tricks of math I knew.

And they were few, the tricks of math I knew, but as I sat at the tables in the rooms that were my own, called my own, called "Chip's Room"—the design all mine: social service eclecticism you might call the style, leftover donated scavenged "in-kind" furnishings, books, computers (in Precambrian days of MS-DOS), and other supplies, enlivened with posters, student art work, photographs of children, and fresh-cut flowers I brought in, all arranged invitingly (it looked like a warm place of learning, a suitable cleft for breaking cycles of dependency); as I sat at these tables, inviting my students, cordially, into "the skills network" (another phrase popular in those days), a network I was fooling myself, and had fooled my employers, fooled my students (or perhaps hadn't fooled my students) into believing I myself was part of—a world of gainful employment (one almost writes "painful employment") and making a contribution and voting for the lesser of two evils and working for the greater good and itemizing your deductions and planning for retirement; as I sat at the table trying to teach my students the few tricks of math I knew, the tricks that would help them pass the GED exam or some other exam any exam so many exams to help them break the cycle of dependency, as I sat at the table, amid the artifacts, elucidating the paltry purchase I'd obtained on "subtle mathematics," sharing my crumbs with the battered, with the lumpen, with the wretched, I remembered the words of Basilio, King of Poland, that had impressed me only a few years earlier, when I, another I, an earlier, discontinued I (last year's model), but tiring and flailing at my own flesh, cannibalizing my own earlier work, cannibalizing a cannibalization, the thousandth cannibalization of a cannibalization cannibalized a thousand times—still frustrated and still conflating my frustration as scholar and lover into the cobbled together mingle-mangle quoted from, at length, in Chapter Three (and into the cobbled together mingle-mangle I cobble together, also at length, today):

"You know...that the science I most study and esteem is subtle mathematics, by which I steal from time," and I felt then—or perhaps feel now, in retrospect—that I too was stealing from time, had stolen from time, felt that way as I sat at the table, my table, and in my thieving, in my bounding, in my misappropriation, I understood, in my way, a little, just a little, the beauty and elegance of the subtle science that had for so long been a dead letter to me—a null set (had I really gotten through high school and into and then out of college without having any knowledge of any kind of math beyond arithmetic? how had I gotten into the skills network? how had I broken the cycle of dependency?).

The rudimentary mathematics that I had learned by then, because such knowledge was required for me to teach my students, to convene my table, Caroline had taught me at another table, at the kitchen table of the apartment in the upper story of the Blue Hotel, by flickering candlelight (because we'd gone, involuntarily, our first season together, off the grid, shortly after I moved in—sans gas, sans lights, sans electricity, roughing it, for a season, in Hogarth Hills).

In these flickers that I remember now with love—forgetting, of course, the inconvenience, and the cold showers, the tripping over things and the bumping into walls, just the soft beauty of Caroline's candlelit twenty-one-year-old radiance, the pink face of the ingénue; in these flickers she taught me how to steal from time, taught me alchemy it might as well have been, or conjuring, white magic, taught me arcane and occult and esoteric secrets, esoteric knowledge previously forbidden me—like, for instance, solving for x by using the inverse operation (a phrase that appealed to me, at first, until it occurred to me later that it sounded like a dangerous experimental medical procedure, with a prohibitive deductible that I could never afford to pay, that an out-of-network specialist would someday suggest to me as my only hope for survival), taught me to cancel out, to nullify, all uncertain terms, until only one lonely number was left standing, dignified and proud, isolated and exposed on one side of the equation, while on the other side lay unmasked and apprehended—dragged, finally, to the bar—the variable, the muddle of uncertainty, that had, in its perverse runic obscurity, occluded, for a time—for a time, yes, but, under Caroline's careful tutelage, I always got my man—the term's true, sublime, numerical identity: the quantitative analysis. Caroline taught me, too, in these flickering evenings, about pi, Mesopotamian pi, Babylonian pi, Sumerian pi, and Hebrew pi, the pi of Noah's Ark, Egyptian pi, Greek pi and Roman pi, the pi of the Shatapatha Brahmana, that mysterious ancient non-terminating ratio that (bobbed now, like a cocker spaniel's tail, two digits in, crimped off like a foreskin) built the ziggurats and the Parthenon and the aqueducts, taught me to multiply this mystery number by the square of the radius of a circle within a circle within a circle so that I could find, for all the reasons one seeks to find, the area of the circle that so fatally circumscribes us all, with the circumscription expressed in square units—a paradox I could never comprehend (has the circle been squared? will it be unbroken?). She taught me, too, how to calculate the volume of a rectangular prism (like a coffin, I might have offered as illustration, the end of all measurement, where all variables come out six feet, and the Tolstoyan riddle—How much land does a man need?—is answered definitively). She taught me my proudest accomplishment, the Pythagorean relationship, in which the sums of the squares of the legs of a right triangle (set so neatly at right angles to each other, with cute little tiny dotted-line cubes drawn at the intersection in the diagram to remind everyone of the brief, poignant perpendicularity of everything standing, triangulating what is right, and challenging all would-be mathematicians to sing in a thicket of questions, to solve for all the unknown variables that will repetitively, convulsively, bop them on their heads as they travel down those paths of their lives where the triangles and the thickets and the jumbles and the tangles and the muddles lie) will always, in every case, with no nagging, niggling, whining exceptions (no "not me"-s, "I'm different; I'm not like everybody else"), equal the square of the triangle's opposing hypotenuse, set rakishly at an angle, elegant in its diagonal repose, like a walking stick cupped in Fred Astaire's palm as he waits for the music on the top step of the art deco staircase in the RKO soundstage, still several misunderstandings and a tin pan alley of Irving Berlin from winning, in the last reel, the heart of Ginger Rogers, who, sequined in an evening dress, looks on skeptically, eternally, from the promenade deck. They are frozen in this pose at the rate of twenty-four frames per second, an elegant right triangle in top hat, white tie, and tails, winking mischievously at the parabola of the triangle's desire—curved space, stolen from time,

> There may be teardrops to shed
> So while there's moonlight
> And music and love and romance
> Let's face the music and dance

But, I ask myself now, hadn't I always—years before I'd turned thirty-one and faced the music and learned to solve for x—hadn't I always, feeling about my chest, hypochondriacally, and clutching at my collar, shedding in advance the teardrops there will be to shed, sans moonlight, sans love, sans romance, hadn't I always heard the bells knell each hour's death sentence, heard them toll *for me*, heard them chime, to follow a thread, at midnight (an alter kocker before my time)? And as they knelled, as they chimed, as they tolled, hadn't I also always felt a deep precognitive solidarity with some lines from C. K. Williams' poem "Blades," included in the poet's third collection of original poetry, entitled *With Ignorance*, another of the volumes that had once lined and was later salvaged from the abandoned bookshelf in the Banana Hut parked in a clearing in some woods of Vernon County, Wisconsin,

...something's torn in me,
some ancient cloak of terror we keep on ourselves because
we'll do
　　　anything,
anything, not to know how silently we knell in the mouth of
death
and not to obliterate the forgiveness and the lies we offer one
another
　　　and call innocence.

But I was thirty-one years old now, then, listening to the death-splashed carillons (and I was gaudily exaggerating everything in precisely this way in those days, as I exaggerate them today), thirty-one years old and I had lost myself, and in so losing had begun to obliterate, because I didn't think that I could get them back, thirty-one years of lies and forgiveness, which, though I couldn't know it then, I *would* get back, with interest, and sooner than any such a sinner as I ever deserved to. This sense of loss, this obliteration, was the first of two such "fallings off," as I also described whatever it was that was happening to me, and, in my aimlessness and soul-sickness, my desperation, this loss, this obliteration (crisis, sorrow, sickness) prefigured, like an early draft in an out-of-town tryout, the second falling off, from which I would not recover so quickly, having, the second time, so much further to fall (farther to fall? father to fall?), hitting the cold earth hard, audibly cracking prematurely decalcified bones diagnosed by then as osteoporotic—likened, in fact, by one doctor, after he clutched and poked and felt about my so easily-fractured ribs, and pointed an accusatory index finger at them, like a Dr. Tulp's anatomy lesson, to limbs fallen in the forest that look sturdy enough to get you through the slough and out of the mire and on to solid ground, but step on them as carefully as you will and they collapse into their own rot, into your own rot, your own mire; a second, but this time it seemed irreversible loss (unless I could write my way out of it; if one can write one's way out of such things), an obliteration that would fall fourteen to eighteen years after the first, depending on how you reckon it (either way a pretty long run—not *The Mousetrap* or *The Fantasticks*, but a pretty long run), prefiguring it because history, which is another word for loss, another word for obliteration, repeats itself twice, the first time as tragedy and the second time as farce, a tragedy of lies and a farce of forgiveness, self-lies, and self-forgiveness, in my case, all a sham and all called innocence. The first self I lost, I lost hard and "tragically"; the second self, hard and farcically, though history may yet prove, if history proves anything, that yesterday's tragedy is today's farce and today's farce is tomorrow's (and tomorrow's and tomorrow's) tragedy (more likely, though, it's all farce); the loss seemed particularly gingered with goat song then (or something like it) because the self lost in the transaction, tragic or farcical, had been so recently minted, like the limited pressing of a commemorative coin, only three years prior to its having been, for obscure reasons, withdrawn from circulation. But the self I lost wasn't a coin, though it was embossed, and it wasn't a ghost, though it haunted: it was a life, and because the world's a stage, it was also like, one may as well admit, because the comparison is inevitable, not so much a poor player on the stage as a company of them, raging and unresolved, each set against the other, strutting and fretting with no motivation, and no direction, in endless chaotic rehearsal and bitchy backstage backbiting, bombing in New Haven, tossed on the pavement from the lobby of the Taft Hotel for failure to pay the bill, but, demoralized and in disarray, somehow cobbling together a revised second act and managing a preview at the Winter Garden, or the Longacre, or the Music Box, and then waiting up all night at Sardi's—or Toots Shor's, or the Cub Room—for the reviews to come in, and when they do, when the stagehand slinks in from the newsstand with seven or eight miles of daily newspapers in his mitts and a po' boy sad sack hangdog expression on his face, and the notices are bad, and the show, which will be forgotten, except by a couple of Playbill collectors and the Internet Broadway Data Base, closes after only a few performances, and the house goes dark, but this time the show, like the world, would lumber on, with just enough box office to sustain it (just barely), for approximately three years, and though three years is a long run for a Broadway show, it is a short run for a self or a life (or a coin or a ghost); a short run, though, that, in my case, has proven to be fairly intricate with ghosts in the history that followed it, intricate with implications pullulating like—I can't help mixing my metaphors—the kudzu tendrils that nearly entangled me in a lifetime of suffocating malarial inertia pawning things to pay my rent in "quaint" apartments of Birmingham, Alabama, kudzu tendrils that would, later, after I had taken my inertia on the road, entangle me in a lifetime of brooding failure and see-through mediocrity, kudzu tendrils that insinuated themselves up and around and over and through all the corridors, ruins, and "fresh starts" that would follow the demise, the fall, the sloughing off of an old skin (as I would soon say, hopefully—and, seen from a certain angle, accurately—as I tore up my chits and cut my losses, and, you know, "let go" and "moved on," strategies that, it would seem, were available to me then—because I was younger and my bones less brittle?).

I had, in turning thirty-one, with the accelerated velocity that starts ripping everything apart at that age, or so it seemed (but if I could only have known then what I would know later, and will, in future, know truly, know authentically—I mean, you know, really know...), ripping apart sinew, ripping apart ligaments, ripping apart neural pathways, ripping apart lies and forgiveness, space-time, everything, botched up and then given up the coveted Biermann Fellowship—a gift the bureaucrats of fortune soon realized had been a mistake, a clerical error—and, as a consequence, I had, that first summer in the Blue Hotel, and a month after I'd turned thirty-one, dropped out of the Contemporary Critical and Cultural Studies program, dropped out of the pre-tenure track, dropped out of my life. I was lucky that time, though (not necessarily willing to be lucky, just plain dumb lucky; I wasn't smart enough, then, to be willing to be lucky). The fall was fortunate, a *felix culpa*, because, as I fell, I also fell into two introductions that would save my life, save my life not in the sense of preventing my death, but in the sense of recuperation, of thrift, Horatio—lost time regained: two introductions—two compensatory allowances, two saving graces—that would allow me a second chance and a second life, a second self that I would later not botch up but abandon, that I would leave behind, throw away, cast off, renounce, disavow. I'd botched up the old short life in and around Tamblyn Hall to clear the way for a fresh start in a new corridor, in some new ruins, waiting tables, as it turned out, at the Chili Bowl Restaurant. I had given up the ghost, the first of two ghosts I would give up, for this fresh start. And the ghost I had given up was a ghost that was a self that had proven, even in its provenance, even in its begetting—but I was blind to this—to be unsustainable, and had proven it again shortly thereafter when it was put to the test, because the self that I thought I had lost, the ghost I thought I had given up, could not have been lost because it had never really been found—only approximated, dressed up in, like mommy and daddy's clothes; the dim half-educated *misprision* of the self-taught man or the peculiar and "interesting" mistake of an outsider artist, a self-deluded cargo cult, essentially, enshrined around a desire called "literary intellectual" (a loftier-sounding precursor to "grassroots educator"; a gnosis later abandoned for a praxis in my self-mythology) and, worse, the desire had metastasized, looped back, recombined, like a scary Hollywood dream sequence, with earlier cargo cult fantasies of Angela Davis, fist held high, and Abbie Hoffman chanting something out of *Zabriskie Point*, cargo cult fantasies of, in Althusser's words, "the desire called Marx" (first, in your quest for whatever it is you think you are questing for, you cite Marat and then you wind up citing Louis Althusser, two butchers; the former butchered the "enemies of the revolution"—or am I confusing Marat with Robespierre?; the latter butchered his wife): I (who butchered a few enemies of the revolution myself, at least in my mind, but largely spared my wife) wanted to be—to come to cases—yearned to be, something called "a literary intellectual doing radical work as a literary intellectual" (a gnosis that is a praxis), a self-delusion I'd borrowed, of course, from a book, a book that had been lent me by a professor, one of only a small handful at UAB who were not resistant to the specter of "theory" haunting English departments at the time. The book was called *Criticism and Social Change,* and the author was Frank Lentricchia, a macho-mustachioed university Marxist dubbed, by Maureen Corrigan, in a blurb on the book's back cover, "the Dirty Harry of contemporary critical theory"; a back cover that also features a famous photo of "the enforcer," as Corrigan also calls him, looking pretty goddamned menacing; with his arms crossed, he leans against a stone wall, scowling, challenging all comers, a culture hero (at least to me) and enforcer who double-dared any son of a bitch, literary intellectual or not, but especially literary intellectual, in or out of, but especially in, the academy, to say that you *couldn't* do radical work as a literary intellectual, an assertion, by the way, that I—sadder now, but hardly any wiser, and having succumbed, more or less, to my own "outsider" version, or *misprision,* of the "incumbent nihilism" that Chris Bladick, in another back cover blurb, praises Lentricchia for being in "the frontline of resistance" to—understand today was already a delusion way before I ever got hold of it. I stayed up all night (mis)reading the book in those graduate student days at UAB, underlining and writing "Yes!" in the margins, vowing early the next morning, when I closed the book, to pursue a career as a university Marxist "doing radical work as a literary intellectual," even though I was an intellectual, literary or otherwise, in pretension only, and self-deceit (and maybe goatee beard), and even less of a radical, except in (borrowed) opinions, slogans, posturing, and crude self-important indignation.

This delusional, self-aggrandizing self, jury-rigged and jerry-built, that I'd cobbled together from the bits and pieces of "op-positional culture" I'd found lying around in my backyard, cul-tural detritus that had penetrated even unto the benighted precincts of near-suburban Birmingham once-removed to bohe-mian-*manque* Southside, was a self-cobbled self cobbled late in the game, when I was twenty-seven or twenty-eight, an age at which the more go-getting, or more mature, or steadier, or just plain competent of my cohort had all-but-dissertated, or were, some of them, the real go-getters, already on the market, shop-ping their CVs around at the MLA convention. Deluded as it was, though, and as late, as false as it was, and as unsustainable (as I suspected even then), this self was, for me, almost opera-tional, sort of, in a way. It was efficacious enough, at least for a short while, to form the basis for a fresh start, for any kind of a start that could be kindled in the dead ashes of all my earlier previous false starts as a feckless half-ass undergraduate slacker who couldn't (is this what was bothering me?) get over my par-ent's divorce, couldn't get over what it had done to everybody in it, or maybe couldn't get over some truth it told about who everybody already was before the divorce had done whatever it was the divorce would do, couldn't get over how the world had always been (it didn't need a fall, the world; it had already fallen, and it was, like a fallen soufflé, advertised on the bill of fare as such), and because I couldn't get over my childhood, couldn't get over the world, I couldn't grow up either, and took nine years, and as many years more, it seemed, of excuses, to earn a bachelor's degree. And then, after first borrowing three thou-sand dollars from my mother, a portion of her share of the (mea-ger) proceeds from the sale of the split-level, except it wasn't a split-level, that had been falling down since my father's strategic retreat from the Oedipal triad, and even before that, falling down like a house of Usher, or a house of Atreus, I used to joke, out in the suburban sublime of Willow Way, to go to Europe for six months, in the days when one could go to Europe for six months on three thousand dollars (to embark, that is, on the

"Grand Tour" that had been a chapter in the story of my life to come that I'd half-plotted out when I was a self-abusing boy lying in my semen-soaked bed sheets looking up at the Liberty Bells and Trinitarian spires imprinted on the Early American curtains of my room, planning for and dreaming of the rest of my life, but feeling, even then, feeling especially then, the unreality of planning for a life, or, more poignantly, the unreality of having a life to plan for), and, returning home from my Grand Tour, "experienced"-up (but still knowing nothing), completing my last semester and finally graduating from college, I enrolled as a paying student in UAB's terminal M.A. program (called "terminal" because that's where it all ended; no Ph.D. was offered; but it wouldn't end even there for me, who had failed my comprehensive examinations, who couldn't even earn an M.A., much less a Ph.D.). I enrolled as a *paying* student because I couldn't, on my own, get a teaching assistantship because I didn't know how to interview for a job (I still don't know how to interview for a job), didn't want to think of it as a job, didn't even understand that it *was* a job, and wouldn't, moreover, have wanted it if it *had been* a job, couldn't and wouldn't and didn't want to have to think of anything, of any endeavor, any experience, any undertaking in terms of doing it because it was the means to something else. That's what I told people, that's what I told myself. My rap was I hated the kind of "instrumentalism," always a favorite shibboleth, or anti-shibboleth, of mine, that leads to career advancement, that leads to success, that leads to self-fulfillment, self-sacrifice, and self-realization, that leads to love, happiness, and tenure, despised it, but also envied it, was transfixed by it, in others whom I resented, envied, despised, or even loved and admired, despised (and loved and admired) not only these other people's "instrumentalism," but also the "utilitarianism" (another shibboleth, or anti-shibboleth) of their choices, despised the greater good and the lesser evil, despised, resented, envied, loved, and admired the way almost everybody I knew had realized, in their own eyes and everybody else's, some vendible, yet still proud, outpouring of what the world called their "potential," the way they had all grown up, gotten on with their lives, and had so willingly, it seemed to me, but surely they would have said otherwise (or maybe not), accepted the universe; the way they put away childish things, updated their CVs, and, working to "change the system from within," had, with dignity and professional *sangfroid*, gone so trippingly to market. (I had never put away *my* childish things; I was still a child, a *grown* child, with a motto—a mission statement!—borrowed from the epitaph of Guy de Maupassant: "I have coveted everything and taken pleasure in nothing.")

Because I didn't know how, nor did I want to know how, specifically, to return to the issue of paying my own tuition, to impress the Concentration in Composition and Rhetoric at UAB, the profit center, or "cash nexus," as I called it, of the English department, where the preferment of teaching assistantships was granted or withheld, granted to graduate students tapped or punched in recognition of excellence in scholarship, leadership, service, and character (or was it conquest, war, famine, and death?), withheld from me (my declaration of interest on the application and attitude at the subsequent interview had been adjudged—and rightly so—"flippant" by the Concentration), I couldn't get the teaching assistantship I'd twice applied for without the eventual intercession of the Concentration in British and American Literature.

The intercession came in the form of a *deus ex machina* when a friend and champion, an Olympian, but a reluctant Olympian, in the Concentration in British and American Literature (they were like gods, the faculty—at least they seemed like gods to me, then) power-played, demanded, or just plain snatched (I never heard the full story), an assistantship for me, and then gave me a jingle at the aluminum factory where I was lucky enough to be employed (on temporary assignment), to let me know I could put in my notice and join the bottom rung of "literary intellectual." (Of course I later failed my master's comps and was

reassured I didn't need an M.A. to accept the Biermann Fellowship but later learned I did and had to give up the fellowship
and take a job at a chili restaurant.) I'd applied, in the meanwhile, to three Ph.D. programs—Duke, because Fredric Jameson, who had by then eclipsed Frank Lentricchia, also at Duke,
as my favorite university Marxist, was there; the University of
Pittsburgh, because Gayatri Spivak (my second favorite university Marxist—who had, glamorously, "rebarbatively," Colin
MacCabe once wrote, appended "feminist-deconstructivist" to
the patronymic) was there (at the time; she has of course moved
on to any number of prestigious posts); and Milwaukee State because I saw a poster announcing the Biermann Fellowship on the
wall in a hallway of the English Department on the second floor
of the Humanities Building (formerly University College Building No. 3; under either designation my first experience of campus brutalism) and happened to have a pen and a notebook in
my pocket (but not a pocket of a blazer; I didn't wear blazers
then) and jotted down the address (not the web address, not yet),
and soon after sent off my application packet (application, statement of purpose, letters of reference, two essays—one decon-
structing the hell out of Wallace Stevens; the other beating
liberals over the head with Zora Neale Hurston) to all three
schools, and waited to hear from my future: one rejection (Duke,
of course) and two offers.

I thought, until very soon into my first semester at Milwaukee
State, that I'd finally found myself at last, only to learn that I
couldn't hack it, didn't have the stuff, and besides I was going to
lose the Biermann if I couldn't pass the master's comps I knew I
would never pass, though I pretended for a while that I was going to take them and pass them the next summer, and when I
finally, after admitting to myself, and, later, admitting to the bureaucrats at the graduate school (The Program in Contemporary
Critical and Cultural Studies didn't care if I had an M.A. or not;
it was the graduate school that cared; though by the time the
threats from the graduate school started pouring in, nobody in

Contemporary Critical and Cultural Studies had any interest in fighting my fight for me; nobody would be sorry to see me go), that I *wouldn't, couldn't,* and by August of the following year *hadn't* taken them, and wouldn't have my master's degree by September, the deadline I'd been given, and would therefore have to forfeit my Biermann and because I didn't have the money to pay the tuition on my own, or the will or desire, anyway, to continue humiliating myself, I would have to drop out of the Contemporary Critical and Cultural Studies program, and lose the self I thought I'd found and now—then, because now is always then—I didn't know what the fuck I would do next, though within a few short months my friend Martin O'Brien (the first of the two introductions—the second was of course Caroline—that saved my life) would take a leave of absence from his job as a teacher at the Lourdes Valdez Education Center and arrange for me to cover for him during his absence, and I would get the famous "baptism by fire" I would brag about later, and in so covering, in so burning, I would find myself again, or find another self I could be, another self in which I could thrive and prosper and buy eighteen acres in Vernon County, and, later, a Dutch Colonial revival on Newhall Street and finally earn a master's degree and be friend and teacher to countless scores of boys and girls and men and women, who needed me, and appreciated me, and loved me, most of them (many of them?...some of them?), the self of all my former selves, of all my selves at all, that I miss the most, that I grieve over, because, as I see it now, this self was happy but didn't know it, couldn't know it, except very briefly near the end, happier than it would ever be again because this self was closest to the deep self that lies, platonically, within, if such a thing exists, but then in further retrospect, I understand now that, even before I'd found this self, when I was between selves, when I was turning thirty-one years old and was waiting tables at the Chili Bowl restaurant and didn't know what the fuck I was supposed to do next, when the gas and the electricity had been turned off at the Blue Hotel where I lived with my wife, Caroline, whom I loved with all my heart—whom I love still with all my heart—and the fat almost feral cat I also loved (still love, still grieve for), even then, especially then, when I was broke and had no prospects, no ambition, no career, and no hope of one, I was happy; I didn't know it, and I couldn't or wouldn't know it until eighteen years later, but I was happy then, if only in the sense of something that Adorno said,

> He who says he is happy lies, and in invoking happiness, sins against it. He keeps faith who says: "I *was* happy."

The Happy Journey to Burnwell and Gardners Gin

The illuminated clock (except it wasn't illuminated), that sat kitty-cornered from the house on Schlegel Street, the clock that was known in the neighborhood as the "Polish Moon" (except, as already stipulated, the clock was not, in fact, known in the neighborhood as the "Polish Moon"), served, the reader will recall, as our living room clock in those days, in the early days, knelling each hour's death sentence, as I, having only the year before turned thirty, had begun melodramatically, and prematurely, to intone; knelling it like the "cock of red feather that crew before the clocks," in Wallace Stevens' "Hymn from a Watermelon Pavilion," the cock of red feather that, whenever I hear a cock crow, or think of a cock crowing, reminds me of a cock that crew once, twenty-four years ago (as I write this today), in Walker County, Alabama. This was the first time I brought my then new wife down south, in a rented car, down Interstate 65, ramping up onto that cross-country coronary stent after first negotiating the pot-holed arterial havoc of the greater Chicago area, and then easing into slow, flat, snowy, unending Indiana (it was snowy because it was Christmastime, and slow, flat, and unending because it was Indiana), and farther, further (father) deeper down into three-dimensional Kentucky and Tennessee, and, finally, plumbing the downward most red clay swale, dipping down into Alabama, where the highway reaches its terminus, if one follows it all the way to Mobile, which we didn't; we stopped the car in Birmingham, where I had first seen light of day.

And once there, once in the thicket (I had learned, in my fourth grade Alabama history class, that "Alabama" means, in the Choctaw language, "I clear the thicket"), on the Saturday morning after our arrival, we followed Old Highway 78 down from the outskirts of Birmingham to the two-lane blacktops cutting through pine plantations disguising scars of strip-mining operations, when somebody bothered to plant over them, across rusting cast iron bridges spanning the muddy Black Warrior River, where my father had been baptized, circumcised, or offered up in sacrifice (I get my sacraments, and my testaments, mixed up), and down coal roads littered with shotgun shells and snuff tins and shards of broken depression glass, that led to the old white clapboard houses (except Mimi's clapboard had been clad, circa 1971, because she was the forward thinking grandmother, in brown brick with black mortar to simulate a suburban split-level of the era, to simulate, in fact, the brighter green of Willow Way, which represented, in its rejection of all things rural, the future of the family's hopes) and to the ancillary outbuildings listing on each acreage (a garage built into the side of a hill off Mimi's driveway, with a mother-in-law apartment upstairs, except the mother-in law for whom the structure had been built had long since made her way to oblivion); and dotting what was left of Ma Maw's spread that had once, so many years before, seemed sprawling—a Hill Ranch, a Spanish Bit, a Furies, a Reata—lay the ruins of a barn with the roof caved in, ruins the color of driftwood, the color of backroads, and a dilapidated smokehouse, also splintered driftwood-gray, with lightshafts pouring in and out of myriad knotholes and crevices like golden blood flowing from action movie exit wounds, that looked, each of these crumbling structures, in their almost comically southern-iconographic tendency toward decline, like the hulks and husks Walker Evans had photographed sixty years earlier in two counties lying approximately two hundred miles south-

southwest of Ma Maw's, in the heart of the Black Belt, where cotton, not coal, was king, and tenant farmers, not wage slaves, were beaten by time and by the human depredation consequent upon capital investment, the uncalculated cost of buying cheap and selling dear, into the dirt they planted and ploughed, not crawled down into.

Old white clapboard houses, one updated, the other a throwback, where my grandmothers lived, widows eking out their dotage on slender mites dispensed like prim Methodist sprinklings (both grandmothers were Baptists and doctrinally inclined to full immersion) arriving rural free delivery in official-looking envelopes with cloudy plastic windows sent out the first Monday of each month by the United Mine Workers of America and the Social Security Administration; mites supplemented, in Mimi's case, in the relinquishment of treasured parcels of land treasured once like parts of a body; these were the vast woods I had played in, climbed trees in, and got lost in, and where I'd so often set out in search of the dark and murky frog pond, more of a slough, though, or fen, my pond, a leaf-clogged pond/ mire/slough/fen crisscrossed with birch limbs rotting like the bones-to-be of the middle-aged iteration of myself that the half-remembered primitive boy-insect antecedent of the man I would become, that existed always on the precipice of adult consciousness, when I thought back on the pond and the woods and that time, the hellgrammite father to my imaginal man, could never have comprehended, had the hellgrammite spotted the imago, glimpsed it in the corner of a compound polyhedral eye, taking it in multilaterally, cubistically: a visitation, or shade, of the later man-bug I'd become, half-man half-bug at my last skinshed, ashamed and crouching in winged and bloodied exo-skeletal adulthood-to-come, in a beam like heaven of spider-cabled leaf-and-needle dappled light across the water *this near-insect was the boy that had once stalked Mimi's woods, cautiously, like a poacher side-stepping mantraps, in a trance almost, his lips chapped and a blister bursting in his shoe, his pants too tight and tearing red welts into the delicate skin covering the outward bony ridge of his protruding pelvic girdle, the place where a six-gun would have rested had he, like other boys his age, wanted to play cowboys and Indians, or too loose, and his belt too big, and having continually to pull his trousers up as he negotiated, haltingly, the rough terrain, his shirt scratching a nipple raw because he had forgotten or neglected or refused to wear an undershirt, never comfortable in his childhood, not entirely fluent in the language* a pond patrolled by hovering darting flying squadrons of dragonflies like barnstorming stunt pilots; a mysterious oozing primordial tide pool I wonder, now, did I imagine, like any or all of the rest of my childhood, or the other life that followed, that I could find only on the eighth or ninth of ten searches, because landmarks, and other such points of reference, are unstable when you are a child: shifting, transmogrifying, disappearing— bridges that burn, tapes that self-destruct, the little lady you thought you were keeping your eye on in a game of three-card monte but when the card is flipped reveals some other less ladylike fate for the fin or sawbuck, or fool that you are, c-note you've invested in your shining hick credulity—and don't always stay in the same place; searches conducted every summer when I was a child spending half my holidays at Mimi's and the other half at Ma Maw's, the woods I would later seek to resuscitate

—peu de gens devineront combien il a fallu être triste...

so I could lose myself in them again, in eighteen acres of a wooded hill situated in far-off Vernon County, Wisconsin, approximately thirty-one counties and a thousand miles north-northwest of their primordial antecedent, twice-removed, that had, in its way, begot them, but these woods we would keep intact, keep thicketed throughout, at whatever expense, because we could afford the luxury: and besides there is no coal in Vernon County to be strip-mined; though—our virtue not entirely cloistered—we have resisted offers from various timber concerns, to prune, at some profit to ourselves, we've never inquired how much, the trees the roots of which hold our hill together, but then again my wife earns a fair salary doing whatever it is she does, so we can afford to budget for virtue.

Parcels sold off, small lot by small lot, when, finally, as the ink in Mimi's bank balance began to bleed from black to red in the heart-sinking unfailing way that ink eventually does, her earlier once-tenable refusals of strip miners' offers to purchase her mineral rights (offers twirling malevolently in my imagination, at the time, like the mustaches of stock villains) began to crumble like the dirt daubers' nests that caked the roof and walls of Mimi's and Pa Paw's garage, the garage that subtended the mother-in-law suite, scattered scary-looking entemo-archaeological sites abandoned years before like ancient Anasazi ruins but that occasionally still housed laggard daubers, that had, for unknown reasons, declined to join the ancient migrations, fearsome-looking wasp-like things but without the venom and could not sting (I always pictured dirt-daubers in my mind when the sermon drifted, as sermons will, toward Corinthians on the occasional Sunday mornings Mimi was able to get my brother and me out of bed—the smell of biscuits baking and ham frying helped—and into church: "O death, where [is] thy sting? O grave, where [is] thy victory?"); venom-less creatures that still scared hell out of me when they emerged, bumpily, herky-jerky, like a silent film projection from their dusty hogan/tombs.

Mimi tithed her ten percent at church, but donated, in addition, another ten, at least, and usually, in the ecstatic throes of a stubborn, if joyful, form of self-abnegation, considerably more. She made this sacrifice, she said, because the first ten percent was the Lord's due, was what she, a sinner saved (what sins had *she* committed?) owed, and the second, and any further supererogation, was a gift she freely and lovingly and gratefully made. And so, to pay her tithe (or, more accurately, to pay the supererogation: the line in the ledger, god bless her, wherein her ink bled black to red), she sold off the woods; sold off parts of my summers past, not just *my* summers, but it was my summers I was thinking primarily of; sold them off parcel by parcel, until there was nothing left but a tear like an open mouth in the crumbly red clay earth, planted over in time with neat rows of scrubby pine.

Two grandmothers: One the model of the ever-complaining valetudinarian I would eventually threaten to become, documenting, for the misery of everyone around her, each continuing grief and discomfort, every ache and pain (dull, sharp, throbbing, radiating, shooting, referred: o the manifoldness of creation!), having spent my mother's childhood, as my mother would later recount it, in bed having a spell

—Mother's tired and needs to rest

rising only to hack at things and shoot them or to hagride her husband (long-suffering and uxorious, unknown, unknowable, terse in expression, quiet for decades, couldn't say or wouldn't say: dumbstruck from chivalry or life's repeated blows, I will never know).

Think back, back to the memory you revive (the memory you revise? the memory you revile? I'm trying to make an allusion to Merle Haggard's song about his mother, called "Mama's Hungry Eyes," but I can't hear the words clearly when I listen to the song, and all three usages are cited on the various lyrics/ringtone websites, once you get past all the pop-ups). Think back to the long ride home from Mimi's and Ma Maw's; to your mother crying at the awfulness of the two hours or so she has just witnessed of Ma Maw's lashing out and hacking at, her tearing down, of the good gray father, tired, gray, and silent, the father she adored.

You and your brother, sunburnt, mosquito-bit, and dirty from the dirt of the country, are half-asleep in the back seat of the Galaxie. You wear no seatbelts; your shoes are on the floorboard; the windows are rolled part way down as cigarette smoke wafts from the front seat and a baseball game is turned down low on the radio. The announcer's voice gently singsongs the news, that had some significance then, had some significance for a slice of time discarded now, that there has been a swing and there has been a miss. The tops of trees roll by in the purple dusk turning red and pink and orange and lavender and magenta as the nuclear family, tender, helpless, still intact, approaches the great northern expanse of the city, where steel mills (now defunct) spit their hell, ravishing in its lung-lacerating pre-postindustrial hydrocarbon beauty, into the vast everlasting and indifferent firmament above...

Rising also, my grandmother on my mother's side, to enumerate, in hateful shrill monotone, as my mother would also later recount it, the every flaw of each of her four children, the flaws of some—again, as recounted by my mother—enumerated more shrilly than others, passing on to them her own spoken and unspoken hurt, her own spoken and unspoken sorrow, dependent, now, Ma Maw, because she had never learned to drive, on her children, or the three, that is, of the four children who had remained in the vicinity, to wheel her from doctor to doctor, from appointment to appointment, putting on a friendly face to strangers, nurses, and receptionists, but snarling, venomous, herself (and could breathe easy) only when she was safely back in the car and out of earshot of polite society; she rose also, this Ma Maw, before Pa Paw died, from her sickbed, before dawn, to bake biscuits and fry ham and stir gravy, and slosh Pa Paw's coffee into the cup from which he'd pour the boiling black brew into his saucer to sip it, and pack his lunch into his pail, and tamp his tobacco into his bowl, and gather his pickaxe for him, and his coal shovel, and iron his coveralls and light the lamp in his helmet and send him down into the underworld to mine for the family's living, to mine for the coal the dust of which was destroying his lungs but his heart, a silent savage fist in his tight chest, would die first before he could live long enough to cough out what would have been, had he held on longer, the last of the life that he had already forfeited.

The other grandmother, also widowed, but sound of mind

and body and hearty of spirit, hating germs and sin and foreign wars (and card playing and swearing and strong drink), not given, like the other, or the grandson she loved so, her first, to despair, to morbidity or agonizing reappraisals, an upright club-woman, active in the community, driving still the 1967 Mercury Cougar that my Uncle Jimmy had left behind when he went in the service, driving it heroically, like Neal Cassady apostro-phized by Robert Creeley, a blur of grandmother and racing ma-chine, eternally seeded, in cybernetic splendor, in every heat of all God's Wacky Races.

Driving the car, because she was driving it for Christ's sake, very fast (though in nearly every other respect, when her con-science allowed it, Mimi was law-abiding, rendering unto Cae-sar and all that) and getting tickets, lots of tickets, the bane and scourge of deputy sheriffs and state troopers, lying in wait, like Death does, but with mirrored sunglasses, fat asses, and little Hitler mustaches.

Driving, for Christ's sake, from meeting to meeting, from ap-pointment to appointment, from training union to training un-ion; visiting the sick and the lonely and the dying, bestowing soup and bandages on the hungry and the afflicted; never stop-ping, always moving, a cosmic force for hygiene and righteous-ness and peace, for justice and salvation.

Piled—in fact cramped; she was long and lean, Mimi was, streamlined, like her ride, and beautiful to the end—in the space age cockpit (with its competition instrument panel, toggle switches, and overhead console) of her shiny pale green boss-ass muscle car sitting on three hundred and ninety cubes of fierce, gasoline-sucking displacement in a mighty four barrel V8 (with, by the way, a literal hole in the floorboard on the passenger's side to parallel the figurative one on the driver's, scaring hell out of me when I rode shotgun on her missions of mercy; Why did I never ask how the hole got there? I think it was because I liked the mystery of it).

Never stopping, always moving; teaching Sunday School on

Sunday and Vacation Bible School in June; substitute teaching all the subjects at Dora and Cordova and Sumiton High; taking extension classes from Samford University, and almost, but not quite, finishing, before she died, the degree she had started so many years earlier, when the school was still called Howard College, my father's alma mater; and, entrepreneurial, operating, with my Aunt Retha, a kindergarten in Aunt Retha's house in Sumiton, and, in addition, selling Luzier cosmetics on the side; for relaxation (a low priority), swimming with her cronies in the public pool in Jasper, and, when she finally wound her way back home, tending to her garden, riding her stationary bike to stay in shape, and reading and re-reading the Bible she had, effectively, memorized, troubled though she was by all the killing, all the smiting.

Two grandmothers: both still living, but not for long, in the country, what was left of the country (strip-mined, ravished, junked, and clear cut); the country and the grandmothers that Caroline and I, recapitulating the progress of weekly pilgrimages of my childhood (strip-mined, ravished, junked, and clear cut, as all childhoods are), had driven down from Milwaukee and up from Birmingham to see *progenitors who had not themselves inaugurated the hurt, had not inaugurated the sorrow, sweetened in time with picnics of fried chicken and potato salad and ice cream hand-cranked in the yard; a birthday party with punchbowls and paper hats and cake and candles; occasional small kindnesses, acts of remembrance, gifts or mementos: handkerchiefs, gloves, a scarf, a sweater, a billfold in calfskin or cordovan; a wedding with a ring bearer and a flower girl and maids of honor with Brother Somebody-or-Other laying on the Jesus; an anniversary; a graduation; the birth of a child; the memory of a picnic, a party, a kindness, an embrace; the sorrow (and the sweetness) that ended, always and fatally, in the terminus of the grave, where nothing is remembered and nothing is hoped for; they had, instead, inherited it themselves, inherited the hurt, inherited the sorrow, inherited the sweetness, inherited it all, and had then blindly, somnolently, trundled it along, passed it down like a family heirloom, like*

*a gene (a gene for disillusionment), like hand-me-down clothes (clothes
that don't quite fit, almost fit, but don't quite), though they could have
stopped it there, could have stopped it then, if somebody had been there
to tell them that they had a choice which anyway they didn't have could
not have had else why go on they would have asked and seem though
they are dead to be asking now*
    why go on?

They went on, though, Mimi and Ma Maw, and then died
themselves, as had their respective Pa Paws before them; they
died as had the even older old people they had known, old people older than any old people will ever be old again (nobody
who is old anywhere is ever as old as old people are old in the
south), old people who had been born in the century before the
century that just passed, old people who were old enough to
have known people who had known slaves, old enough to have
known people who had owned slaves, old enough to have
known people who had been slaves: Granny, for instance
(Mimi's Pa Paw's mother), and Mama Jones (Mimi's mother),
widows themselves of old people dead long before I was born
(descendants, and progenitors, of long generations of widow
women solemnly entrained in an ever-receding column of grief),
alive in their nineties and wouldn't let go, couldn't let go, both
tended to, heroically, self-sacrificingly, by Mimi, because that is
what one did then, or maybe that was just what Mimi did:
Granny, withered, incontinent, and on-and-off demented, her
hands a pair of desiccated claws shaking with Parkinson's Disease and reaching for a bedpan under an iron bed in a smelly
sickroom piled with a scary assortment of antique orthopedic
appliances; and Mama Jones in the mother-in-law apartment
over the garage with her hand on a panic button rigged by Pa
Paw that buzzed when pressed in hideous electronic cacophony
in the hallway of the updated brick-clad clapboard fifty or sixty
yards away, summoning Mimi when the widow was in need,
which she wasn't often because Mama Jones was not as sickly as
Granny (and she was, moreover, able to travel, almost to the end,

spending half the year with a daughter married to an aerospace engineer, or poodle mortician, or extra in the movies, or something like that, who lived in Sherman Oaks, California, down the street from My Three Sons and The Brady Bunch, as I imagined it, one of Mimi's seven sisters, I forget which one, Athalie, Beulah, Clarinda, Elspeth, Lavinia, Mavis, or Alma Mae—she had one brother, whose name was Robert).

They all died, these old people, but later than anyone thought they would, or sooner it seemed when the news, awful to some and a relief to others, sometimes awful and a relief at the same time, was announced and received, their exits staggered like curtain calls at the end of a performance, lesser players and then the headliners: Granny first, my first death, and the only one I cried over until Mimi; Mama Jones was next: she expired in California, and was buried there with the more prosperous relations in attendance; then came Ma Maw's Pa Paw, who died at age sixty-five in a hot August when I was at band camp, trying to learn the half-time drill; then it was Mimi's Pa Paw's turn, in October, 1980; Ma Maw died next, a couple of years after I had relocated to Milwaukee, Wisconsin, leaving all her grandchildren a thousand dollars each.

Mimi, who left nothing behind, having given it all away while she was still living, was the last of the old people to go…

When trying to get my brother and me out of our beds on Saturday mornings for the hour and then some drive out Old Highway 78, the drive Caroline and I recapitulated some twenty years later, depending on when you reckon it from, our mother would explain (gently, remorsefully, already grieving) that Mimi and Pa Paw and Ma Maw and Pa Paw were old and would be dead, possibly in our childhood, and we should enjoy their company while we can. But we wanted to stay home on those

Saturday mornings and sleep in and watch cartoons in our "feet pajamas" and then get dressed and go out and play with our friends, to ride our bicycles down the grassy swoop behind the O'Brien's house, crashing like Vietnam into the ditch at the bottom of the hill, and build forts and fires and play army and hide and go seek in nearby wooded lots soon to be "developed," and tackle each other to the ground in games of football *except it was touch on the driveways separating the front lawns that made up the field (two front lawns was a football field, the opposite sides of each driveway were the end zones, and crossing unscathed the far limit of the driveway was a touchdown), but Jack Siple was tackled on the driveway, accidentally, one November game day, his knee flesh torn from the bone of his knee now exposed, the driveway red with blood and pink and gray with flesh and bits of bone and marrow and cartilage, and Jack yowling in pain beyond mercurochrome, just as he would yowl again a few years later when the ceiling of his father's bedroom would be similarly splattered red and pink and gray, but this time with the brains of his father, a butcher by profession, and given to drink, possessing, like his boys, a crew cut, a penchant for brawling, and a hick accent and bad grammar (the Siples said "ain't," which my parents particularly didn't allow; and, a Siple specialty, "y'allses" as the possessive of "y'all"), who had run one evening at suppertime from the dinner table to the master bedroom, and blown off the top of his head with a shotgun; Jack, the story went in the neighborhood—though no one ever knew what really happened—had been the one to rush into the bedroom when the family, huddled in the kitchen, had heard the blast, and was the one, the story also went, to wipe the mess from the ceiling; when I heard the news, at school—my family had moved to Willow Way by then, leaving behind the dead and dying of Wedgeworth Drive—I felt guilty for the grudge I'd held for Mr. Siple from when my brother and I had several years earlier spent the night at Jack and Lydell's (Lydell was Jack's baby brother) and had been looking forward all day to watching Rock Hudson and Paula Prentiss in Howard Hawks'* Man's Favorite Sport?, *but when it was time for the Late Show, Mr. Siple changed the channel and insisted on watching wrestling, and we called our father to come pick us up and we went home in a huff, two little lords (you know the lord I mean), and watched the movie in the comfort of our more refined home, where people didn't watch wrestling or say "ain't" or blow their heads off with shotguns (there were no firearms, and no deviations from standard English, in the Blackwell household).*

The last time I saw Jack Siple—except maybe in passing at school— was two weeks before Jack's father's suicide, and my brother and I invited Jack and Lydell to go with us to Lake Alhambra, a kind of poor man's country club that my father had gotten the family into by joining the Shriners, but never attending any meetings or wearing a fez or driving a tiny car in a parade, just joining so the family could go to Lake Alhambra and swim in the pool, and Jack and I discovered a cave in the cliffs overlooking the lake just as it was about time to go, and we made plans to come back and go spelunking, but then, a couple of weeks later, Jack's father killed himself and, wait a minute, now I remember, the last time I saw Jack was at Jack's father's funeral [closed casket] and he was looking pretty sad and somehow we were never friends anymore and then Jack started running with Chick Adderley and Spit Madigan and Pudgy St. Cyr on the wrong side of the law and he turned into a kind of nasty customer and they finally wound up—Jack and Chick and Pudgy, at least; I don't know about Spit—in jail, where I imagine them still, in stripes and in need of a shave, sharing a cell, sharpening a shiv and planning a jailbreak, Beagle Boys numbers 176-167, 176-671, and 176-176, respectively.

But, I was saying, every Saturday it was over the river and through the trees on another happy journey to Trenton and Camden.

—There's nothin' like bein' liked by your family

Our first stop was Ma Maw's (her house was closer, first in), for lunch and horselaughs and racist colloquy; for scavenger hunts in the loft of the barn (still-standing then, though listing precariously, adding a sense of danger, of something ventured, the loft that had been used for at least three generations of forbears as an attic, where the past came close to disclosing its cold secrets, and treasures and knick-knacks and curiosities could be found and were free for the taking); and for shooting BB guns at tin cans: the city slickers shot BB guns, the country mice shot .22 caliber rifles. If it was Christmas and Pa Paw was alive, we'd troop, the whole family, except for Ma Maw, who needed to rest, down to "the Park" they called it, a large wooded tract, 100 acres or so, since clear cut (to finance my year at Harvard; just kidding, not with my ACT scores, or my high school GPA, or, basically, the cut of my jib) that Ma Maw had brought to the marriage (she always acted like she'd married down), located three quarters of a mile or so up the road from the house (also part of Ma Maw's portion) and Pa Paw would shoot mistletoe out of the tops of tall trees with a rifle, enough for everybody to take some home.

Then it was up the road to Mimi's for a second lunch and some more refined conversation and Bible stories and a game of scrabble and looking through old photograph albums and walks in the woods and a nap.

And so, following ancient precedents, recapitulating the progress of the weekly pilgrimages of my youth (this was our first Christmas together, and Caroline's first sojourn in Dogpatch), wending all the backroads leading back in time, we stopped at Ma Maw's first, bumpety-bump over the railroad tracks that I was nervous, as I'd been as a child, to get across, clear of the tracks and the oncoming train I always imagined I heard hurtling our way (there were no guard rails or flashing lights to warn of approaching trains, just an old faded sign, with bullet holes, listing cock-eyed on its rusted iron post, admonishing, in a little poem just seven syllables and a seasonal reference short of a haiku, "Alabama Law: Stop, Look, and Listen"). Upon safely clearing the tracks, we made a quick right and wheeled up the long gravel drive bordered in kudzu-softened barbed wire that led, finally, to a little sort of a parking lot under a mimosa stand, where we parked the car and then climbed up, two or three steps at a time in my case (the way I had climbed them as a child), the railroad-tie stairs (upon which my country cousins and I had so many years before played games of rock school—I, as things would eventually play out, the only future teacher of America among us; believe me, as bad as I feel about my own failures, you don't want to hear whatever became of the country cousins) that led to the steps that took one up to the screen porch, through which callers entered the house. We paused for a moment at the top step (or I should say *I* paused for a moment at the top step… remembering things), and as I opened the screen door I heard, as I remembered I would, just before I opened it, the sound of the rusty spring squeaking *the screen porch where, approximately twenty years prior to my bringing Caroline down to meet the folks, my younger hellgrammite self—sun-tired, shaggy, stinking, hard to get in the bathtub or in a barber's chair, dreading the impending return to school, but trying not to think about it, as the soldier on leave tries not to think about the war that he will have to return to, spending, at Ma Maw's, the second half of the summer vacation the first half of which I had spent at Mimi's—lay in an orange hammock, with green and white fringe, riffling through a cardboard box full of hand-me-down comic books I'd brought from home, a beautiful cache donated by a neighbor's kid who, his mother said, had outgrown them (these were older comics, an eighth of a generation older, enough time to mean that the former owner of the books might have had, a few years later, to have gone to Vietnam: this was the decade when if you were a boy every year older you were was one year closer to Vietnam; when the year you were born could determine, and sometimes did determine, if you had to die, and, of course, in the attempt to avoid or postpone dying, to kill), sipping sweet iced tea through a straw from a mason jar as the summer rain blew pink blossoms off the mimosa tree in the front yard and a train whistled in the distance; the rain that smelled so good misting in, a little of it, through the mesh of the screen, which also smelled good, like metal, cooling things down, baptizing my bare feet, foreshortened and crossed like Jesus at the ankle near the foot of the hammock, sufficient, then, unto myself, but with the comic books protected from water*

damage, because, having smelled the rain before it came, I had moved
the box to a safer position on the porch away from the screen; and then
the train, the whistle of which had prepared all ears for the thunder that
was to come, approached nearer, in thunder and rattle and screech,
scaring birds away, and lizards and mice, on tracks that ran practically
in the front yard of Ma Maw's house, crossing the road that Ma Maw's
driveway turned into, the gravel driveway that ran partly parallel to
the tracks, down a small embankment from them, the tracks upon which
my mother had fallen as a girl, chasing her friend Christine, earning a
small raised purplish-green scar on her knee that my brother and I al-
ways made her show us, and tell us the story of how she came to get the
scar, but when my brother and I revised the story and told it back to
her, our mother was trapped on the track as the train approached and
rescued only at the last minute (by Christine? or had Christine tied our
mother to the tracks and then an unknown do-gooder, our father, per-
haps, had come by to rescue her, returning a few years later to marry
her?); the same train that my mother, when she was a child, had known
the engineers and brakemen of, engineers and brakemen who would toss
her comic books and candy as the train passed, and later when she was
a teenager would slow the train down slow enough to let her (and
Christine) climb aboard and they would get a ride to Birmingham,
where they would take in a second-run movie at the Lyric, or if they'd
saved enough nickels, a first-run at the Ritz or the Melba or the Empire,
and get a small bite to eat at Britling's Cafeteria or the café on the mez-
zanine of Loveman's department store, and catch—on the train's re-
turn trip to wherever it was it was going back to—a ride back to the
yard and the mimosa tree and the house and the barn and the smoke-
house and the lassitude and boredom of country living, to the loneli-
ness, and the, what do they call them? the simple pleasures: ice cream
lightning bugs June bugs tadpoles polliwogs rock candy calico gingham
polly wolly doodle all the day; the train whose tracks smelled of creosote
the good smell I always liked smelling like the subway in New York
smelling like the railroad ties piled up by the smokehouse where my
brother and I and our country cousins, collaborating, for once, like
drones in a happy beehive, made a fort in the early friendly days of

summer one summer, before things began to rot in the heat, and where, in the rotting days, we repaired one afternoon, crawling into our cozy cave after a morning of fighting and arguing and teasing; Baldry Euell—my older cousin, older by a year—and I had been picking on my younger brother and on the four girl cousins also in attendance, two of whom who lived in a house trailer in a fenced-in corner of Ma Maw and Pa Paw's property, lived there with their mother, my mother's fat sister, accentuating her girth with loud and lavish caftans, large gaudy jewelry and even larger hair, and their daddy, a short man with a red face whose first name was two initials, who was a plumber or some such, and always had a toolbox in his hand, and who for some reason had something against Catholics, calling them fish eaters (I once pointed out to him, when I was a child, that Catholics only did that on Friday and during Lent, and then only the more observant of them, but my uncle said that even though I was right about that, he still liked the epithet and would continue using it...), always finding some way to introduce this particular prejudice (every man his specialty) into family conversations already laced with, or consisting primarily, of prejudice; two of the girl cousins were, technically, Baldry Euell's younger sisters, but more like cousins than sisters since Baldry Euell had been, for reasons I never understood, abandoned as an infant by his mother and father, and left to be raised by Ma Maw and Pa Paw before the girl children had been born (but Baldry Euell never expressed any regrets about it, at least not to me), a boy child banished, preemptively, from the Oedipal triad now nuclear family that resided mainly in Texas, but traveled around a lot because Uncle John Daddy (which is what my brother and I, for reasons no one can remember, called Baldry Euell's father) was in the service (Uncle John Daddy, who was mean and a drunk and a braggart and a wife-beater and, later, a suicide—and he swore a lot, too—could tolerate—this was my theory—no potential usurper in his kingdom); he did, however, and this was much later, after he'd abandoned his wife and daughters as he'd several years earlier abandoned his son, drive a pretty goddamn cool car ("goddamn" was Uncle John Daddy's favorite swear word): a sixties-something Karmann Ghia convertible, a car that I took great pleasure in riding in the

*one time my uncle visited the family at Willow Way and angered my
mother by shooting birds from the trees in the backyard, sitting on a
bench on the deck not yet rotting and brandishing the weapon he carried with him at all times—just as, approximately twenty years later,
he'd anger my mother again by turning the revolver on his own
damned self; the same visit Uncle John Daddy took me, in the Karmann
Ghia that I admired, to a sporting goods store in nearby redneck Center
Point (Killough Springs Forest was more genteel) to buy me the pocket
knife my own parents, striving, upwardly mobile, would never have
thought to have wanted me to have, a knife still, by the way, in my
possession, rusted, and packed in a drawer among my souvenirs...*

*We'd been playing motorcycle gang, Baldry Euell, my brother, and
I, with bandanas tied around our foreheads and iron crosses hanging
around our necks, bandanas and iron crosses we'd bought, along with
some incense, fat leather watch bands, fluorescent paints, and an assortment of rubber Rat Finks, at a sort of combination head shop and
five and dime in Sumiton, dubbing each other with menacing motorcycle gang-sounding aliases; I was "Link Chain," "Link" for short, and
Baldry Euell was "Wolf," but Baldry Euell and I had nicknamed my
brother "Daisy," making him cry, and then taking the only two bicycles
on the property for ourselves and making Daisy ride a tricycle and not
letting the girls play at all, or, more precisely, giving them the role of
terrorized townspeople, and teasing them as we circled them again and
again, raising dust and calling out rude names, pedaling harder and
harder, circling round and round, the dogs following, yelping and bark-
ing, Daisy trying to keep up on the tricycle he was too big to ride circling circling circling a menacing blurry red blur of mean childhood
boy-cruelty ("all twelve year old boys," Leslie Fiedler once wrote, "are
Germans"), but then tiring of this mayhem and fearing we'd gone too
far and would be told on, Baldry Euell and I explored the gentler sides
of our boy natures and instigated a ceasefire and a little truth and reconciliation (notice both the mayhem and the truth and reconciliation
were the big boys' ideas), a concordat to be concluded in the railroad tie
cave/fortress that we'd built together in earlier peaceful times of mutual
cooperation; in this cave we huddled together (I was, for my part,*

feeling some small stirring in my loins at the close proximity to female flesh, admittedly not particularly fetching female flesh, but then it was pretty dark in the fort, and desire is a fucked-up thing), the whole crew, welling up like drunks with human kindness overflowing, swearing oaths of allegiance and friendship and brotherly and sisterly and cousinly love, love for all mankind, so that many years later, when I read about "the green stick" and the "Ant Brothers" of Leo Tolstoy's childhood, I could make a "text-to-self connection," one less noble than the Count's, but a connection still, when I remembered the Ant Cousins of my own childhood huddled in the railroad-tie fortress:

> When I was five years old, and my brothers Dimitri and Sergius six and seven, Nicolas announced to us that he possessed the secret which, if known, would make everybody happy. There would be no illness, no trouble, nobody would feel anger against another, and all would love one another and become "Ant Brothers." (Probably he meant the Moravian Brotherhood—Moravskiye bratya—about which he had read or heard; but in our children's minds it was Ant Brotherhood—Muraveinye bratya.) I remember that the word "ant" especially pleased us, reminding us of the ants in their hills. We even invented a game of Ant Brothers. We crept under chairs, placed boxes around them, covered up all chinks with handkerchiefs, and sat in the darkness pressed against each other. I remember that I used then to have a particular feeling of love and tenderness, and I liked the play very much.

> The secret of the Ant Brothers had been disclosed to us; but the great secret—how to banish all unhappiness from life, all disputes and anger, and to make people happy for ever—this secret, as he told us, Nicolas had written on a green stick, and the green stick was buried near the road along the hollow by the old wood...

> The ideal of the ant brethren clinging lovingly together, not under two chairs covered by handkerchiefs, but under the wide, blue vault of heaven and embracing all mankind, has remained. As I believed then in the existence of a green stick on which was written the secret

which would do away with all evil in humanity and give great hap-
piness, so I believe now that there exists such a truth; this will be
divulged to mankind and all promises will be fulfilled.[16]

But of course the secret of the stick was lost and the concordat soon
unraveled and discord was visited back upon the yard, and the teasing
and cruelty was resumed. *Baldry Euell/Wolf is dead now, the country*
cousin, one year older than me, one year closer to Vietnam, whom I had
played coal miner with as a child, picked ticks off Ma Maw's beagle
Sandy with, and smashed the mites to bits with hammers, shot at rusty
tin cans and old bottles with BB guns with, dipped snuff with (once),
snuff provided by an ancient withered old man wearing overalls and a
pin-striped brakeman's cap outside Purdy's old-fashioned store that
still had a working potbelly stove in it, and possibly a cracker barrel,
but I might be making the cracker barrel up (there were definitely crack-
ers in that store, though); the once wannabe-yippie cousin who had
given me a copy of Steal This Book *that he had stolen from the Rexall*
Drugstore in Dora, but whose politics reverted soon enough to redneck
racist southern bile, and who grew into a mean and bitter and hateful
man; Baldry Euell, who as a child always wanted to be a coal miner
when he grew up (an ambition that I, growing up in an upwardly mo-
bile milieu, could never understand), grew up to be a coal miner, taking
early retirement, getting into lots of drunken brawls, gaining the rep-
utation of being a mean and nasty and dangerous son of a bitch, stock-
piling guns, racking them in his "pick 'em up," and finally getting
himself killed in a gun battle with some other redneck sombitch over a
girl that I can only imagine the...well, the skankiness of.

And so Caroline and I, down from Milwaukee and out into
the country from Birmingham, recapitulating the progress of
weekly pilgrimages from my childhood, stopped at Ma Maw's
first, and Ma Maw, in a wig, because she'd lost almost all her
hair, acting sweet in the way that made my mother chafe because

---

[16] Quoted in *The Life of Tolstoy* (1911) by Paul Birukoff.

she remembered the other side of the old lady's personality, said "Ya'll come in," and we went in and we sat with Ma Maw in the living room that was partially illuminated by the green lights of a silver-metal Christmas tree and the twitching blue of the TV set resting on a cart in a corner of the room.

Ma Maw poured us some strong coffee that tasted good, that tasted like getting ready to go somewhere, that tasted like waiting for somebody to come home.

We drank the coffee black because all Ma Maw had was non-dairy creamer. There was a bowl of cinnamon-dominated pot-pourri on the coffee table and a *TV Guide* and a *Jasper Daily Mountain-Eagle* and tissues and a magnifying glass and some pill bottles and a bowl of unshelled pecans, filberts, and walnuts with a nutcracker in it.

When I smelled the cinnamon, the smell Ma Maw's house always smelled of (cinnamon potpourri, to be precise, and ham and coffee and creosote and citronella-scented furniture polish and gardenia-scented soap), I remembered the last visit I'd paid to Ma Maw's house before I moved to Milwaukee, when, during the visit, an old friend of Ma Maw's from finishing school (just joking about finishing school) came to call, unannounced, though it was Ma Maw's "at home" day (just joking about Ma Maw's "at home" day); a sad lady with sad pouches under her eyes buried in a beautiful sad wrinkled face, who, in her sadness, and the cash-poor, genteel, almost-aristocratic sounding cadences of her speech (and the slight hint of an alcoholic beverage I thought I detected on her breath), put me in mind of sensitive, lost, tormented, and cheated out of her money Aunt Birdie from Lillian Hellman's play The Little Foxes, *a production of which I had recently seen at the Town and Gown Theater in Birmingham (and would later see a way-too-smart "deconstruction" of at The New York Theater Workshop). She was toting under her arms two bulging paper sacks tied with twine nearly bursting with fifty or sixty years' worth of marvelous paintings she'd done on scraps of cardboard and torn pieces of other paper bags, beautiful, unframe-able paintings with raggedly biomorphic edges, colorful, rich and imaginative, but dark somehow, in their stirring un-sentimental evocation of the natural world, and humankind's lonely place in it, examples of what they used, condescendingly, to call "folk," or "primitive," or "naïve art," but now they call, condescendingly, "outsider art," and Ma Maw, not even looking at the efforts of her childhood friend, her life's work, tried to shoo the lady away, but the lady stayed.*

She stayed for a long time.

I tried to buy some of her pictures, but she wouldn't sell them. She said she would like to give me some of them, would like to give me the ones I loved the best, but she had never been able to bear to part with any of them.

It was a gloomy day outside. It was Christmas then, too…

We sat in the living room for a long time, Caroline and I on the couch, Ma Maw in her recliner, but with the footrest down, talking and drinking our coffee, talking about old times, talking about new times. Caroline and I talked of new times. All of Ma Maw's times were old times.

Ma Maw had a bag of shortbread cookies that she opened up, and a big white and blue china platter that she put them on (the Willow pattern I think you call it, with birds and boats and willow trees and a bridge, fence, and pagoda), and two smaller plates to catch the crumbs. Caroline and I ate our cookies. I dunked my mine in my coffee. Ma Maw didn't eat any.

Then an old rooster gave out a croaky cockle-doodle-doo in the yard, but a kind of a partly-swallowed half a cockle-doodle-doo, like roosters give sometimes. Impressed by the strange calls of the exotic fauna of the Deep South, Caroline looked up from her coffee and asked, sweetly, "What kind of bird was *that*?"

The Polish Moon, Part Two

If there is a sin against life, it lies perhaps less in despairing of it than in hoping for another life, and evading the implacable grandeur of the one we have.

Albert Camus, quoted by Geoff Dyer in *Out of Sheer Rage*

"O cock of red feathers that crew before the clocks," mouthed I, robustiously, tearing a passion to tatters, back at the Blue Hotel, cracking Stevens's hard c's like a stern classicist correcting the general public's bad Latin, as the Polish Moon knelled another hour's death sentence, knelling it hard like a shrieking bleeding Jesus bird hung high on an ancient rusted nail hammered in the sky above (but with a view of ravaged Walker County below, and of the junked-up ditches of Five Mile Road, the wattle and daub of Wedgeworth Drive, and the split-leveled future at Willow Way, and, farther off in the distance, the National Portrait Gallery, and, a little closer—closer in distance, not in time—the Harrington Hotel, the Smithsonian Institution, the Ford Theater, the Bureau of Engraving and Printing, and the seven states you can see from Lover's Leap atop Lookout Mountain, and all, all the campus brutalisms I had known, and all of those to follow: "Look, Peter, I can see your house from here"), startling me, startling me at every crow of the clock. I—who, if I'd borne a tattoo, a gesture I didn't need (like the "people, places, and animals" on the back cover of Philip Levine's *Not This Pig*, "the ones who live at all cost and come back for more, and who if they bore tattoos—a gesture they don't need—would have them say, 'Don't tread on me' or 'Once more with feeling' or '*No passaran*' or 'Not this pig'"), would have had mine say, "*Timor mortis conturbat me*," or "*Es ist alles lächerlich, wenn man an den Tod denkt*,"[17] or "Mr. Bungle sends his regards," or "*kina hora* pu pu pu" —was disturbed, yes (as an organizing principle of my life!), by fear of death, but also by fear of death's analogue, its précis, its "executive summary," the gloves it wore, and sooner or later took off: passing slipping obliterating time (but how do you put that in a tattoo?). And so every time Jesus squawked the hour, if there was company in the house or I was alone, but in those days there was company in the house, I would, after warming up the audience with my "cock of red feather" routine, entertain my ghosts, I mean entertain my guests (or bore them to death because they'd heard it all before), with an old-fashioned entertainment, a sort of vaudeville wedged in the ever-changing program of masques, mummeries, and magic lanterns; of forfeits, snap dragon, and *tableaux vivant*; of whisk-and-swabbers, ruff-and-honors, and battledore and shuttlecock; and, as the evening wore on, and the blood alcohol content rose, mumblety-peg, Russian roulette, and a policeman strapped to the back of a bear and thrown in the Milwaukee River: an old-fashioned entertainment that began with my slowly and portentously—pretentiously!—unfurling an accusatory right index finger (Reader, none of this is true)

Slowly, I turn; step by step, inch by inch…

and pointing it in the direction of the cuckoo cock Jesus chirruping in the sky, and continued, after a pause just long enough for an angel of history to pass, with another mouthing, declaimed this time in three-dimensional southern drawl, an aristocratic variant borrowed from Shelby Foote, courtly star, in those days, of the Public Broadcasting Service (and by the way, as far as I

---

[17] "Everything is ridiculous, when one thinks of death." (Thomas Bernhard)

could tell, only slightly reconstructed apologist for the Confederate States of America, but I wasn't endorsing his politics, just borrowing his drawl), a speech I'd memorized as a teenager in my bedroom in split-leveled Willow Way, when I'd stayed up all night reading *The Sound and the Fury*, vowing early the next morning, when I closed the book, to become a writer, a novelist or a poet, I wasn't sure which, either way morbid and sensitive and chronophobic and elegiac in disposition even then, as I suppose all teenagers are, but especially the sensitive ones, the speech that Quentin Compson's father Jason Lycurgus Compson (I read Faulkner then, I read Faulkner now, the way morbidly sensitive "emo" teens today read morbid vampire-y YA) declaims as he presents his son with the watch that will serve, hokily but effectively (like the sled in *Citizen Kane*), as the weenie that drives the sad narrative and sickly denouement of Quentin's distracted monologue entitled "Part 2: June 2, 1910" (*Did you ever have a sister? did you?* I never did, but I could sympathize)

— I give you the mausoleum of all hope and desire

As I declaimed, a mature sugar maple (since demolished, in the interest of progress, or maybe it had gotten sick), lush and zaftig in the lovely Wisconsin summer, all the more poignant for its dramatically all-too-brief a lease, brushed its limbs wantonly against the kitchen window.

— I give it to you not that you may remember time

Often, on Sunday mornings, as I watched the maple dance, and mourned, in advance, an inevitable loss, I would unfurl yet another accusatory right index finger (I felt I had a sort of series of whirling hands of them, like a dancing Shiva, except *all* of my fingers were pointers) and point it in the direction of the temporary efflorescence outside my window that I loved so well (the efflorescence, not the window, although I liked the window well enough), and, after pausing long enough for one more angel of history to pass, I would declaim, in a different kind of regional-specific three-dimensional accent (Connecticut WASP I guess you'd call it, with a little bit of Newport thrown in, an accent borrowed from Thurston Howell III, star, in an earlier era of my evolving television consciousness, of the Columbia Broadcasting System), some pertinent lines of Wallace Stevens that I'd memorized as a teenager when I stayed up all night reading *Harmonium*, vowing early the next morning, when I closed the book, to become a poet, this time definitely a poet:

> Death is the mother of Beauty; hence from her,
> Alone, shall come fulfillment to our dreams
> And our desires. Although she strews the leaves
> Of sure obliteration on our paths—
> The path sick sorrow took, the many paths
> Where triumph rang its brassy phrase, or love
> Whispered a little out of tenderness—
> She makes the willow shiver in the sun
> For maidens who were wont to sit and gaze
> Upon the grass, relinquished to their feet.
> She causes boys to bring sweet-smelling pears
> And plums in ponderous piles. The maidens taste
> And stray impassioned in the littering leaves.

And as I piled my plums and littered my leaves, in the brassy, sweet-smelling days before I set out on the path sick sorrow took,

> —I give it to you not that you may remember time

I—whispering a little out of tenderness—invoked often the phrase "Death is the mother of beauty," when I sang the splendors of the short-lived Wisconsin summers I loved so well

—but that you might forget it now and then for a moment

the heat and the humidity of which, or the never-ending repudiation of the one in favor of the other, that native Milwaukeeans—Teutonically obese from a lard and suet soaked diet of *Braunschweiger* and *Sauerbraten* and *Schweinshaxe* and *Spanferkel* and *Schlachtschüssel* and liverwurst and headcheese, etc., with three pale yellow wax beans, decanted from a dusty tin, served on the side (a wan and insipid North Country gesture they called "vegetable"), washed down with tankards of beer chasing tumblers of brandy old fashioneds (1-2 jiggers of brandy, 2-3 dashes of Angostura bitters, a lump of sugar, and a splash of water, muddled and served on the rocks), or vice versa—never tired complaining of, when, for a half an hour each summer, the temperature rose a small degree above absolute zero on the Kelvin scale; a meteorological anomaly that was a blessing to me, temperamentally cold-natured (and skinny like a scene in the life of Bohemia; consumptive-looking, but I was in good health in those days), and who, practicing for a senescence that would come sooner than I imagined, tended to wrap myself up in a shawl and toss a little plaid blanket over my knees even in the dog days.

—and not spend all your breath trying to conquer it

I would also quote Stevens, the bit about death being the mother of beauty, when practical-minded colleagues at work questioned my extravagant (decadent, even, I think some of them thought) habit of keeping fresh cut flowers on my desk—orchids, usually, or poppies, veronica, anemone, ranunculus, lisianthus, mountain lilies, pentas, bluebottles, cosmos, nasturtiums, or cleomes—cut flowers that DIE

—because no battle is ever won he said

instead of the more practical potted plants favored by practical Middle Westerners that, with a little care, will live indefinitely (the potted plants, not the Middle Westerners—though they didn't seem to notice it, or, if they did, they didn't consider it to be a topic worth developing an obsession over, death being, after all, "just another part of life," etc., etc.).

—the field only reveals to man his own folly and despair

These same practical people, who knew neither folly nor despair and who stoically regretted nothing, also urged me to stop throwing my money away on rent and to save it instead for a down payment on a house, a duplex, preferably, so I could collect rent on the spare flat to cover the mortgage, and maybe even turn a profit, because as a renter I was neglecting the moral imperative to "build equity," a religious rite not just in the Middle West, of course, but in the Middle West especially, it seemed to me.

—and victory is an illusion of philosophers and fools

(Upon listening to these urgings I would sometimes change my tactic a little and bring out my heavy artillery, wheeled in from the Russian front, and recite a passage I'd memorized as a teenager when I stayed up all night reading...oh, never mind...would recite, in fact, a statement attributed to Count Leo Tolstoy, who really nailed it this time, I thought, when he asked the musical question, from high atop the Yasnaya Polyana, overlooking the "already tall and dark green grass, and forget-me-nots and the dead nettles, and everything – most of all, the waving of the birches along the '*preshpekt*'"[18]: "Is there any meaning in my life that the inevitable death awaiting me does not destroy?"

---

[18] From the Yasnaya Polyana website.

Except, I sometimes pointedly substituted, in my usual zeal to overstate my point, the word "equity" for the word "meaning"—not necessarily, in the context of Milwaukee cheeseparing, such a far-fetched substitution.)

Many years later (and the many years laters kept piling up, like plums, like catastrophes, like debt from the future, like the cosmic bend of space-time itself), force-retired from active life, a ghost holed up in Walt Whitman's Brooklyn, trying to write it all away

> *I too lived—Brooklyn, of ample hills, was mine;*
> *I too walk'd the streets of Manhattan Island*

but drifting in my febrile dreams from Whitman's Brooklyn, still ample, still living, to Whitman's Camden, dying now as Whitman had died there, paralyzed, too, by stroke, and diminished of lung, its ribs crushed by the abscess in its chest, and moaning, as Whitman had moaned, or Newark, eighty-seven miles northeast of Camden, might have moaned, the Newark that Philip Roth had beat his escape from and Amiri Baraka had beat his escape back to; or Paterson, sixteen miles due north of Newark, but with a protrusion of the Garden State Parkway to Rutherford, might have moaned: William Carlos Williams' Paterson, "in the valley under the Passaic Falls / its spent waters forming the outline of his back /…on his right side, head near the thunder / of the waters filling his dreams"; and Allen Ginsberg's Paterson ("High over Passaic Falls," the ecstatic beatnik shaman scribbled, in "mid-career," on the back of a photograph of himself overlooking the precipice of the thunder of waters that had, with the consciousness-expanding aid, it seems, of a nickel bag entheogen, filled his dreams, too; "December 1966," the inscription continues, "…Mayor of Paterson subsequently issued warrant for arrest of A Ginsberg after declaration at Paterson YMHA Poetry reading that pot smoked at Passaic Falls had enhanced visionary mortal aspect of roaring water flow at moment of this photo…Case dismissed for lack of evidence February 1967"); and Junot Diaz's Paterson, Junot Diaz, who wrote a touching, if necessarily diminished in expectation, and yet in spite of itself/because of itself in its way transcendental, early twenty-first century gloss on, or post-script to, Whitman's expansive and world-embracing nineteenth-century anaphora of a good gray self-singing self, that could serve as a reductio ad absurdum *(or "executive summary") of what can still be sung of a self in our own sad era of dearth, 152 years down the line (a line as long as a line of Whitman[19]) from the publication of the first edition of* Leaves of Grass, *a self reduced by now to a grammatical fiction (but of course the* reductio *to which I allude is, by now, itself a cliché—old beret, old porkpie, old mortarboard); indeed might also serve, heuristically, as the secret motto for the book I labor now, clot by clot, neuron by neuron, and ganglion by ganglion, to finish writing: "'Nothing else has any efficacy, I might as well be myself'…'But your yourself sucks!'…'It is, lamentably, all I have'"; the Paterson, also, of Ruben "Hurricane" Carter, lying 52 miles east of thriving Parsippany-Troy Hills Township (up from 17th place in 2006 to 13th place in 2008 in* Money *magazine's list of Best Places to Live in the United States), former home of Greystone Park Psychiatric Hospital, the institution where Carter's chameleonic and (in a brief return to form as protest singer) righteously (and tunefully—if growlingly) exculpating ballad-eer[20] had undertaken his famous hajj (this was, of course, several years prior to the balladeer's taking up the accused middleweight's cause), to meet with his idol Woody Guthrie, an idol who, in his own career, had taken up a few causes of his own, and an idol who was dying there, at Greystone, in Parsippany, writhing in the degenerative effects of Huntington's disease, the guitar he could no longer play languishing in an unswept corner nearby, a machine too tired to kill any more fascists; and, in another kind of apocalyptic refraction, another kind of killing (and exemplum, I can hardly have been the first to point out, of Bronx, not in this case New Jersey-born, Don DeLillo's oft-cited brocard, and stately lament, from* Mao II, *"What terrorists gain, novelists lose"), the Paterson of Hani Hanjour, Salem Alhamzi, Nawaf Alhamzi, Saeed Alghamdi, and Mohamed Atta: "I suffer all the time: I have no relief,*

---

[19] Or Ginsberg, or C. K. Williams, another New Jersey poet, born in Newark.
[20] Bob Dylan.

no escape: it is monotony—monotony—monotony—in pain."

The house on Schlegel Street had been nicknamed "the Blue Hotel" (by generations of local rock, punk, roots, blues, funk, polka, salsa, klezmer, bluegrass, and zydeco musicians, various aggregations of whom had lived and rehearsed there at one time or another, including, during the years Caroline and I were in residence, the tenant, unfortunately a drummer, who occupied the flat below) because, like its namesake in the Stephen Crane story, it was painted the color of a great blue heron; and also because its narrow wooden slats, beginning to warp in a distressed, almost sepia manner, had never been clad in the ubiquitous vinyl or aluminum siding, and, to add to the distress, had been "antiqued," like the long-gone piano in the long-gone basement of my long-gone childhood home, splattered not this time with paint, but pocked with bullet holes, which, along with the large display window, with lace curtains, of a former storefront, and a bit of Victoriana detailing in the cornice of its front gable, lent the structure a certain look of the old west; I often joked it was really only a façade in a studio back lot, and one gentle push would send the whole illusion crashing to the ground...and, in a sense, I was right

Smile when you say that, Blackwell...

In the winter, the former sugar bush, the maple that had danced before, denuded now and raving, the skeleton of a madwoman collecting plastic bags, served as a macabre image of death and transfiguration, flailing her bones in despair and pathetic fallacy against the roof and sky. In the cold spring, as cold as winter, iron cold, Faulkner would have called it, Caroline and I, shivering, rheumy, and red-blotched, leaned over the comical exploding vaudeville stove (a relic of the fifties) that had been fired up so many times—when we were not in arrears with the gas company or the larder empty due to seasonal adjustments or market downswings—to poach and braise and sauté (and blanch and grill and bake and deglaze) the copious spinning bubbling housemade *plats du jour* and tasting menus of all yesterday's parties, in the days before considerations of trans fat, acid reflux, bovine growth, high fructose, partial hydrogenation, and genetic modification had rendered taking one's daily bread such a walk on the razor's edge, back in the days when I was still a famous cook—famous amongst my friends, anyway (so many friends then); friends who have, since then—and as already intimated—grown up; and in growing up have outgrown me, have moved on and picked their spots and made their choices and paid their dues and defended their dissertations and saved up for a down payment and taken a beating on their 401Ks and uploaded their CVs to LinkedIn and posted pictures of their children on Facebook, etc.: the *beouf en daubes* and *moules marinière* and *coqs au vin* and *pots au feu* and *boudins blanc* and *kigs ha farz* and *pissaladieres* and *osso bucos* (except I followed James Beard's old recipe that substitutes ham hocks for veal shanks because even then, even in carnivore days, I drew the line at veal), fried bats, like the ones they sell at the Atocha Station in Madrid, with a dipping sauce of arctic honey, shreds from the shin of an ape, prog-rock tongues of lark in aspic, New Zealand Hu-Hu grubs, Oaxacan *chapulines*, ludevisk and puffin heart, kid seethed in its mother's milk, served with vulture and kite after their kind (*treif*, but hearty and delicious), locust and wild honey, frog spawned in a blind man's ditch, thousand-year-old egg (coddled in a pipkin, just because I liked to say "coddled in a pipkin"), fretful porpentine *au jus*, Tang dynasty warthog, and of course the bubbling *sine qua non* of ambitious middlebrow cookery everywhere: "the fearful *cassoulet*," as Alexander Cockburn once dubbed the inevitable French provincial stew in a very funny extended barb, published many years ago in the *New York Review of Books* (an article I remember puncturing, at the time, so many of my pretensions in the kitchen, and by extension, other rooms in the house), taking on such best sellers of "gastro-porn" (did

Cockburn coin the phrase, once a put-down, now an honorific?) as *Simple French Food, French Provincial Cooking,* and *Feast Without Fuss,* for example, charmingly categorizing these tomes as versions of pastoral, and scolding, by implication, their Cuisinart-wielding yuppie nouveau gourmand readers (predecessors of today's young and apparently ravenous "foodies," hedonistic and salivating twenty-somethings you see lined up for blocks outside Momofuku Ssäm Bar on Second Avenue, dreaming of "an *amuse-bouche* of English muffin soaked with whipped pork fat..." followed by an entrée of "uncooked fluke in a wash of buttermilk, yuzu and Sriracha."[21]).

We leaned, in the cold spring, as cold as winter, but wetter, and often even darker, over the comical exploding vaudeville stove and, peering out the window under which the stove rested, we monitored the bones of the mature sugar maple for any hopeful signs of buds. But it never happened that way, because one day the tree was dead and the next transfigured, lush and zaftig again. And by the time the day was done the leaves were yellow, orange, red, purple, brown, and finally dead again—raked in ponderous piles, and hauled away. The tree is gone now, a Google map quest will reveal, the kind of map that shows you, like a crystal ball or a magic lantern, pictures of the places that haunt your reveries, that leave you, in their absence, sad and desolate and homesick, that leave you asking (literally in the case of the upper Midwest), "*Mais où sont les neiges d'antan?*"; whether the tree was lost to blight or urban renewal or some asshole wanted a better view of something he thought he needed a better view of, I will probably never know, but the Blue Hotel remains. If you walk past the house, even today, you can hear the drummer in the lower flat beating out his furious tattoos, and practicing his flams, paradiddles, and ratamacues; he has since bought the building, and rents out the upper flat to cover his mortgage.

---

[21] http://events.nytimes.com/2008/05/07/dining/reviews/07rest.html

And in my drifting, in my premature retirement, holed up in Walt Whitman's Brooklyn, I meditated on the old complaint of the dead and dying, the old complaint of the world, insinuating my own loss into it, but a loss falling infinitely short of its mark, like an arrow from Zeno's quiver, a loss incommensurate to the world's abiding monotony, a loss incommensurate to real suffering, but nevertheless my own tiny splinter of the true cross: "I suffer all the time: I have no relief, no escape: it is monotony—monotony—monotony—in pain." Because real suffering belonged, commensurately (remember "In the Ghetto," "Indian Reservation," and "Tobacco Road"), to black people, to Native Americans, and, by extension (see Let Us Now Praise Famous Men*), to poor whites (but I wasn't poor), to Jews, to the Palestinians of Gaza and the West Bank, to Tutsis, to the African peoples of Darfur; to people diagnosed with actual, not imaginary diseases; to the captive, the lost, and the abandoned; to the tortured, the mangled, and the flayed; to the trafficked; to the genitally mutilated; to they that mourn and to they that are persecuted for righteousness' sake; real suffering, commensurate canonical categorical world-historical real suffering belonged, as well—belonged because of a curse ("Fukú americanus...the Curse or Doom of the New World": Junot Diaz,* The Brief Wondrous Life of Oscar Wao, *page 1)—to Dominicans (residents of the eastern two-thirds of La Isla Espaniola, not the brotherhood known as Ordo Praedicatorum, founded sometime in the 1200s to stamp out heresy, though for all I knew, they suffered, too—as did, god knows, the heretics they stamped out), a point, a sense of belonging (to history, to the world), that, familiar though I was with a similar curse that had hit closer to my childhood home in Birmingham, Alabama (conceptualized usually, though, not as a curse but as a sin—an original sin, for which there is no remission, unlike in the case of the original original, which, by the way, seems trifling in comparison, eating some fruit for Christ's sake), I may or may not have understood, intuited, or known (in retrospect, I'll allow it felt like a curse) in the six years (four of which I spent daytripping in the Dominican diaspora, and two "processing" the experience) that preceded the night (one night last week as a matter of fact) that I stayed up all night reading* The Brief Wondrous Life of

Oscar Wao, *but a point, a sense of belonging, that I'd sussed out pretty well by first light the next morning when I closed the book, vowing to become a writer of post-colonial experience, and getting myself to sleep by counting, instead of sheep, a flock of dangling floating blurbish book jacket adjectives, like those flapping elegantly, effortlessly across the front cover, back cover, and frontispiece of the paperback edition of* Oscar Wao *that I had finally bought when I found the book (a knock-off version from the U.K.) for sale in a stall on Bleecker Street while I was giving visitors from Milwaukee a walking tour of the West Village, adjectives I dreamed would someday find their way onto the dust jacket of my book, entitled* Slowly, I Turn, *or* Mid-Career Retrospective, *or* Due to An Earlier Incident, *or* Smile When You Say That, Blackwell, *or* Muddled and Served on the Rocks, *or* A Swing and A Miss, *or* The Path Sick Sorrow Took, *or* Skin Shed, *or* I Clear the Thicket, *or* A Ghost Holed up in Walt Whitman's Brooklyn, *or* Our Own Sad Era of Dearth, *or* Clot by Clot, Neuron by Neuron, Ganglion by Ganglion, *or* An Arrow from Zeno's Quiver, *or* Already Tall and Dark Green Grass, and Forget-Me-Nots and the Dead Nettles, and Everything, *or* Curlicues of Fatigue, *or* A Fallen Soufflé, *or* Palimpsestic Regolith, *or* Concerned, Distressed, Worried, and a Little Vexed, *or* A Self-Cobbled Self, *or* Glimpsed in the Corner of a Compound Polyhedral Eye: *"a raucous delight," "full of nerve, gutsy and delicious," "funny, arch, and sad," "haunting," "acute and bad-tempered," "gorgeous and lyrical," "a marvel of beauty and imagination," "startlingly vivid," "spirited," "manic," "compulsive," "gifted," "dazzling," "beguiling," "auspicious," "gut-busting," "exquisitely wrought and magical," "technically breathtaking," "jam-packed," "sprawling but sprightly," "flip, hip, smart, and very funny," "sassy and philosophical," "funny and self-laceratingly candid," "an intriguing, magnetic, genre-rattling book," "luminously original in style and form," and "page-turningly enthralling and charged with the power to move."*[22]

---

[22] *Note: This list also includes raves from the dust jackets of books by Elif Batuman, Geoff Dyer, Hilton Als, Rachel Cusk, Gary Shteyngart, Ben Lerner, and maybe some others that I can't remember now.*

I had postponed reading the book until I'd been two years off the ghost ship and out of Inwood, though I read the first few pages whilst still a swab abaft the beam, read the first footnote, which outlines, in précis, the terrifying career—emblematic, I thought, of all "administrative leadership," constituting a primer in total quality management—of the infamous skipper, I mean principal, I mean dictator, of the Dominican Republic, Rafael Leónidas Trujillo Molina, who ruled the eastern two-thirds of La Isla Espaniola between 1930 and 1961, ruled it "with an implacable ruthless brutality" (reminding me of my own jefe, though my governor, the ghost ship's governor, I mean, had a sentimental side as well—but then I guess all dictators do) when the book came out, and it was lent me by a colleague and fellow midshipman, but I couldn't bear to read any further, couldn't bear to go on (I was a sensitive chap, a delicate white boy), couldn't bear, I would have been ashamed to admit, to think about anything Dominican besides what I had to to get through the school day, and to forget what I had to forget to get through the night; the thing is I already felt like I was suffering, in my own way, from some kind of contact "fukú," and the less I knew about it, or the less I thought about it, the less likely any of the shit would stick to me.

Because New York is a small world or the diaspora is a small world or I am a small world (as Kafka said, "Either the world is so tiny or we are enormous; in either case we fill it completely...."), the colleague who'd lent the copy of the book to me, the copy that I had read a few pages and a footnote of, before abandoning it—as I would soon after abandon all the beautiful children that I loved so well, and the school that in spite of itself because of itself I loved anyway (something I knew then but am forgetting today, maybe have to forget or the remorse and the loss and old complaint of the world would be too great, would break my heart)—this colleague, it turned out, turned out to be—no kidding—the brother-in-law (to be) of the Pulitzer Prize winner himself, the brother-in-law (to be) of Junot Diaz. But he wasn't a teacher, this colleague; he was a counselor who worked at the school but not for the school (an important distinction, like being a civilian employee of the police department). He was, moreover, a real mensch, one of a small handful of smart and caring toilers in the canefield up in Inwood that I admired, a real Catholic Worker (in the figurative sense I have invented for anyone as lovingkind as Dorothy Day or Michael Harrington, though he might also have been one in a more literal sense: I didn't know him that well so I couldn't say. At any rate "Catholic Workers," in the sense that I use the phrase, made me—an atheist, but a Protestant atheist, justified by lack of faith alone, without good works—feel ashamed, like a dream long since forgotten that had come neither true nor free, my old dream of being a professional do-gooder)...

It gets cold in Milwaukee, Wisconsin, and the winters last from fourteen to fifteen months a year; the snow piles deep and the winds gust hard off Lake Michigan. The sun never rises. This is the country where they invented the "wind chill factor," but I, usually a strict subjectivist, always disputed the idea that anything could "feel" colder than it actually is. Caroline had taken a course in meteorology in college, and tried to explain the wind chill factor and other hard facts and underlying principles of the physical world to her backwards and dreamy husband (as a child curled up with my World Book Encyclopedia, I had skimmed—or skipped altogether—any article having to do with science, and taken only the barest requirements in high school and college), but I resisted reality, and astonished her with my basic ignorance of how things worked, where they came from, what happened to them, and how they changed, how they always changed...

Caroline was a video artist when I met her, a video artist and sometime performance artist, who was busy in those days interrogating and subverting the male gaze, racialist narrativity, hegemonic discourse—name your (phal)logocentric poison. She also co-produced a cable-access television program that showcased the interrogations and subversions of other promising young video and performance artists. In fact, as a performance, or as a college prank (and I couldn't always tell the difference), she'd almost married a fellow student in her Theories of Contemporary Performance seminar (she was also going to school then, and for many years afterward), drawing his name from a hat in which the names of several of her classmates had been thrown; the idea was that the group would get married together at City Hall and then—I assumed...hoped—file for divorce, in order, presumably, to interrogate and/or subvert the hegemonic discourse of "marriage," but the plan never reached its fruition. The boys, apparently, got cold feet.

Caroline and I were, a year or so later, ourselves joined together in matrimony (drawing, essentially, each other's name from a hat), by a Court Commissioner who usually worked divorce cases, a lady attorney who was thrilled to join together rather than tear asunder, and who had an office in a building across the street from City Hall. The bride was ravishing in a 1940s vintage silk tea dress, gray, with little pink and cream flowers. The groom, who would not quite have been taken for ravishing, also wore gray, a 1930s pinstripe suit of worsted wool, drape cut, single-breasted, that had been Mimi's Pa Paw's, a suit Mimi had given me, along with a few other treasured effects, when Pa Paw died. Also in attendance were Arthur, who was my best man, and, serving as Caroline's maid of honor, Kirsten Stoltmann, a friend Caroline had met in her Theories of Contemporary Performance class, and very nearly one of Caroline's sister-wives in the mass performance art wedding that a few months earlier had not come off.

We hadn't originally planned on getting married at all, preferring to cohabitate happily absent the blessings of God or the decrees of the state, as we'd been doing for almost a year, until Caroline read the fine print on her financial aid application and worked out that she'd be eligible for more financial assistance if she were married to a man without an income (me) because she wouldn't have to report her parents' earnings (Caroline was only twenty years old at the time). Ironically, she gained her independence by getting married.

We had met at the Chili Bowl Restaurant, near the corner of Oakland and Locust Avenues, in the spring of 1989, when communism was falling and Madonna studies were rising. It was the kind of a day that Benjy Compson, in *The Sound and the Fury*, calls "bright cold," when snow was piled high on the sidewalks and there were ice hazards to dodge and the sun was shining. A sweet and slightly pudgy *Mädchen*, uniformed in a black apron over a white Oxford blouse and navy blue chinos, shod in the usual comfortable (but in Caroline's case smart) service sector lace-ups, her hair (which was tied in a bun) dyed an improbable color of red (candy apple, maybe, or fire engine), holding a pad and pencil in her hands, glided over to my table, or so it seemed to me at the time, and took my order (seafood chili and a beer; I was in those days what we now call a lacto-ova pescatarian, the most generous concession to PETA I felt I could make at the time). Her lovely face was the face of a dairy maid in a Thomas Hardy novel, pink and healthy and fresh (Kirsten had cast her in the role of an ingénue—and me in the role of a sleazy strip club emcee—in a funny campy video she made about the rise and fall of a Hollywood color test girl), but a dairy maid with a crooked *film noir* (or screwball comedy) smile, the face of an ingénue, but a wise-cracking ingénue (a cross between Gene Tierney in the early scenes of *Laura*, maybe, and Rosalind Russell throughout *His Girl Friday*, or, now that I think about it, a cross between Tierney and Russell and Linda Darnell, in *A Letter to Three Wives*, but pinker, healthier, and fresher than any of these actresses, and Caroline wore scarcely any makeup). I was ensorcelled. (This was a little less than a year before our wedding day.)

I was well into my second semester as a Biermann Fellow, still faking my way through the free-floating signifiers and abyssal aporias, procrastinating studying for the master's comps I had failed almost a year before at the University of Alabama at Birmingham, deluding myself that I'd sit for the exam that summer and somehow pass the goddamn thing this time and keep my fellowship and earn my Ph.D. and get a tenure track position in a charming campus idyll somewhere where I'd publish and not perish among the sweaters, smiles, and glee clubs, and somebody going out for the junior varsity something or other...

I wasn't alone when I walked into the Chili Bowl that day. Arthur was with me, and we were both hauling heavy bags of French theory and discontinued fragments of the western canon, to flog later, and lighting up crumpled Marlboro reds we kept digging for in the pockets of our vintage overcoats. Arthur and I had a few weeks earlier taken our flat together on Bremerhaven Street, the flat with the bellowing lout and the screeching harridan downstairs, and the gunplay, and the no stove in sight, from which we would shortly be evicted, and where we had, upon settling in, only a few nights before walking into the Chili Bowl restaurant, thrown a successful debauch attended by all the prominent seminarians in the department, including the sexy feminists. (We had to have the party catered because we couldn't cook anything ourselves—you know, since we didn't have a stove.)

I had, only a week or so before, broken up with Little Red Riding Hood, whom I'd kept on ice since the Halloween party, and had, around New Year's, started dating, half-heartedly and on the rebound, except she was the one who broke up with me, putting me out of her bed in the middle of the night, because, she said, she had no patience for my (it's been a number of years but I think these are the words she used, or some of them) "whining, crying, self-pitying self-absorption."

I first spotted Caroline sliding a pie into a rotating case, something with meringue on it, each peak glistening under the fluorescent light with a little bead of syrup. I can't remember now any of the bantering that ensued when she came to take my order, but there was bantering and there may even have been flirting. She laughed at my jokes, and I laughed at hers. She said, early in the exchange, sizing up the situation as it was laid out before her, "Oh god, you're a *grad*-uate student."

I was a *grad*-uate student, all right. She had my number, but I was too shy to ask for hers. She was cute, though, and I tried to screw my courage up, but my courage wouldn't screw, and the opportunity passed. I'd been a flop with chicks since 1966, and, still gun-shy, I let several more opportunities pass on several subsequent visits to the Chili Bowl.

And then there was a coincidence, a coincidence that came to light over brandy and sodas in the bar at Chez Gaston Monescu, a coincidence that was officiated by Azhar al-Shidyaq, who would finally get the opportunity to play the role of matchmaker he'd so wanted to play.

How it happened was Azhar and I were at Monescu's, and I was telling my pal about the cute girl with the pies and the apron and the crooked grin I was too shy to ask out. As I described her, Azhar's brow went a little quizzical, suggesting something like dawning recognition, and when I mentioned the name of the restaurant where Caroline worked, Azhar started laughing hysterically, like somebody laughs at the end of a John Huston movie, like Walter Huston and Tim Holt laugh at the end of *The Treasure of the Sierra Madre*, like Humphrey Bogart laughs at the end of *Beat the Devil*. His eyes got big and bright and sparkly, and a smile spread out across his face, a big pleased-with-itself smile that was also a smile of surprise that was wondering why, after all, why was it so surprising?

"Of course! Why didn't I think of it? I know this girl. Her name is Caroline Schultz. She's my roommate!" (I had been to Azhar's house a few times, but Caroline had always been out.) Azhar and I both remarked the coincidence, and then the little *shadchen*—who, I later found out, when his attempts to help me solve my little problem with Tallulah McIlhenny had failed, had wanted to fix me up with Caroline's friend Claudia—started rubbing his hands together and planning some matchmaking.

A week or so later, Azhar invited me over for several shots of tequila and big plates of linguini with clam sauce. (I don't know why we were having tequila with our linguini, but we were.) When Caroline came home, at about 11:30 p.m.—she'd been to a concert with a friend—Azhar bolted up suddenly, his napkin falling to the floor, and, after picking up his napkin, he excused himself from the table. Citing a previous engagement, he grabbed his coat and hat and flew out the door, leaving Caroline and me to our own devices, the devices we've been at, for richer, for poorer, etc., etc., ever since...

But before making any commitments, which we would make soon enough, our first stop was a neighborhood bar called the Amethyst Inn, where, embarrassed about being left alone together in the apartment, we promptly set out to when Azhar made his exit stage right, and where Caroline cured me of the hiccoughs I'd brought on myself by chasing, at the Amethyst, Azhar's shots of tequila with several mugs of beer. Trying to impress Caroline, I had quoted Chekhov when she told me she had a new cure for hiccoughs that really worked: "When a lot of remedies are suggested for a disease, that means it can't be cured." But Caroline's cure—biting a pencil held as far back in the mouth as possible, and leaning your head forward while swallowing a glass of water upside down—really worked.

(Years later, I taught the hiccough trick to hiccoughing students on the Ghost Ship, inviting students so afflicted to come up to the front of the classroom where I would make a big dramatic production of things, hamming it up and making like a magician with nothing up my sleeves, presto change-o. For the rest of the school year there seemed to be at least one case of hiccoughs a day, an epidemic you might say...)

Caroline was in college when I met her, and for several years afterwards, like me taking nine years to complete her B.A. This was partly because of financial considerations, but also because, also like me, she was always changing her major, changing her mind, and couldn't get her life started. Mainly, though, it was because she shared yet another habit of mine: the habit of dropping courses she had for one reason or another stopped attending (she'd gotten behind in the reading, an assignment was due and a deadline was missed, and then another deadline, and then another)—sometimes dropping the classes officially at the registrar's office and receiving a WP ("Withdrawn Passing") on her grade report, and sometimes, when she'd missed the deadline to withdraw, dropping the classes unofficially, by simply not attending them anymore, earning "F's" by default, and later retaking courses she had in this manner failed, earning good marks the second time around, and bolstering up her now waxing, now waning GPA. (Unlike me, though, Caroline never dropped a class, officially or unofficially, because she was afraid she'd made a fool of herself with irrelevant or tendentious or obscure or not-thought-out or just plain dumb comments she'd made at a previous class meeting, or, more usually, because she couldn't think of any clever contributions to add to class discussion, or even if she had any clever contributions to add, couldn't figure out how to get her oar in the water, and so remained silent, or—a specialty of mine—because she'd turned in a paper, for once on time, but was afraid to come back to class on the day the professor had promised to return papers, less for fear of receiving a bad mark than for the mortification of reading the professor's comments, comments that, she was sure, this time, would expose her as the *poseur* she knew herself to be, and never returned to class because she was embarrassed about the long rolling sentences, elliptical structure, and far-flung digressions, the ornate, arch, mincing, and self-conscious prose style marked by unceasing parenthetical expressions, endless qualifications, interruptions, and second guesses, the creeping ellipses and flowering dashes trailing clouds of semi-colons, all the foreign borrowings, with hand-drawn diacritics—remember I was "keyboarding" out my well-wrought urns on a typewriter—hand-me-down quotations, references, and allusions, all the strong strange extreme statements, loud boasting joking provocations, unearned *Weltschmerz*—I was in my twenties for Christ's sake; but have I, in my fifties, earned it now?—and pretend sophistication, all the posing and the posturing, and the fact that she, I mean I, didn't really know much of anything at all—knew nothing, in fact—but acted like I did and wrote with the false authority that I did.)

One course Caroline didn't drop, thankfully—for me and for the remembrance of things past—was a creative writing class, a creative writing class in which she wrote her first and, sadly for the reading public, her only short story to date, though I encouraged her to write more, as did her teacher, who gushed, "Your story is filled with sophisticated touches. Actually, I wanted to write only one word on it: magic."

In the course of the eighteen or so years following its composition, the story had been packed in mothballs and carefully preserved in archives, transferred from attic to attic and basement to basement in apartments and houses on Schlegel Street, Hölderlin Boulevard, and Newhall Street in Milwaukee, Wisconsin; and from there freighted, along with what was left of everything else we had ever owned, across country, first to a self-storage facility on a frontage road off Old Highway 22 in Clinton, New Jersey, and shortly thereafter onto Manhattan Island, where it was stored, along with all the other traces, remnants, and orthographic projections of our earlier lives, in a small closet in a small third story walk-up on West 76th Street, and then in an even smaller closet in an even smaller walk-up on 2nd Street, in Park Slope, Brooklyn.

For a few tense weeks, though, in the very recent past, following yet another expensive cartage across country, the story was presumed lost, despite desperate attempts to find it (desperate attempts on my part; Caroline isn't as grasping of the past as I am, or as fearful of losing things; and also she wasn't completely sure she wanted me, when I asked her if I could, to include it, as a point of reference, and because I like it so much, in my own first attempt at creative writing). The story was presumed lost, along with several other items of varying use, exchange, and sentimental value, including: the by-then rusted pocket knife that my Uncle John Daddy had bought me all those years ago, when, swooping down, as he did that one time, with his swear words, his pistols, his death wish, and his poor man's Porsche, on the then still-plumb split-level, but it wasn't a split-level, on Willow Way; several spare pairs of thick-lensed reading glasses with magnification factors approaching those of an electron microscope; some tiny bottles of aromatherapy oil: menthol, camphor, and wintergreen; patchouli, sandalwood, and vetiver; frankincense and myrrh; lilac, lavender, and geranium—carefully wrapped in layers of plastic and tinfoil as a precaution against leakage; at least two books: a thick bright-blue paperbound printing of *Infinite Jest*, "bright book of life" and "tremulation on the ether,"[23] that I had never finished reading; and a copy of the *Collected Poems of C. K. Williams* (I have had to google poems of Williams' that I want to quote); and, finally, a treasured vintage *Playbill*, dated "Week beginning Monday, April 3, 1950," that Caroline had picked up for me at a stoop sale in Park Slope, a *Playbill* with Katharine Hepburn on the cover, in the role of Rosalind in *As You Like It*, posing charmingly, in leotards, cape, and puffy sleeves, as the shepherd Ganymede, sitting atop a rocky outcropping of the Forest of Arden, her hands resting on a bended knee and her head raised slightly as her eyes gaze knowingly, confidently, stage left, into the wings of the Cort Theater, and into the long arc of theater history.

This presumption of loss (of the knife, of the essential oil, of the spectacles, of the D. F. Wallace, of the C. K. Williams, of the *Playbill*, of Caroline's story, and possibly of some other things that haven't been remembered yet) had been made in the disoriented transitional aftermath of a traumatic gut, space, and time-wrenching cross-country "strategic retreat" back to glacial and scarcely-populated Milwaukee, Wisconsin (or so it seemed to me when, upon my arrival, I continued my New York habit, unknown in the hinterlands, of walking places, and wondered, as I

---

[23] D. H. Lawrence.

strolled, where the fuck everybody was), until the items, the story and the *Playbill* at least, were re-discovered, found by Caroline stashed, we don't know how or why, in a fat folder bulging with my medical records, principally having to do with recent harrowing visits to two different, but equally fiendish, gastroenterologists, but I'll spare you the details of that saga.

Entitled "Steam Cooks It," the story, a charming evocation of the early years, the beginning of the *Saturnia regna* Caroline and I had left behind, and had moved back to Milwaukee, trying—futilely, we understand now—to recapture was, in fact, only the day before yesterday, or so it seems, found by Caroline. I had been mourning its loss, and had been counting on, before I realized it had gone missing, using the piece to help me get back into writing the somewhat fictionalized memoir I had had to put on hold for a couple of months as I organized our removal from the city of our dreams, packing our belongings under the influence of a terrible month-long prophylactic course of antibiotics (sensitive like a neurasthenic gentlewoman of the Old South, or a Victorian novel, I am laid prostrate by antibiotics: and by antihistamines and anti-depressants and decongestants and bisphosphonates, etc.) that my doctor insisted, though it isn't standard treatment, not without tangible evidence of infection, or risk of infection, on prescribing when I presented with a tick bite, the bite of a tick never definitively identified as a deer tick, a bite acquired on the first hike in the woods that I had taken in years (except for the time in the Catskills when I was chased by a bear and took a spill on a slippery rock and fractured a rib and almost a wrist, but that's another story; and I wasn't really chased by a bear, though I did *see* a bear, in a car—I was in the car, not the bear, but still, you can't be too careful with bears), during a reconnaissance trip to Milwaukee to secure an apartment, and, when our belongings finally arrived—those that successfully made the journey (we had to wait a week for them, sleeping on an air mattress that slowly deflated every night until by morning all the stale used-up phlogiston had seeped back to its origin, wherever its origin is, and we tossed and turned on a bit of rubber stretched along the parquet in a bedroom several multiples larger than our old Upper West Side and Park Slope digs combined, with our first summer sublet on the Lower East Side thrown in, and paying almost a thousand dollars a month less in rent than we'd paid at any of these former hovels, but missing already the thrill, that we never really lost, of living in New York City)—unpacking them, free, finally, at the unpacking, of the diarrhea and brain fog and anxiety and torpor and flu-like symptoms effectuated upon swallowing, twice daily, the horrific capsules of toxic Doxycycline, bulbous and tasting of the sulfur of hell (free of the diarrhea and flu-like symptoms, but, let's face it, not entirely free of the brain fog, or the anxiety, torpor, and taste of the sulfur of hell).

The story is reprinted here, with Caroline's kind permission, permission granted with some reservations, and a certain near disappointment that the story was found, a story that, albeit with a reversal or two of gender, various mix-matched transferences of character traits, and other instances of the exercise of a free hand, comes pretty close to capturing—keeping in mind Kleist's caveat: "But paradise is barred and the angel stands behind us; we have to go all the way around the world and see if it might not be open again somewhere in the back"—something of the mood of the particular paradise lost *touched though it had been with sadness and care we could scarcely remember* the vanished Arcadia, the *Saturnia regna* so impervious, as are all the vanished Arcadias, and all the *Saturnia regna*, to recapture (and I had been duly warned, in seminary days, when the abyssal aporias should have hardened me up, against the sin of nostalgia for the metaphysics of presence), tempting one to such mad, blind, expensive, and extraordinary efforts at blind hopeless sieges and failed raids on the passage of time, as moving one's gear, and one's soul, and deliberately making this move of one's own free will, planning for it, suffering for it, across the country from Brooklyn, the World (the world that we would only once, and for a brief interregnum of just seven years, know a little of and even make something like a home in), to a new imagined *Saturnia regna* we thought we saw coming into focus, in the ice and snow of Milwaukee, Wisconsin, as it had before, a million years ago, in the nineties:

Steam Cooks It

by Caroline Schultz

On humid days, the hollow wooden door filled the jamb so completely that Henry needed to use a special combination of coercion and charm to get in. As he turned the key, he gave the knob a quick tug and then lurched against the door with his right shoulder. The door squawked open.

"Hello?"

"Hello!" answered Liz's voice. Henry walked back out to pick up the paper sack of groceries that he had set on the hallway floor. He put it down on the kitchen table, and with a reverse maneuver locked the door.

Liz was in the living room, sitting low in the nappy green chair and reading a magazine. Her knees were bent and her bare feet rested against the coffee table. She swiveled right and left. The fan was blowing on slow, and low-down sun was streaking in dusty layers through three windows.

"Wouldn't it be cooler in here if you pulled the curtains closed?" asked Henry.

"Are you hot?"

"No," he replied. "Just a little."

He moved across the room to sit on the arm of her chair. He kissed her on her forehead and cheek. "How's my darling?"

"Fine, now that you're home." She kissed back. "How're you?"

"Good. Kinda tired."

"The new Nation came today."

"I see that."

"The weirdest thing. That crossword clue that we couldn't figure out, about the 'tatters of the soul,' the answer is 'healthiest.'"

"I don't get it."

"Neither do I. But all the ones that we filled in we got right."

Henry got up and went into the bedroom, pulling off his sweaty clothes. He walked naked into the kitchen. He shouted to Liz, "What was the one about permitting no concealed weapons?"

"It was SHOGUN."

"Oh no! We should have gotten that. I picked up some food."

"Yeah, I did too."

As Henry started loading groceries into the refrigerator, he noticed the huge bag of raw okra that Liz had bought earlier that week. He smelled into it. "Do you think this okra is good still?"

"I'm not sure."

He turned on the radio. The dial was already

fixed at one of his three stations. It was the one he usually listened to when he was home alone. A woman's voice, deep and friendly, spoke from the machine.

"Caller from Elmer, go ahead."

"Hello?"

"Yes. You're on the air."

"It seems to me I always hear people like Ms. Arnold talking about what parents aren't do-ing, without offering what I'd call constructive criticism. I mean, can't we expect our educa-tional system to do its job? I'll hang up and listen."

"Mary Arnold?" asked the gentle voice.

"Well, Barbara, I think the caller made sev-eral interesting points. What I'm suggesting to parents, and what I discuss in chapter three of my book, is the importance of cooperation between parents and teachers. Teachers can't do it alone and neither can parents. What I'm saying is they need to collaborate on learning."

"Let's take another call…Red Bend?"

"Hi. Yeah, I was wondering if your guest was familiar with the entomology of the word 'educa-tion'?"

"It's from the Greek, isn't it?"

"The Greek? It means 'to lead out' and if you think about it, it's leading people out into the world and enlightening them. Thank you."

"Yes, and one of the ways parents can 'lead children out' is to make learning a fun and natural part of everyday life. Etymologies are, in fact, a good example of the kind of knowledge that both fascinates and stimulates."

Henry wondered if Liz could hear the program in the living room. He hoped not. He reached down and twisted the dial half a notch, to his second station. A man who sounded like Dick Cavett was saying, "…and Soweto." Behind his voice, Henry could hear young men arguing in fast words. He couldn't understand what words.

"…until then, police are restricting travel in and out of the township. In Johannesburg, I'm Martin Kruger."

A teletype machine swept in. "You're listening to the National Radio Network. The time is twenty-nine past the hour."

"Good evening. I'm George Daniels and this is Cross Currents. The family-owned retail store was once a fixture of American life. During the past decade, however, this institution has been inching its way toward extinction. Amy Notario filed this story."

Amy spoke with clear, nasal concern. "David Halverson has been running Halverson Hardware for thirty-seven years. Before that, David's father operated the store for eighteen years. When David retires, his son Alan hopes to follow into the

family business as well. But by this time next
year, the Halversons may have to…"

The telephone rang. Henry listened as Liz
answered it.

"Hello? Oh, hi Emily, how're you? Just fine.
Well, how about eight or so? No, except for maybe
some wine. Swordfish, roasted sweet potatoes, and
some kind of salad. And for the sweet potatoes I
thought I'd try this recipe for a coriander and
cinnamon sauce. Okay, great. See you tomorrow. I
will. Buh-bye."

Henry was looking forward to his parents'
visit. They would hang out all night, like four
old college friends, smoking cigarettes. Liz was,
after all, only nine years younger than Henry's
parents, and in certain ways she had more in common with them.

Liz had a way of handling things, the sort
of things Henry avoided because he didn't feel
quite qualified. She had brought into their marriage a dowry of cookbooks, garlic, and indus-
trial-gauge pots and pans.

The most important thing, they agreed, was
to know the world. Henry was not a reader. She
read for both of them. At dinner parties, he
would vividly describe Liz's positions, which he
passed off as his own.

He would look hopefully to her for substan-
tiating statistics, historical precedent, or the

name that was on the tip of his tongue. "Reagan budget director, the one who wanted to abolish the Jobs Corps...?"

"You mean David Stockman?" she would ask him without condescension and yet knowing that that was the name he was looking for. She knew because the two of them, had, last Thursday night, stayed up very late trying to determine the proper solution to urban-American poverty.

Liz came into the kitchen and took a can of Falstaff from the fridge. "Say, did you pick up that James Beard book?"

"Yeah, it took me a whole hour to find it, though. It was in the 'TX' section, which for some reason is in the basement on the other side of the building from most of the other books."

"I don't know why they use the Library of Congress system. Dewey Decimal is so much simpler."

"Well, the problem isn't so much how the books are organized as where they're housed."

A woman on the radio was talking about endangered salmon in the Colombia River. Liz went on. "With the Dewey Decimal system, all you have to do is find your subject in the card catalog, memorize one short number, and then go to that section to find shelves and shelves of what you are looking for."

Henry switched the radio band to AM and

turned the dial to his third station. "You can do the same thing with Library of Congress. Besides, most libraries have replaced their card catalogs with on-line systems."

On the radio, Steve Lawrence was swinging. "When an irresistible force such as you, meets an old immovable object like me…"

Liz held her ground. "I prefer the card catalog. It's tactile. It smells good. The words are permanent, not simply flickering phantoms."

Henry decided to try and use up the okra. He would make gumbo. He went to the bookcase along the wall, pulled out four cookbooks, and sat down with them to flip through the indexes. "I kind of like using the computer. It's fast and you can make a really complete search."

The song ended. "That was Steve Lawrence and his tigress wife."

Liz said, "I bet congressmen don't even go there." They laughed.

They listened to the music. Henry rinsed the okra and cut it crosswise into thin slices that looked like cartoon flowers. When they were all cut he poured the flowers into a big saucepan, added water, and put it on the stove to simmer.

With a flourish of lush violins, Nat King Cole began to lullaby.

"Is this 'Stardust Memories'?" asked Liz.

"You mean 'Stardust'? Yes it is."

"I thought it was 'Stardust Memories.'"

'No, you're thinking of the Woody Allen movie."

"Are you sure?"

"Pretty sure."

He rinsed the cutting board. As he started to prop it up in the drainer he noticed that one side was still slimy with okra gum. He poured on some more soap. "Liz, would you be willing to cook up some brown rice while I chop vegetables?"

"Sure, it takes about forty-five minutes, right."

"Yes, as long as you keep it covered. Did Stokely Carmichael write this?"

"You mean Hoagy Carmichael? Wait—here comes the part where he sings it."

Henry mouthed the words as they came: "My stardust melody, the memory of love's refrain."

PART TWO

A Joke in this Vein

Concerned, distressed, worried, or a little vexed, possibly—but if vexed, indulgently so—at a kind of unwholesome Hamlet-y "sicklied o'er" cast of mind he felt he could discern underpinning an alarmingly morbid program for Internet-based research (into diseases and the current doings of old school chums) that was described in great detail in a string of communiqués he'd been receiving from his old friend from Contemporary Critical and Cultural Studies (and thereafter) *These were in-between days, incapacitating and Brian Wilson-ish, pullulating into weeks and months and years and galaxies of Internet-enabled hypochondria, self-canceling* folies du doute, *agonizing reappraisals, and deep-tissue prostration* Arthur Redding, the tall Texan from Ohio, tenured now in Canada, President, in fact, and C.E.O. of the English Department at a once well-funded "plate glass university" (or so they are called in England, which Canada, looked at from a certain angle by an American, seems sort of like; certainly in the way of orthography) that was finding itself by then, at least on the arts and letters side of things, in the throes of the usual free-market gut-renovation (and fighting, by the way, the good fight there, with dual citizenship—Arthur I mean—as he had once done with only one passport at Milwaukee State, where he helped organize a union for TAs, but in this latter case fighting to preserve, rather than change, a system from within; ironic, isn't it?: the "change agents" represent reaction now and the status quo is "socialistic"), the same tall Texan who held a cool rag to my forehead on so many vomitus and excreta-laden evenings and early mornings over the years, advising me, wet-nursing me, buoying me, diapering and powdering me, keeping me steady; running out, when necessary, to wherever he needed to run out to to keep the bourbon, in those days, and the Marlboros and the lemon Cokes on chipped ice coming, but tenured now, and successful, with four good books out: this good Arthur— concerned about his friend, distressed, worried, or possibly feeling a little vexed at me—watching uneasily from a high window in his upper-"storey" office (as he might have learnt to have spelt it by then) the continuing dissolution of the Canadian welfare state below, and dressed in his customary black velveteen gown, with attached cords, stoles, and aiguillettes, twirling a mortar-board in his hand (thinking as he did that with a little practice he could learn to spin plates), brushed away with his free hand the stack of my letters that were piled on a corner of his desk and said to himself softly (as if he'd recorded the words afterwards to mimic an internalized soliloquy in a television play and then a sound engineer had played the scene back and dubbed them in—at least that's how I saw it in my mind's eye, heard it in my mind's ear), but resolutely, the way a stout-hearted Canadian would say it,

"By God, I'll shake the lad from his acedia…"

And thus resolved, the old boy pushed his finger down hard on the intercom the piled letters had previously obscured, stubbing his toe on the Victorian limb of his desk as he did so (Arthur was big—"The Shtarker," I used to call him—and put his whole body into things, and besides, the limb jutted out like a gnarled great root of a tree, threatening to trip all passersby, something Arthur had spoken to the department property manager about on several occasions) and buzzed in a secretary or a graduate research assistant or a girl with a sexy overbite from the steno pool to take a letter (I had it in my mind that the secretary, research assistant, or girl from the steno pool, each a team player and willing to do whatever was necessary to push the program

through, sat in Arthur's lap as he/she took the governor's dicta-
tion, but this was a PC campus and there were strict guidelines
concerning such obviously exploitive forms of dalliance, and Arthur was a righteous man, a bit of a schoolboy as a matter of fact,
so the image I had in my head was only a fantasy, a sad projection of the sad state of my own sad psyche); the letter that Arthur
composed on this occasion—pacing the floor as he dictated (remember, please, that nobody was really in his lap, so he was free
to pace), throwing his arms behind his back as he did so and
clasping the wrist of one hand with the thumb and forefinger of
the other, stooped slightly with furry eyebrows and thick-lensed
spectacles like Groucho Marx, but without the cigar because the
goody two-shoes at the office for blah blah blah made him go
outside to smoke—included, along with a handful of very funny
jokes (he was a witty fellow, Arthur was, good with a quip), and
some practical recommendations for coming to grips with my
newfound situation (unemployed, unemployable), the following excellently observed sally, and unassailably sound piece of
advice, worthy of Nick Carraway's father, that I, though turning
it over in my mind scrupulously ever since, would, predictably,
and spectacularly, fail to heed: "Don't you know, old man, that
the Internet is good for only two things: [A.] pornography and
[B.] buying airplane tickets?"

A long-standing off-spin bowler of the male gaze and dedicated Sunday wanker (but wanking, ceremoniously, on the other
days as well), I had been, since Caroline taught me how to use
the Internet circa 1996 or 97, a devoted, if somewhat shame-
faced, follower of nearly every single one of the beckoning oda-
lisques lounging luxuriantly at the numberless hyperlinked se-
raglios of the World Wide Web, and for this reason I stipulated
[A.] readily enough, but in the weeks of prostration, etc., that
pullulated (and the months, and years, and galaxies) following
hard on the shattered heel of my forced retirement (as I so nom-
inated it, and still do; *rightly or wrongly, I still nominate it*), sur-
feited-up to my chin with my admittedly small share of the

thousand natural shocks of the non-virtual world, I had by the time Arthur's adjuration came piping down the line stashed my passport in a bureau drawer and stopped traveling altogether, had ceased all the rambles I'd more than half-entered the teaching profession to be able to afford the time to take.

My forced retirement I called it: my manic statement...my grand renunciation...my career suicide (only just career?)—for that is what I had done, I had killed myself; that is what I had done as that is what I'd always longed to do, to kill myself in some form or another, but not literally, not a literal longing, just a sort of cyanide tablet of the mind in case I fell into the Russians' hands, an escape clause, a pis-aller if things got desperate, if things closed in, but only a fantasy, something I would do in my mind, in theory, in the abstract, not something I'd really do in the phenomenal world, in the world of the ten thousand things, if only because of the story I had read about the man who jumped off the Golden Gate Bridge before they put up the suicide barriers and—a miracle—survived the plummet, survived the impact, living to report, upon catching his breath and clearing his mouth and beard of the winkles and whelks that had collected there, that he'd been struck, after falling a few feet, a few yards, a few miles, watching the cold choppy saltwater grave he'd chosen for himself approach faster than anything had ever approached anything else before, faster than love, faster than youth, faster than disappointment; had been struck, as he tumbled, as he fell, with an understanding not so much of what he would be losing as with an apperception of a kind of flaw in the reasoning that had led to the act, an intimation that there might in his life that had come to seem to him untenable have been hope after all, that things could get better, or hadn't been as bad as he thought they'd been, that he hadn't looked at this thing from every angle, hadn't considered every option, that many of the more pressing of his problems could be solved, or at least mitigated, that the harm of the others could be reduced, things could be managed, accommodations could be made, and he began to regret the consummation he'd so devoutly wished, the quietus he'd sought to make in the cold blue drink of the bay, and then he survived, like a miracle, but here's the kicker because there's always a kicker in these kinds of stories: a few weeks later he jumped again, but this time no miracle, this time his quietus was consummated and he sank to the bottom of the sea and drowned.

"So beautiful, or so what," Paul Simon, who is seventy years old now, sings mournfully, exultantly, on a radio turned down low in the next room. Is he singing about the man on the bridge ("a raindrop in a bucket / a coin dropped in a slot"), the man on the bridge who is each of us, or maybe only some of us, or maybe he's just the man on the bridge who jumped off twice (the first time tragically, I suppose, the second time farcically)? A raindrop or a coin Paul Simon may or may not have ever heard of, peering *as I peer, peering as we peer* over the guardrail before he takes his descending flight *my flight, our flight* or, in a breath, in a gasp, as he leaps out into the blue paint-by-number sea-and sky-scape (painted, in my imagination, in the same fog-filtered Technicolor hues that accompanied Kim Novak's similar, if less spectacular, leap into the bay in *Vertigo*), tumbling, turning, spiraling in the windy gyre of his expiring grasp on things, "losing his stomach" in his descent. (Like the boy in the backseat of a Ford Galaxie of nineteen-sixty-something long ago, as his father, long and lean with the curly hair, speeds up a little, as he always does, a very small smile cracking just a little on the side of his face, as the car approaches the familiar dip in the long lonely shoulderless sideroad between Argo and Flat Top, where the winding cut-off merges left onto Old Highway 78 on the ride home from Mimi's and Ma Maw's, the boy laughing with relief as his stomach, upon clearing the dip, falls back like a ball into a mitt to its home in his soft abdominal cavity where he felt so many of the things he felt...)

"So beautiful, or so what," Paul Simon sings in the next room, as I go down once more into the smithy of my soul—well maybe not the smithy of my soul, but I go down somewhere (the doctor's office of my soul?)—to tear or to coax or to eke out, in the cold gray drizzlygray, the kind of gray without any blue in it, of a peeling-paint heat pipe-hissing early morning in the neverending Novemberdecemberjanuaryfebruary (and, let's face it, Marchaprilmay) of Milwaukee, Wisconsin, a few more pages (a few more paragraphs: a sentence; a clause—subordinate or independent; a word; a morpheme—free or bound; "the scant drip," Don DeLillo calls it, "the ooze of speckled matter, the blood sneeze, the daily pale secretion, the bits of human tissue sticking to the page") of my confession, spiritual autobiography, *cri de coeur*, advertisement for myself, and *apologia pro vita sua*, the executive summary of "an empty house on Weed Street / across the road from a vacant lot."

> You know life is what you make of it
> So beautiful, or so what

But what had I made of my life? I who had longed since I was a boy to be, if not dead—no it wasn't suicide I devoutly wished, not exactly—then *hors de combat*, out of the fray, excused from duty, absent without leave, on sabbatical in my own world in a clearing alongside Mimi's pond free of lesson plans and report cards and parent-teacher conferences, free of observations and "learning walks" and performance appraisals and standardized tests and comprehensive examinations and strategic planning and goal-setting and data-driven instruction, free of principals and assistant principals and executive directors and development directors and human resources directors and grant monitors and literacy coaches. As a child I had dreamed of finding a way to get out of going to school, and later to get out of going to work, of being hospitalized maybe, but with nothing too serious but still requiring quarantine, something that would provide an open-ended unchallengeable doctor's excuse, dreaming of suicide but dreaming, too, inchoately, or seeming to appear to have been so dreaming (I imagine now I must have fit, certainly in Birmingham days of flannel shirts and greasy hair and yellow teeth and jaundiced lock-jawed anomie, but in Milwaukee, too, and in New York, somebody or other's idea of an FBI profile of a potential domestic terrorist), somewhere in a primitive preserve of the brain stem, in some small place near the top of my spine where thoughts that later get expressed or never get expressed begin or die, where they aren't even thoughts whatever they are just images and feelings of love and hate and rage and fear and something's wrong, dreaming of turning my suicide inside out like a shirt coming off my back and going in the hamper, like primary narcissism graduating to anaclitic cathexis, like lovehate seeking the object of something it wants in the sense both of something it lacks and something it desires, dreaming of not exactly suicide, sort of, but dreaming too almost also of not exactly murder as well: domestic terrorism: *attentat*: propaganda of the deed: Charles the Jackal: only in my head, though, but not even there, a thought crime un-punishable even in an era of Total Information Awareness in which know-nothing senators, blank-faced and seer-suckered (as I imagine them; I never look at TV—can't bear it—just listen, sometimes, to the radio), crouch on their haunches like satyrs in the neo-classical ruins of the Republic and bray, in that piquant olio of sanctimoniousness and depravity that is the specialty of the house in the dining rooms of the GOP, advising, for instance, torturers and all the other layers of the national security state on how to handle whining coddled evil-doers when they ask, hypocritically, for a lawyer: "You tell them, 'Shut up, you don't get a lawyer.'"

Shut up, you don't get a lawyer

Murder only in my head (sort of like Jimmy Carter in a by-gone era lusting in his heart, in confessional splendor, in the pages of *Playboy* magazine; still a sin, though, but, you know, mitigated) but not really even there, not really even in my head, murder, though, sort of, or a more or less devout wish for it, gathering mass then losing it then gathering some more somewhere in a dry bumpy bone-spurred gulch of my spinal column, pieces of it tossed up into the soft jelly of my medulla oblongata, other shreds sluiced into radiating nerves and dissipated into fingertips tapping like a restless leg, or reduced to a demi-glace in an obscure partly atavistic gland of the endocrine system that contrives helplessly, hopelessly, to keep the race from killing off its kind, and incorporated into my semi-functioning sort of self, into the psychopathology of everyday life: this would be a different way of taking arms against a sea of troubles, this almost-murder I sort of devoutly wished, a way of being "proactive," of doing something not just talking about it...

There is a joke, in fact, in this vein, this vein of doing something not just talking about it, that I used to tell Caroline as I headed out of a Sunday morning, hobbling on my stick (in a season when my foot, swelling and subsiding for a bit and swelling again as then in its grief it was prone to do, was swollen sore: a dingy yellow moon of a swollen foot, waxing gibbous and fallen to the earth), heading out to make my way across the park; these were Upper West Side days, when the first hopeful blush of "I'm going to be a schoolteacher" had faded, replaced like a bad blood transfusion with the full dread apprehension that not my coming to New York—and I was always careful to make this qualification—but my coming to New York to be a schoolteacher, had been a mistake, and that the mistake was a near fatal misstep that would fester like a wound and poison my life at the root, reminding myself, as I slogged to wherever it was I was slogging to, creeping in my petty pace, of (not Macbeth, but) Philoctetes, my very own, I would later come to realize, Ancient Greek archetype of myself, an archetype, the ultimate and most literal one, of someone who steps in something and suffers the consequences (or learns to make do, in some hideous way, with new less desirable circumstances, as he waits, incapacitated and alone, for the god in the machine to fall out of its apparatus, like the guts of a shot up soldier...).

I had, funnily enough, as coincidences go, thrilled as I was then, and thrilled as I would remain, even in the pullulating years, as the wound suppurated, as the world suppurated, at all the maddeningly rich and manifold opportunities for cultural enrichment that the city had—as if in a kind of settlement awarded in compensation for injuries incurred in a gear of its machine—laid at my feet, hobbled also, in those days, perhaps on one of the Saturday nights that preceded one of the Sunday mornings that I hobbled across the park and made my joke, but hobbling on this occasion downtown...

Or hobbling, rather, down a trapdoor like a manhole like a grave that opens, at fairly regular intervals (in most sections of Manhattan), to one of the cascading falling flights of stairs that tumble down long and never-ending (if you are lame) dark and peel-y patterned old and haunted angularly-winding funhouse mining chutes that dump—eventually—their frenetic, twittering, exultant, beat-down, compulsively-achieving, just-getting-by, just-getting-started, halting, lurching, stop-action animation human loads onto a platform that is a ledge on a precipice or a sandbar in a river, depending on the line, or the station, where commuters cling to walls or grip stairwells or pylons or girders and clutch to their chests enormous bags laden with purchases and lesson plans and prospectuses and blueprints, with time-lines and flow charts and case studies and first drafts, frozen-looking (and time-distorted like an Einstein thought experiment in a tram of Zurich) to passengers looking staring gazing gaping out window slits that look like sleepy eyes of express trains ghosting by at dizzying hyper-speed passing through the station down the middle track; half-seeing, in a hazy mote of a lazy eye, near a floater and a fallen lash, and then for only a fraction of a second, magic lantern phantoms of themselves in earlier aspect, or later, or in tenses we don't use in English, remnants or traces of what used to be or might have been or is yet to come, that, once espied, these awkward shades—ghost actors that have made their entrances too early, or too late—evaporate into little clouds of cartoon smoke, each pillow one stop smaller than the pillow that puffed before it; they are sad-looking and afraid, the waiting faces, or at least, and maybe only, my apparition of them, with strange exaggerated features, smeared noses, plug eyes, tufted foreheads, spavined shins, and ruptured shoulders, chewing on things with mouths sliding down chins, swallowing hard and spitting out gristle, sinew, cartilage, and bone, tamping down a cigarette on a crinkly pack for later, packing and unpacking and repacking their bags, adjusting straps, tying laces, zipping zippers, lashing lashes, plugging the electric bud of a crimped cable in an ear, and, once the juices start pumping, wagging their hands in the air like Sunday, as they bob their heads, eyes alive, eyes dead, nodding personal assent, mouthing lyrics like liturgy, or singing, some of them, their psalms out loud, as if they are all alone whistling or humming in a darkened house or singing in a choir with other people, which they were, which they are; alone and with others, descanting mournfully, hopefully, tenderly,

Will you still love me tomorrow?

their thumbs tapping little boxes of Marshall McLuhan, telegraphing signals, friending some motherfucker, defriending another, or downloading an "app," fulfilling the true and final purpose of the upwardly mobile little digit's—when it's not out hitching a ride or sticking itself in a pie, that is—hard-won opposability, anxious, all, to arrive somewhere, only to depart and then arrive and then depart and then arrive (and then depart and then depart and then depart), waiting now for a connection to somewhere and a deliverance from somewhere else, a connection and a deliverance that is emblemized in an illuminated number, or a letter of the alphabet, like a third eye glimmering in the squinting brow of an engine hurtling down in the distance of a train that approaches…

And from such a platform as this, for a few minutes, leaning on my cane, I halted happy hopeful and inconsolable, with lineages of my own unrecognized consanguinity—twice, thrice, six degrees removed, or perhaps only a single scant meiosis apart—that had assembled there, a flash mob or temporary beehive, dirt daubers nestling in the guano-spackled cliff-platform, mutated hybridized cross-pollinated sons and daughters and nieces and nephews, and assorted other progeny—those dying generations—of the ancient seed of Shem, the ancient seed of Ham; the seed of Gomer and Javan and Japeth and Cush; the seed of Nahor and Arphaxad and Riphath and Madai and Mizraim and Lud; of Aram and Canaan; the seed possibly of Phut; pea plants in an experiment of Mendel, or of Yakub; the lines of descent mottled in their generation: bleached, blanched, dyed, stamped, or burnt hard by history, hard by circumstance; by accident, absence, whim, and wandering; by custom, disaster, and accursedness; by persecution, plague, and fury; by movement, migration, eviction, and retreat; by exile, expulsion, exodus, and long march; by scourge and by scattering; by dispersal down eons through mountain passes over ice fields across scroll plains across till plains across lacustrine, sandur, and abyssal plains; across peat bogs, pine barrens, mud flats, land bridges, and lava flows; across deserts, cirques, arêtes, and sloughs; feet sunk in yardang, feet sunk in loam; feet sunk in loess and in blowout; feet trudging down taiga, over karst, across scowle and scree; columns of ants swimming icy rivers, crawling out of rubble, out of barbed wire, out of corrugated tin and abandoned cars and broken glass and burned-out basements, out of detonated houses, switching yards, dead of night; transmogrified therein, in the cauldron, in the crucible; in punctuated equilibrium and in graduated phylogenesis; made divergent in aspect, way of life, accoutrement, and visage; in demeanor, stance, song, and armor; in blanket, medicine, and observance: bent straight, flat, or coiled up kinky; pounded long, broad, or coming up short; abandoned, exonerated, or betrayed; exalted, denied, or let go of; disparaged, elevated, or sacrificed for the greater good; drunk, sober, palsied, agued; anointed by God, by hook or by crook, or looking the other way; indulged, taken in, married off, declared redundant; arriving somewhere falling, fainting, flailing: shaking out settled or itinerant; hunting or gathering; toiling or tinkering; netting or gleaning; joining or casting; sowing, tilling, reaping, or tatting: in declension sinned, sinning, sinned against; a worshipful company, slick and handy—ad hoc, sliding scale, tenure track, by appointment, on assignment, bespoke and off the rack—of mercer, fletcher, draper, farrier; of sutler, sailor, soldier, store buyer; of webmaster, rag picker, grave digger, market analyst; of personal trainer, fundraising executive, vice-president for mission impact, dean of student affairs; sinking or swimming; stag or drag; getting a living or going a-begging; counting a blessing or cursing a fate; sitting in the gods or in the stalls: every stop in between, every exception to every rule, resting together, now, all of them, all of us, in a cleft of the rock of the world after the deluge before the fire next time.

Until, finally: first a squinting light in the dark damned distance; then a roaring gush and a clamor and a clank and a harsh hot wind, a jinn in a sirocco of the MTA, a burning bush emerging, being born, coming forth: an ark of deliverance come loud, like a thunder screeching, with sparks and electricity burning, the smell of water on electricity, rats scurrying, small fires extinguishing themselves on the track, and little bursts of steam, little eruptions, belches, farts; and when it, the train, like a rusted out out-of-date carnival ride, twittering machine, or Dadaist *métamécanique* crashes into its complete stop and then collapses, with a tinkling bell tinkling like a doorbell like the tinkling sound of a teaspoon tapping on a brandy snifter late in the evening of a late night supper when a drunken relative or friend of the family is trying to get everybody's attention because there's something he's been waiting for just the right moment to say; and then the something to say: an injunction, pre-recorded, a ten commandment come down, burbling forth from rock, from burning bush, from for all god knows a jar in Tennessee, an injunction, a commandment, giving not of bird or bush, that reads, except it is spoken—and this is pretty good advice in general, for young and old alike—

"PLEASE USE ALL AVAILABLE DOORS"

and all the available doors, making a swishing sound and then a clank, tumble open like a curtain in one of those old voting booths (in the days before chits or chads or whatever they're called), parting, bi-valve, like a clam or glottis; and then another commandment ensues, comes down, burbles forth, in the form, this time, of a caveat, firm and loving, entreating all who would enter to enter loving, to enter wisdomed up and fully apprised, to enter justified:

"STAND CLEAR OF THE CLOSING DOORS, PLEASE"

(Further excellent advice that applies in all areas of life, not just rapid transit)...

And so enjoined, so forewarned, the human company—mumbling, twitching, scratching, holding back, giving it their all, yearning, searching, resigned, sighing in concord, snorting in enmity—aware, now, of the risks and prepared to follow instructions, fall, like birds out of the sky, down from the nooks and combs they had in waiting claimed for themselves, clefts and sockets in the wall in the keep of which they'd held firm, holding their temporary piece of ground, watchful and vigilant, marking it, delimiting it, pacing its perimeter, twisting in place, and as one, with one blank face, shaking off an old skin, they step forward like a motion study or a film of the Lumière brothers, little figures moved by unseen hands across the platform deposited finally at the threshold, a new beginning, whereupon they clamber aboard on tiny legs with flailing arms, clothed in coats of skins bearded old terrible but sentimental Yahweh had sewn for them in by-gone antediluvian times when he sent them forth from their once-garden to till the ground from whence they were taken, coming in, all the way in, and quickly, before an available door can take out an eye or a tattoo or a hair extension, or snap off a finger, the diamond ring that had adorned the digit's lower joint bouncing down the track and settling, finally, after rolling a long time, an eternity, really, alongside a chewed Dorito package in some dirt near the third rail, raising, as it settles, a silent and tiny mushroom cloud of dust...

They maneuver aggressively, they think subtly, this swarm, this consanguinity, myself included, for an empty seat, or an almost empty seat, and, finding one, those who are able, the fittest of us, and the best adapted (in a gesture of kindness that does not surprise me very much, I am, on account of my cane, *noblesse obliged* into a seat, grandfathered in, so to speak, by the one social Darwinist in the fray who, apparently, has second thoughts about the war of all against all), we squeeze ourselves down into each other's flesh, massing together like melted wax figures into a solid lump, but keeping a small slight distance apart, holding on cautiously, thinking ahead—with an admittedly counter-scriptural thought to the morrow—to an eye or a lip or a cheek or a thought or a dream or a memory recognizably our own, or something like our own; or maybe we are toy figures crammed in a chest, animate, though, but dead-like; and then another announcement, this time from a human voice straining in the automation, a human voice that has wrested control of the public address system from the carefully modulated voice-coached enunciation and institutional-sounding rounded tones of the recorded message, nasalizing, this thin reed, in whiny gravelly-throated switchboard-operator outer borough plainchant, the following, ungrammatical, I've been told, adjectival prepositional phrase (apparently it's the adverbial that's called for: "because of...," or "on account of"), that had reverberated so many times before in my ears, and in the ears of all New Yorkers, or at least the straphangers (both in and out of the beautiful chthonic garbage, rat nest, and creosote laden sinuses of the city that I loved so well, the city and the sinuses, where people are moved, or where they are not moved, where they are taught sometimes, in the crowded dim fluorescence of a carriage of the underground, to keep still), with the details adjusted for the particular occasion (these were occasional poems):

"Due to an earlier incident at…Smith and 9th Street," say, "or Jay Street/Borough Hall, or Canal Street, or West 4th Street/Washington Square, or 14th Street, or 34th Street/Penn Station, or 42nd Street/Port Authority, or 59th Street/Columbus Circle, or 125th Street, or 137th Street/City College, or 145th Street, or 175th Street, or 181st Street, or 190th Street, or 203rd Street/Peter Minuit Academy…, this F train, or this A train, or this 1, 2, 3, 4, 5, 6, or 7 train, or this B, C, D, E, G, J, L, M, N, Q, R, S, T (they say, some day, when they finish the 2nd Avenue subway), V, W, or Z train, will be delayed indefinitely, and then, when finally, after several false starts, it starts moving again, it will be re-routed, and run express where you expect it to run local, and local where you expect it to run express, and along the way will stall from time to time, again indefinitely, in tunnels between stations, lurching forward, getting your hopes up, and then stalling again, arriving eventually, this train, at some as yet unspecified coordinate in space and time, of buried latitude and subterranean longitude, a coordinate that will lie, possibly, a few blocks, or a few miles, or across town from your intended destination, or the destination you thought you had intended, or maybe nowhere near it, perhaps not even in the same borough, perhaps not even in the same town; arriving, what is it Kandinsky said?, 'Not here, not there, but somewhere…'"

And once this message has been repeated eight or nine times, with loudspeaker malfunctions obliterating the part of the announcement that you, or any other particular straphanger, may have been waiting to hear, the part of the announcement that pertains to your travels, the conveyance will resume, finally, its something like a forward thrust and churn its heavy heaving slotted parabolic rocking passage down dusty dirty sooty dead men's tracks buried in shale beneath schist in caverns carved like grottoes hard and everlasting in the ruby, jade, and golden beryl-lighted realm of Pluto's lair below Hell's Kitchen, East Harlem, Sutton Place, Williamsburg, Turtle Bay, Gramercy, Chelsea, Bensonhurst, Koreatown, Kip's Bay, Little Italy, Bay Ridge, Bed-Stuy, DUMBO, Ft. Greene, Astoria, Crown Heights, Jackson Heights, Washington Heights, Hamilton Heights, Morris Heights, Morningside Heights, Mott Haven, Murray Hill, Clinton Hill, Sugar Hill, Cobble Hill, Carnegie Hill (I love repeating these names; they sound like music to me, like poetry...), and, having stalled and double-backed and crisscrossed the roiling, rocking island(s—and mainland) many times, will arrive, has arrived, does arrive, did arrive: not here, not there, but somewhere...

Will arrive, has arrived, does arrive, did arrive: downtown, on one of the Saturday nights that preceded one of the Sunday mornings that I hobbled across the park after making my joke: downtown at a pulsating cell kind of like a casket, not a coffin-casket, though kind of like that, too, but a casket like the caskets in *The Merchant of Venice*—it felt like a fairy tale box, this station did, a box buried beneath the ground—in Soho near the frontier of Tribeca that I had, from the vantage of several stations prior, anticipated, watching and listening the way for, shouldering myself back into the rucksack that I'd rested for the journey's duration on my lap, lifting myself up by the swan's neck of my cane, and with my free hand gripping the upper rail, pulling my weight, clumsily, ploddingly, down the aisle of the car (that rocked so herky-jerky, shifting like time) towards the door, worse for the wear but happy when I alighted, getting my land legs back, in another tiled station, another relay in the vast circuitry that pulsed in all directions and in me, the electricity I could not contain, the unbroken thrill of living in New York City, the city that never did, though capable of intimating that it would or could or that it may yet, betray the heart of any of the slobs (sentimental, hard-bitten, or the usual combination of the two) who had ever loved her (this unbroken feeling, this electricity, is something else I would reject, would throw away, grieving as I grieved then and grieve yet for the loss of the old *Saturnia regna* in Milwaukee, Wisconsin, touched though it had been with sadness and care I can scarcely remember, anticipating, even then, the grief of the loss I would feel later, when I had thrown over the hard-realized dream of the city for an idea of recapturing a time and a place I would discover I could, after experience, only be a ghost in, a ghost of volition: a phantom of the *pis-aller*): a station like a casket like a tiled and shining relay from which I climbed back up out of like climbing the shrine of an underground mountain, a shrine situated a few crooked cobbled storied blocks past converted warehouses and factories that once housed artists, only rich ones now and Mary-Kate and Ashley, from one of the tiny black box theaters where I passed so much of my time in the dark, a theater that occupied a storefront occupied today, I have reason to believe, by a wine bar, or a nail salon, or a neo-charcuterie because things change I have to keep being made to understand, because New York, as the president/C.E.O., except they don't really call her "president/C.E.O.," of The New Museum said in an article I read somewhere, applauding the destruction of fusty old buildings and the construction of banal new "edgy," "buzzy," "cutting edge" ones (these aren't her words; these are other words I hear), because New York, she said, isn't a museum (which is true, a museum is a thing that New York is not), where I, also not a museum (well, sort of a museum, and a bit of a culture vulture, my pockets crammed with crumpled, annotated, and cross-referenced "Goings on About Towns" and *Village Voice* and *Time Out* listings; I lived in New York, but I was still a tourist, a tourist who delighted, even though I was only a tourist, in playing cicerone to visiting Milwaukeeans and Birminghamians), had hobbled my way to to take in a revival of John Jesurun's brooding, poetic, and elliptical I don't want to say "deconstruction of" because that's not the word I'm looking for, "meditation on" maybe, or "rendering of" Sophocles' own meditation on, or rendering of the ancient Greek archetype of myself: that old Achaean sad sack with the bad foot, Philoctetes *a performance in which, caught up in the brooding and the poetry and the ellipses and the sore foot (but swooning, mainly, at the uncompromising bitterness of the protago-nist, and pinched tight in the folding, flip-up pair of pliers that always seemed to be my seat in all the little black boxes where I would spend a dark happy reverential proportion of my seven mixed years in New York), I half-winced and half-knew, my own foot aching in sympathy with Philoctetes', and, because my shoes were too tight, bleeding like one of Cinderella's stepsisters' in the Grimm Brother's (and the Ste-phen Sondheim and James Lapine) version of that story (I'd had, during the performance, because of the swelling, to take off a shoe and, out of embarrassment, try to hide my disgrace by cradling my unshod foot surreptitiously against my thigh, in a kind of pieta) —half-winced and half-knew, minutes into the production, that I was staring down the long tunnel of history like the barrel of a gun at the flickering ghost of my own Christmas future peering blankly —eyes diverted a bit, cast down, a little sheepish —back up at me...*

But on this occasion, the occasion of the joke, the joke in the vein of doing something not just talking about it, I hobbled out across the park, in the morning after the performance of *Philoc-tetes* it may have been, a drunken-looking figure staggering in the morn mist, dragging my foot as if to plough a furrow in the Great Lawn, an elderly shepherd leaning tentatively on my stave, a shepherd emeritus, as I slogged patch by patch across the park down past the boards of the Delacourt Theater round the dew-mottled blossoms of the Shakespeare Garden up the winding steps to the rim of the ramparts of Belvedere Castle and into the woods of the Ramble and, clearing that thicket, battling my way through a blur of wedding parties posing for pictures on the Bow Bridge, getting up to the Bethesda Terrace and wending then past the Bandshell that always looked to me like the ruin of an earlier civilization that had once lived in the park, Etruscans, maybe, or Toltecs, to the Mall, presided over by its stately elms (they really are stately, those elms; you kind of understand what the word "stately" means when you walk through them), and from there out of the park, after stopping first to buy a bottle of Poland Springs from a vendor with a push-cart, exiting through the Children's Gate at Sixty-Fourth Street, backtracking then six short blocks up Fifth Avenue to the neo-classical portal of the Frick Collection, tossing my empty water bottle in a trash can, and making my way in to look at (compen-satory) pictures...

I say it was a Sunday morning that I hobbled across the park because on Sunday mornings in those days, and as far as I know these days too, admission to the Frick was, is, "pay what you wish" (I, for my part, paying what I wished, dropped, typically, a quarter into the attendant's outstretched palm and thought as I did of Top Cat in the old cartoons tipping the doorman with a coin on a string he then reels back with a yank into the front pocket of his purple waistcoat, by the way the only article of clothing Top Cat ever wore, except for his matching purple porkpie hat; of course both the vest and the hat appeared, in my childhood, at least during the series' first go-round, as matching shades of gray on my family's black and white television set, which would be replaced, before long in the bright green sixties, as the family fortune grew, with a nice fat color console; but then I, too ashamed to contribute anything less than $5, even to the estate of an "industrial statesman," which is what they call rob-ber barons now, am lying about the quarter).

The joke, to come to cases, that I told, not so funny a joke, re-ally, more of an outsider's idea of an insider's wink, was that I was heading out across the park to visit not the Frick, but the Sasha Berkman Collection. That was the joke, that after the rev-olution, in my alternative timeline, the museum would be re-named to honor Clay Frick's would-be assassin, the anarchist Al-exander Berkman, and Jack Sprat boyfriend (at least in my im-agination, Berkman was lean) of zaftig Emma Goldman (extent photos confirm "zaftig"). (By the way, when I pictured these two culture heroes, I saw, in my mind's eye, or I guess heard in my mind's ear, Molly and Jake Goldberg of 1038 East Tremont Avenue, the Bronx: "Yoo-hoo! Is anybody ready for the revolution?" This, I suppose, is because, staving off the dread of the Monday morning that would follow so hard in just a few hours, at 5 a.m., as a matter of fact, when my alarm would go off, I listened, every Sunday night, in those days, to Max Schmid's Golden Age of Radio program on WBAI.)

"Honey, I'm hobbling over to the Sasha Berkman Collection."

I was dreaming, in this gag, of a day when all the scores will be settled and/or all truth reconciled (I, in this mood, preferred of course the former), a day when the last shall be first (and the first shall be on the gibbet; or at the very least in exile) and society has inscribed on its banners the slogan, "from each according to his ability, and to each according to his need," as the state, like an aging parent moving from assisted living to the full-care ward to the hospice and then on to the sweet hereafter, withers away somewhere off on the horizon, and the Land of Cockaigne/Erewhon/New Jerusalem/Shangri-La (name your antidote to whatever it is poisons you) materializes triumphantly in the mist, a few eggs having, regrettably, been broken in the process, means crushed for an end like the little smudges, "dots" he calls them, that Harry Lime (who has loomed as large as the shadow he casts across black and white post-war Vienna, before diving back down into the city's sewer system where he will soon meet his end—has loomed, indeed, as large as Orson Welles himself—in my imagination since I first saw *The Third Man* on the Late, Late Show as a boy, thinking I was watching a horror picture, adjusting the vertical hold on the Magnavox that always started to roll at critical plot turns, sitting on the floor up close to the set and trying to keep the sound down low because I wasn't supposed to be up so late)...the little smudges that Harry Lime, from his own sort of heightened perspective, wipes, rhetorically—premises in a syllogism—from the floor of the Weiner Wurstelprater to teach Holly Martins a lesson in enlightened self-interest that is, at least doctrinally, the opposite of communism...

It was a different way of taking arms against a sea of troubles, this almost-murder I sort of devoutly wished, somewhere in my endocrine system, a way of being proactive, of doing something, not just talking about it, not just writing a somewhat fictionalized memoir (which is of course a pleonasm—"somewhat fictionalized memoir"); every sensitive man, woman, and nonbinary in America—beaten down by something socio-historical, or undone by a conflict within, but rising...rising: getting clarity, illumination, (crushing) self-knowledge, what you will; i.e. redemption (and for that matter every *in*sensitive man, woman, and nonbinary in America—but it's usually a man—disgraced, or soon to be disgraced, and worried about his or her or their, etc.—but it's usually his—legacy to posterity and/or, with a view toward more immediate prospects in the large but rapidly evaporating present, trying to crawl his way back into the public's good will)—is writing a somewhat fictionalized memoir (or in the case of those awaiting the vindication of history, hiring a ghost to do it for them). This I am hardly the first to point out, though good people across the land keep getting their feelings hurt and their trust betrayed, they say, by writers who are supposed, they believe, to tell them for chrissakes the truth (the truth, by the way, that they already know, or think they know: the truth that there's a shitstorm coming, that now's the time to buy, that all will be forgiven, that the answer is within yourself, that the chickens are coming home to roost, that god or history or biology or the dominant culture is gonna cut you down), but, like philandering husbands, or evangelists who solicit prostitutes, or undergraduates plagiarizing their term papers from the Internet, these memoirists—would-be *litterateurs* and on-the-make politicians alike—are, eventually, caught out in their dishonesty and/or hypocrisy and vilified in the press and in the pulpit and at the water cooler when it is revealed that they have—to the degree that it can be proven that they have and to the extent to which anybody cares—invented episodes or made up dialogue or fudged overdoses or prison stretches or brushes with history, that they have misrepresented, for example, the horror or the squalor or the splendor of their beginnings, the horror or squalor or splendor they overcame against long odds and with very little encouragement and no government handouts or trust funds or foundation grants or help from god (or maybe it was the handouts and trust funds and foundation grants and help from god they overcame) on their way to the (life-affirming, always life-affirming) redemption their stories, by prior arrangement or contractual agreement or the conventions of the genre, must always end with, because "what the American public wants," as William Dean Howells put it over a hundred years ago, "is a tragedy,—with a happy ending," getting into a spot of bother for their deception, some of them, with Oprah Winfrey, but I believe I read that she subsequently forgave the most famous of these blighters, the poor devil, as, in time, she forgives all those who trespass against her...

"If there is any substitute for love," wrote Joseph Brodsky, "it is memory," but memory is a fickle brew, fickle as love, fickle as truth (universal or *sous rature*), "truthful" or "untruthful" only to the degree that it needs to be to hang together as a story, or to appear to so hang, to fill in the blanks, the way the eye fills in its blind spot with the material it finds at hand, a "truth" all the more poignant, all the more urgent, in light of an observation that Angela Carter once made that I have, since starting out on this memoir of mine, kept sloshing on the back of my tongue like some wine I'm about to spit out: "The end of all stories, even if the writer forbears to mention it, is death." All memory is in this sense "recovered memory," prodded and coached, in circumstances it has not chosen for itself, by the material conditions that have produced it; it is, like the self (and the eye that feeds the self), jury-rigged and jerry-built, slapped together, subject to retroactive interference...

It is, moreover, leaky, like a body, or a faucet, or a corrupt administration, unpredictable, dangerous, self-revealing, a stand-in for desire: it is what the eye sees when it looks inside itself, and this inwardness, or consciousness of self, is all blind spot.

Maybe love/memory is a series of displacements set in the blind spot, or some other obscuration of the optic disc: an interpolation or an inference, or, if I remember my propositional logic correctly (I somehow passed a course in symbolic logic in college, but can only now remember the funny names for axioms and proofs and theorems and things; I never took a course in optics), a hypothetical syllogism or heaped upon coadunation—or string concatenation—of destructive dilemmas, modus ponens, exclusive disjunctions, bi-conditional eliminations, and ass-backwards De Morgan's theorems.

If P implies Q, then R implies S.

If S implies T and R implies Q and either Q is false or S is a syntactical consequence of T or R is true and P is a syntactical consequence of S, then either P or Q is false or S is true (but knows in its heart that it is false).

Therefore...something.

(Or, as Anne Carson put it in the title of her Ph.D. dissertation, and this is the true syllogism of life, "Odi et amo ergo sum.")

In any case, at a boarded-up theater in an Orpheum circuit of the mind, in my mind, a spring is heard to spring offstage

—BOI-I-I-N-N-G

and a cuckoo clock cuckoos,

—CUCKOO CUCKOO

like in a Tom Stoppard play I saw a university production of years ago, as I, for my part, in pre-emptive defense of any breach of covenant that future diligent readers, if there are any readers for me (and one wonders about this sort of thing), diligent, or otherwise, smarting from the bruise of their own betrayal of trust, may attempt to bring to light, cite here, in my defense [A.] William Faulkner, who said, "A writer is congenitally unable to tell the truth..." and [B.] Philip Roth, who wrote, "That writing is an act of imagination seems to perplex and infuriate everyone," as exhibits for a brief I may wish to file that might, this brief, have something to do with the relationship between truth and fiction, memory and desire, desire and vision, a brief that has been written (and performed) a thousand times before in a thousand different venues by a thousand different scholars, a thousand critics, a thousand poets, a thousand sword swallowers, sleight-of-hand men, trapeze artists, and a thousand other assorted circus performers and vaudevillians, brows high or low or in the middle register

—BOI-I-I-N-N-G

working with or without a net, with or without tenure or a steady job, or any job, with or without a full house or boffo box office

—CUCKOO CUCKOO

all more loving and god-fearing and steadfast and perspicacious than myself, who have long since moved on to some new topic I will hear about in a few years, and that I haven't anyway the argument or epistemology in me, or the memory of or desire for either, to make or attempt to make, or even look up on Wikipedia, and will leave to the professionals at the better universities and the higher periodicals, and at Wikipedia, hoping in the meanwhile that my hypothetical readers, thumbing these pages, settling in for *la longue durée,* will fail to notice [A.] the ellipsis in the Faulkner citation, and [B.] that both of these writers were talking about fiction when they said what they said, wrote what they wrote, and lived how they lived. I too, remembering

Brodsky, and mixing in my own proportions a little bit of truth and a little bit of fiction suspended in bits of memory and shards of love (and also mixing in, I see now, as I revise this draft, a little of bit of Frank Sinatra, a little bit of *Man of La Mancha*, and a little bit of me back in high school staying up all night reading Camus, vowing the next morning to be an existentialist), feel that I must say what I must say, write what I must write, and live as I must live, even if I (unlike Sinatra, unlike the Man of La Mancha, unlike Camus, but exactly like me back in high school) don't know how to do any of these things—to say, to write, to live—even if it (and when I say "it" I mean "it all," which is to say everything: the case for memory, the case for love, the case for memory altered by love, and love altered by memory, the case for the self and for the somewhat fictionalized memoir, the bits, the shards, and the justification for each of these, for all of these) is a sham, the thousandth fictionalization of a fictionalization fictionalized a thousand times...

The fictionalization, to come to cases, of a desire for murder that has been sublimated into the fits and starts of a somewhat fictionalized memoir: Another substitution. A backward masking of Don DeLillo: What terrorists lose, novelists gain; "the curious knot," *in my case (!)* (Emphasis mine), "that binds novelists and terrorists [and when I say novelists I mean somewhat fictionalized memoirists]," if I may press my argument, or someone else's, is—and we'll have to go back to Joseph Conrad, via Martin Amis, for this one: vanity and sloth.

See Amis on this point, agonizing over the events of September 11, 2001, looking for answers where there are none—in literature, where one looks for such answers: "In his reading of the terrorist psyche, Conrad persistently stresses the qualities of vanity and sloth—i.e., the desire for maximum distinction with minimum endeavor."[24]

Vanity and sloth: the gold standard not just for blowing

---

[24] "Is Terrorism 'About Religion'?" Included in the collection entitled *The Rub of Time* (Knopf, 2018). First published in the *Wall Street Journal* (2008).

things up and blowing people up and blowing one's self up, but maybe also twin towers in the "creative nonfiction," subgenre "somewhat fictionalized memoir" game, too—*in my case! in my case!*—at least if you reduce the taxonomy down to its smallest most absurd constituent: phylum "creative nonfiction": class "somewhat fictionalized memoir": species *Due to an Earlier Incident*, or *How I Rose From the Dead in My Spare Time and So Can You*, or *Three Lilies and a Moustache*, or *Taming a Seahorse*, or *Twenty Inches of Monkey*, or *How You Doin'?*, or *The Scapegoat's Agony*, or *The Hard Stool*, or whatever I wind up calling this thing. (Is that how it goes, by the way? Phylum/class/species? My "attitude about this sort of thing" has been, as Amis says of his own attitude somewhere, somewhere wittier than his disquisitions on the terrorist question, I think in *The Rachel Papers*, "I don't know much about science, but I know what I like.") I, though blameless, blameless (my murders, remember, were all in my head, although if you ask me I'll tell you that I've always felt this kind of feeling, especially late at night or early in the morning, ever since I was a boy, that I have committed a crime that I've forgotten about; even if I haven't [which I haven't— have I?], my views on these things have been colored by something Norman Mailer once wrote—getting into a spot of bother at the time with Diana Trilling, but New York intellectuals are less likely than Midwestern talk show hosts to offer eventual absolution: "Whether the life is criminal or not, the decision is to encourage the psychopath in oneself"), nevertheless feel implicated somehow in this business of blowing things up, or of wanting to, sort of; it may be the case that, after trying a variety of other strategies over the years ("inefficiency, indolence, dissipation, vacillation, mockery, distrust, 'hypochondria,' non-conformity, bad sportsmanship..."[25]), I have transposed the stirrings in my medulla to the task of writing this somewhat fictionalized memoir of mine (maximum effect, minimum effort:

---

[25] The list is Kenneth Burke's, from *Counter-Statement*, quoted in Frank Lentricchia, *Criticism and Social Change.*

though the effort of writing my memoir is causing me a great strain and the likelihood of my book effecting [affecting? which is it?] anything or anybody is small, very small, even though, inspired as I've always been by Mailer, I would, myself, "settle for" "less [much less!] than making a revolution in the consciousness of our time").

I guess we're back to DeLillo's original complaint, "What novelists lose, terrorists gain," except I, who, like Mama Rose, was born too soon and started too late, had myself—though I'd dreamed of it as a boy, and quickly let go the dream, but am making a last ditch effort now—never got hold of my own piece of that little thing that novelists have, in DeLillo's view, lost; I'd never girded my loins to go out with the big boys on any of the old-fashioned "raids on human consciousness" they used to go on back in the days when they indited their bright books of life with "a condor's quill and Vesuvius' crater for an inkstand…"[26]

And always, in these transpositions and displacements, these stirrings of the medulla, whether the talk is of revolutions or raids on human consciousness, I picture myself skulking about in a London of the mind like "the Professor" with the bomb in his breast pocket (or maybe he's just glad to see you; in any case, there's a "weenie" for you) and the detonator with the twenty second delay, in Conrad's *The Secret Agent* ("horribly prescient" Amis calls the novel), a sort of one-man would-be brain trust fancy-pantsing amongst the book's "dank crew of self-righteous sociopaths," that Ted Kaczinski, speaking of stirrings in the medulla (and dank self-righteous sociopaths), apparently modeled his life after (he has since adolescence, it has been reported, kept a copy of the book at his bedside, even in the cabin in Montana, and presumably still does today, as prisoner 04475-046 in the ADX Florence "supermax" prison, a.k.a., "the Alcatraz of the Rockies"). Also desiring maximum distinction with minimum effort, I want, in the sense of lack, the patience, or the attention

---

[26] Herman Melville.

span, or the mental composure, etc., to have put in the ten thousand hours of practice, let's say, that Malcolm Gladwell (of *The New Yorker*, of TED talks, and of tweets) made famous, the ten thousand hours you have to put in to get really good at something (because people like things in ten thousands: the ten thousand hours; the ten thousand things; the army of the ten thousand in *Anabasis*; the ten thousand martyrs of Mount Ararat; the 10,000 Maniacs; *The $10,000 Pyramid*; I can't do the math: how many days is ten thousand hours? How many weeks? More than six? Do term papers count? Lesson plans? Query letters? Letters of resignation?). I also lack the patience, the attention span, the mental composure, etc., to have sought to take tuition in the craft of writing, at, let's say, a famous writers' school—which I think is how one becomes a writer—in the workshops of which one learns, as I understand it, to "find your voice," "write what you know," "show, don't tell," and "murder your darlings" (And, speaking of what novelists lose and of what terrorists gain, is this what Mohammad Atta and his boys learned, when they slipped so gingerly, like bearded ballerinas, through the checkpoints of the national security state, to enroll in aviation school? Did they, in the predawn of their holy war, learn to find their voice, to write what they know, to show and don't tell, to murder their darlings...?), or however it is a writer learns his craft, or learns her craft, or learns their, zir, hir, eir, vis, or tem craft, if it is a craft, which it isn't, not that I know (who am I to know? and, besides, I have a vested interest in "inspiration," in sloth, in vanity), but I tell you that it isn't anyway:

It's an enthusiasm—literally (figuratively); it is god, imperfect, fallible, wretched and sublime; the kind if you were so inclined you might want actually to worship, or take a stab at...

Listen to Faulkner (but mind the ellipsis): "Let the writer take up surgery or bricklaying if he is interested in technique. There is no mechanical way to get the writing done....Teach yourself by your own mistakes; people learn only by error."

Or, Nietzsche, "Error is necessary for life."

Or, Philip Roth: "The fact remains that getting people right is not what living is all about anyway. It's getting them wrong that is living, getting them wrong and wrong and wrong and then, upon careful consideration, getting them wrong again. That's how we know we're alive: we're wrong."

Or, John Cassavetes, in a different, but related, context...I can't find the exact quote, but it goes something like this: "I admire any director who is able to finish a movie, *any* movie, good or bad."

And, Cassavetes again, talking to all of us: "Say what you are. Not what you would like to be. Not what you have to be. Just say what you are."

And listen, please, to Jan Morris: "Certainly I sometimes think that transient love, the sort that is embodied in a one-night passion, or even a passing glance, is no less real than the lifelong sort. Even imagined love is true!"

I, "wresting," maybe, "a realm of freedom from a realm of necessity," as my old hero Fredric Jameson, riffing on Karl Marx, famously put it, want the short cut, the minimum effort and the maximum effect, a passing glance at contemporary literature, a one-night passion, an imitation of love; I want to get it wrong, which is to say:

I want to say what I am.

And what I am is a two-toed sloth, vain about my cuticles and the lovely cyanobacteria flourishing on my back, lolling upside down in my tree, lumbering slowly to the ground for a few hours each morning to empty my bladder and my bowels and peck at a keyboard with these long sickle-like toenails of mine.

Lolling, aboriginally...

in undergraduate years, in the squalor of soiled rooms in unkempt apartments with dingy bed sheets repurposed as curtains tacked to peeling window casings, lying in my underwear on a dirty mattress on the floor; unwashed and scratching at advanced formations of tinea cruris, seborrheic dermatitis, Pityriasis simplex capillitii, and other red blotching Latinate eruptions, chain-smoking Marlboro Lights, and once a hand is free stroking a familiar purple tumescence with obsessive-compulsive, Tourette-ic motion, concentrating hard as I pump on old memories of brief contact with the soft luxurious flesh of girls, flesh like the inside of a satin ballet slipper, as John Updike put it, or a strange object covered with fur which breaks your heart (Donald Barthelme, but he wasn't talking about what I'm talking about or what Updike was talking about or I don't know maybe he was), the inside of something by calendar day occluded, and disclosed now for an historic moment, like the 76 year appearance of a comet or the blooming of a century plant, a furtive half-gift offered up tentatively, hesitantly, against better judgment and with gathering regret in a parked car or on a dark couch—a part-something, attempted dry hump, aborted, trailing off like a sentence fragment, the beginnings of a pity grope thought better of with a tongue briefly touching a tongue in a wet mouth; hopefully, lingeringly, fingers doing advance work in the field, grazing a nipple within the confines of a brassiere, or creeping down past the limit, tacit or arbitrated, of the elastic band of a pair of panties, inching inch by quarter inch, by eighth, by sixteenth, by thirty-second, and sixty-fourth into the gentle, forbidding protuberance of the pubic mound guarding the eventual warm opening sunk in the short sagittal cleft of the luxurious vulval vestibule, hesitating there, on the bump, the small rise, trembling and ashamed, dying like a swatted insect, until finally I complete my strokes, spray-painting motes of dust floating in sheets like rain of the disembogued sunrays breaking the light-tight close of my lumpenbohemian coffin of a quaint apartment, of the darkroom, the camera obscura in which I lay,

praying but without a god, unless the light is god, dreaming of when I lay my burden down, a blasted valley of ashtrays overflowing everywhere, a little campfire smoldering out in each of them, bits of crumpled paper crumpled everywhere smudged like dirty snowballs, dirty bombs, collapsing towers of books piled in stacks falling over in time-delayed thuds raising clouds of dust like smoke; wrappers of things all around, and empty Coke bottles, empty beer bottles, empty cigarette packets; a torn New Yorker from the year before folded open to Pauline Kael's review of Eraserhead, in which "Miss Kael," as they used to call her at the New Yorker, writes, "Lynch pulls you inside wormy states of anxiety"; Soho Weekly Newses and Harper's and Esquires and Nations and National Lampoons and New York Reviews of Books, and on the local level, Papermen and Bozarts and Southern Styles, yellowing in disheveled stacks on loose planks of worn parquet falling out, dislodging like bad teeth, Village Voice apartment listings spread eagle like a hymnal—because I was dreaming even then of a cozy flat in what is known as old Manhattan: pre-war, doorman, tree-lined, sun-drenched, garden, railroad, alcove studio, flex junior 1, with intercom, locked lobby, live-in super, eat-in kitchen, all appliances, to be let at four hundred dollars a month, at five hundred dollars a month, at six hundred, at seven hundred, at eight hundred, at nine hundred, a thousand, even more (the numbers seemed mad, hysterical, sublime— sublime in the Longinus or Edmund Burke sense of the word)…

too late to go to class at all today and anyway you haven't done the reading or written the response or maybe even bought the books or been to class in two weeks or three weeks or four

too late to withdraw passing too late to withdraw failing another "F" on your transcript

too late for getting dressed for borrowing money for getting a girl-
friend for taking a bath for combing your hair for brushing your teeth
for registering for school for finding a ride to work too late for calling
in sick for pawning things for redeeming them too late to pay the rent
before you have to pay the late fee too late to learn only by error too late
to find the exact quote
    say what you are Blackwell
    say what you are

An Updated Sloth

Speak, memory, say what you are, for as long as you can remember, as long as you can speak: of an updated sloth, having backed painfully into a slightly opened up consciousness, an improvement in personal hygiene, table manners, work ethic, parliamentary procedure, or pivoted in a dream into these things, standing up and brushing the tangles, dirt, and micro-organisms out of its coat, evolving, like President Obama "evolved" (why wasn't he there already?[27]) into allowing that same-sex couples might, after all, marry, or the Republican Party "evolving," somewhat opportunistically, and late in the game, in an announcement of one of its bellwethers on Fox News, into offering up bones for the Latino vote by not, as originally planned, cracking down on the "illegals" among them [Editor's Note: The Republicans changed their minds about this; they decided, since they don't believe in evolution, not to evolve[28]]; think back to that sunlit summer sublet in a dark tenement of the Lower East Side, on the precipice of before it all began, a precipice linked, like a serial comma, the comma-neck of a swan hovering over a young girl in Old Greece, to the chain of events that is in reality a single catastrophe, "eyes staring, mouth open, wings spread":

> The broken wall, the burning roof and tower
> And Agamemnon dead

---

[27] He was.

[28] Later Editor's Note: This material was written circa 2011-2012, before all the *real* shit came down.

I am squatting now (then) in a landing of a fire escape over-hanging Orchard Street, coiled myself—a battered old architec-tural detail, a gargoyle or an ornamental corbel—like the neck of that fluttering, pitiless, generative swan, my fingers poised dra-matically in midair, each talon clinched at the joint and ready to spring, and brought to you by the letter "C" (I felt, in the chutes and ladders of the Lower East Side, fumbling among stoops and overturned garbage cans, like a character—flesh or fabric—of *Sesame Street*); curling, this "C," like a bass clef, or a cat's claw, or like the 5,000 fingers of Dr. T., over the keyboard of the laptop computer sitting at my feet, my head bowing down to it like a beak, reminiscent of the toy piano virtuosoed to comic effect by the precocious Schroeder in the Peanuts comic strip, the laptop I'd sent away for in Milwaukee, Wisconsin (like a boy mailing off box tops to Battle Creek, Michigan), in the predawn of my new life, outfitting myself for the long move (sort of like Hem-ingway outfitting himself for safari[29] at the old Abercrombie & Fitch in Lillian Ross's *New Yorker* profile entitled "How Do You Like it Now, Gentlemen?"), an outfitting conducted, in my case, exclusively on the Internet, under my wife's careful Consumer Report-worthy tutelage; the first of three laptops (and moves) in—what is it now, eight years?—because I have been hard on them (the laptops not the moves; though the moves have been hard on me), as I had been hard when I was a child on all of my old Etch A Sketches, junked one after the other in unplanned ob-solescence, Etch A Sketches that my laptops have, through the means of a kind of deep tactile memory, also always reminded me of, especially when I'm trying to manipulate the touchpad; the touchpad that, by the way (because everything reminds me of everything else, and because writing is, as Norman Mailer called it in one of his last books, "the spooky art"), reminds me further of the indicator, or pointer (known in the business as the "planchette"), that sears one's fortune on a Ouija board (I feel, in

---

29 Except, as I remember it now, he was outfitting himself for a trip to Venice.

the rec room or the spirit cabinet of my soul, like I'm writing this book on an Etch A Sketch or a Ouija board—not a judgment on my laptop, or the Ohio Art company, or the Parker Brothers, but a judgment on my own superstition, arthritis, and steadily-deteriorating fine motor skills), because I'd need a computer to write my lesson plans *tripartite in form(ula)* speak, memory *I would soon learn (because everybody likes things in threes; and that's how they get them, or think they do: with a beginning, a middle, and an end), segmented, the lesson plan, by Great Chain decree, like an insect ("opening meeting," head; "work session," thorax; "closing meeting," abdomen: a blueprint, or* maquette—*theory guiding practice—for administering the sacraments* dance, misery *of "Turn and Talk," "Guided Practice," "Cooperative Learning," "Small Group Instruction," "Authentic Literacy Activities," "Conferencing," "Refocusing," "Students Sharing Learning");* and pursue a subsidized master's degree at City College *located in that mezzanine of Harlem called Hamilton Heights, where I would also find waiting for me more forms and formulae, more theory guiding practice, because everybody had to work very hard to get on the "same page" as everybody else, which is to say everybody had to work hard to get on the same page as Lucy Calkins, the oracle-in-residence (and by now pummeled to splinters Aunt Sally of this piece), ensconced at Teachers College, Columbia University, situated two stops further downtown on the IRT Broadway/Seventh Avenue line, or three stops on the IND Eighth Avenue line, from City College, in the tonier, off-Harlem Heights of Morningside; whenever her name came up, and her name came up, wielded like a cudgel, an appeal to authority, by university profs and administrative functionaries alike, I pictured her talking into a dicta-phone in a wood-paneled office surrounded by calipers and Bunsen burners and phrenology busts and vats with the pickled brains of "emergent readers" in them, rubbing her hands together like a mad scientist, planning the next strategy for effective teaching to be "modeled" by every English teacher—I mean every English Language Arts teacher—in America);* and I'd need a computer, also, to send out all the page after page of self-justifying prolix e-mails that I used to send when I was still in touch with people, when I knew people, and when they knew me, all the old friends and the new friends I'd leave behind, as they would leave me behind, as everyone everywhere eventually leaves everyone else behind…

We slough each other off like the molting, that is called ecdysis, of the cuticula of an invertebrate; we chuck each other overboard, because the dead will bury the dead; we chuck each other over as so much impedimenta, so much marine debris, in a slipstream, in a whirlpool, in a maelstrom or an eddy, retreating from view, getting smaller and smaller, little dots of anthropogenic artifacts buoying and bobbing in the wake of refuse that trails the awful lonely hopeless and clamorous rowing toward god, or something like god, of all us atoms fragmented in an agon, facets in a diamond, all us grasping flailing windowless monads, each "Isolato" cubbied up, indwelled, cocooned, "on a separate continent of his own [and her own, and their own, etc.]," [30] though in the infinity of time, and "in accordance with the eternal laws governing the combinations of [the] eternal play of repetition," which states that "all configurations which have previously existed on this earth must yet meet, attract, repulse, kiss, and corrupt each other again," [31] we seem to catch, standing on a subway platform, holding forth in a classroom, crouching on a fire escape, withering in an apartment, etc., etc., a glimpse of something or someone that has passed or is yet to come, a memory, a projection, a dream, perceptible only for a fraction of a second: a shadow or a shade, a recombinant configuration, meeting…attracting…repulsing…kissing and corrupting: again and again; catching, sometimes, this eye, in an instance of infinite time, which is to say an instance of infinite regret, a glimpse of itself gazing back from its secondary berth in the vitreous humor of the eye of someone or something apprehended, the shade of another monad, another configuration, time-captured, and splayed in an ever-repeating revelation of itself, to itself, giving forth all light, all hope, all feeling

---

[30] Melville.
[31] Heinrich Heine.

[L]et me look into a human eye; it is better than to gaze into sea or sky; better than to gaze upon God. By the green land; by the bright hearthstone! This is the magic glass, man; I see my wife and my child in thine eye.[32]

and, thus beholding, in one another's eye, which is to say each of us in our own, an image, reminiscent, maybe, of a prehistoric insect preserved in amber, or a glimpse of something acheiropoietic—a Veil of Veronica, an Image of Edessa, a faerie flitting in one of the photographic plates that fooled Sir Arthur Conan Doyle—we extend a hand, waveringly, tentatively, like Alice or Orpheus (in Cocteau's version of the story) reaching a hand through a glass, to touch something that isn't there, something we think we see reflected in the eye of another configuration, seeming to recognize in the reflection, trembling there, like something being born, or something dying, a glimmer that Ralph Waldo Emerson, in a vastly different context, or maybe not so vastly different a context, once identified as "our own rejected thoughts"; "they come back to us," Emerson wrote, "with a certain alienated majesty."

An updated sloth; or, sighing, apparently *say what you are* "for the dark downward and vegetating kingdom"[33] of Folivorae and Corydalinae: an updated hellgrammite, pupated in the long winter of Milwaukee into the dashing and resplendent New York City dobsonfly—salt and pepper in appearance, seasoned but aching, young again, sort of (more on this follows), and yearning, draped in the folds of my frayed and over-sized thrift shop morning coat, a Eustace Tilly of the Megaloptera set—that I could see reflected in the chiaroscuro of my computer screen, the "glass darkly" over which I leaned; I had, at long last, sloughed off the hard chrysalis of Wisconsin, and emerged, wings dry, and mandibles prominent, to live my seven days in New York City

---

[32] Melville.
[33] Robert Lowell, "For the Union Dead."

alive enough to spawn and die[34]

ecstatic, now, and pink in the reflecting dew of the new sun in
the new sky, my cheeks rosy like they'd just been pinched by my
Bubbe, a cowlick curling—here it comes again—like the letter
"C," like a little shofar, or one of Moses' horns, in a corner of my
hair, "inscrutable in an inscrutable world,"[35] I felt tempted to
say, as I squatted there, still recovering from the ID section of the
master's comps I had just failed almost twenty years before, because as Nietzsche says, "only something that continues to hurt
stays in the memory," spitting out an echolalia of literary allusion, a spasm of, and I quote from the National Institutes of
Health "Tourette Syndrome Fact Sheet," "repetitive, stereo-
typed, involuntary movements and vocalizations" (but I guess
I'm describing now not then, a distinction that may or may not
obtain), having landed, I can barely remember how, in the world
of Irving Howe's fathers, only a few blocks from The Avenue
Bearing the Initial of Christ into the New World; I had had a bit
of too much coffee (have had a bit of too much today), and I was
feeling—against type—hopeful about the future that was welling up inside me, trying to give it a nudge, egg it on, get it on the
stage before it was ready, before it had time to put its make-up
on and learn its lines and work out its motivation; I should have
known better because I was too old for this sort of thing; my
heart life-tempered, remember, but frangible...

I would, nevertheless, continue to behave like a boy again
though, even after things went all to hell, but in that particular
coordinate in space and time, then, there, in that welling up, I
felt reborn, refreshed, re-baptized, *non in nomine patris*, I would
later learn, *sed in nomine diaboli*.[36] But how could I have known
that then? in that long ago country of hope, "with"—yes I know
I'm mangling up the American Renaissance, failing another

---

[34] Robert Lowell, "Waking Early Sunday Morning."
[35] Wallace Stevens, "The Comedian as the Letter C."
[36] Melville.

master's comp, quoting the whole damned visionary company out of context

> *Identify the author of the following quotation and the work in which it appears; explain its significance:*
>
> *"Our needs interpret the world"*[37]

(calling it "the visionary company" when "the visionary company" refers to a different, but, I suppose, genealogically related, group of other artsy homosocial seers); in that long ago country of hope, "with," I was saying, or Nathaniel Hawthorne was saying, or was about to say, "no shadow, no antiquity, no mystery, no picturesque and gloomy wrong, nor anything but a commonplace prosperity, in broad and simple daylight," the broad and simple daylight, in this case, and commonplace prosperity of "high quality dedicated individuals...raising student achievement in the New York City classrooms that need them the most," a country, a prosperity, and a broad and simple daylight with a shadow, though, *and* a gloomy wrong—picturesque only to the Ku Klux Klan, or any number of morons in the south waving Confederate battle flags, saying it's their "heritage"—that served to bring those conscious of the gloom, and (somewhat self-importantly) determined to remediate it, together,

> *Identify the author of the following quotation and the work in which it appears; explain its significance:*
>
> *"Unhappy is the land that needs heroes"*[38]

from whose bourn I have never, emotionally, returned, the country, and the shadow, and my own cheap (self-important) purchase in the remediation of the gloomy wrong, in which I sat

---

[37] Nietzsche, *The Will to Power*, Book III.
[38] Bertolt Brecht, *Life of Galileo*.

squatting on my window sill (my reading glasses—which were more like a fop's *pince nez* though, because the temples, which is what you call the things that hold eyeglasses on your ears, had fallen off when a screw came loose [I was hard on my spectacles, too], with the temple-less torso lacking the quantum of *pince* necessary to keep them resting securely on my *nez*—sliding, over and over, off the bridge and then the tip of my beak and crashing like a drum roll please onto my Ouija board/Etch a Sketch/toy piano, like a Jerry Lewis routine that didn't get any laughs then and doesn't get any laughs now), attending, all nineteenth century, plume in hand and inkwell in the other, but it was the control knobs of an Etch A Sketch I gripped tightly in both hands, to my correspondence: a dandy, a fop, a bourgeois bohemian.

> *Identify the author of the following quotation and the work in which it appears; explain its significance:*
>
> "*I marched the lobby, twirled my stick…*
> *The girls all cried, 'He's quite the kick.'*"[39]

I'd fallen in, ingratiatingly, in those heady days, young again, I'd deluded myself into believing, with a "group [a 'Fellow Advisory Group'] of lively youth, loud and crowing": high quality, dedicated, earnest, touching, tender New York City Teaching Fellows, Teaching Fellows younger than I was by twenty years, younger by twenty-five years, by thirty years, by forty, by fifty, by sixty, and by seventy years, former professionals in fields other than education and, more predominately—by far—recent college graduates getting a first foot on the island, all of them gleeful in their commission to set the world to rights, "bustling about" Manhattan "and laughing with satisfaction at the stir they made," putting me in mind (now, not then, not in that dawn when bliss was it to be alive, but to think you were young when

---

[39] George Colman the Younger, *Broad Grins: My Nightgown & Slippers and Other Humorous Works.*

you were not was very heaven) of the group of merry-makers that the "young-old man, in a dandified buff suit, a rakish panama with coloured scarf, and a red cravat," that so repulsed Aschenbach in the early pages of *Death in Venice*, had fallen in with, aboard the "ancient hulk, belonging to an Italian line, obsolete, dingy, grimed with soot," docked on the Istrian Coast, waiting to set sail for Venice (commencement exercises for the new crop of New York City Teaching Fellows were held that year, by the way, aboard I forget the name of it, the battleship-museum docked on the West Side in the thirties somewhere near the Jacob Javits Center; I—dandified and rakish—wore to the ceremonies a flamboyant, plumy pirate costume that I'd hired in one of the costume shops that line the side streets downtown off Sixth Avenue: or was it that shop in the soundstage-Greenwich Village replicated at Pinewood Studios—the actual Village is soundstage-y enough—where Tom Cruise rents the costume he wears to Stanley Kubrick's idea of an orgy in *Eyes Wide Shut*?):

> Aschenbach's eye dwelt on him, and he was shocked to see that the apparent youth was no youth at all. He was an old man, beyond a doubt, with crow's-feet, round eyes and mouth; the dull carmine of the cheeks was rouge, the brown hair a wig. His neck was shrunken and sinewy, his turned up mustaches and small imperial were dyed, and the unbroken double row of yellow teeth he showed when he laughed were but too obviously a cheapish false set. He wore a seal ring on each forefinger, but the hands were those of an old man. Aschenbach was moved to shudder as he watched the creature and his association with the rest of the group. Could they not see he was old, that he had no right to wear the clothes they wore or pretend to be one of them? But they were used to him, it seemed; they suffered him among them, they paid back his jokes in kind and the playful pokes in the ribs he gave them.

I was, I understand now, a similarly grotesque species of "young-old man," something my wife understood immediately, sizing the situation up at once later that summer when she joined me in the sublet for a few weeks before we relocated uptown and hunkered down, in a neighborhood more our age, for our long-ish/shortish sojourn in New York City, but it was something she hadn't the heart to tell me then, to tell her self-deluded and sleepwalking husband (she told me later on, though, after I woke up, when she knew I could take it; and I took it, scales—or some-thing—falling from my eyes)...

But in that broad and simple sunlight *by the green land; by the bright hearthstone!* full of the cant and the righteousness and the good intentions of my own high quality dedicated and willing suspension of disbelief, I was, then—like Aschenbach's young-old man—"the loudest of the loud, out-crowing all the rest."

I was crowing, certainly, in the e-mails I wrote that summer, hundreds of them (I was imbued), long *lacrimae rerum* to old pal-y pals my own age or older ("those dying generations" I called this category of friend, or former friend), and quick little mash notes to my new young intimates, with whom I exchanged pri-vate jokes and playful pokes in the rib (the "earnest and tenders" I called this group of lively youth who suffered me among them); crowing, partly (or perhaps mainly) out of (let's face it— *always*) already dawning disenchantment (how does the old Thurber cartoon go? the one with the wife looking over her shoulder at her husband sulking in a chair, and saying, "Well, I'm disenchanted, too. We're all disenchanted"; but I would learn, and this is what hurt, though I'd learned it before, and it had hurt then, too, that not everyone is disenchanted); crowing in the correspondence that I was attending to that bright sunlit sublet morning of so long ago, as I bent my shrunken and sinewy neck over my toy piano on the fire escape overhanging Orchard Street, on the precipice of before it all began, fired up with coffee and new possibilities and the presentiment of I think I've made a mistake.

I wrote two letters that morning: one to an earnest and tender, and one to a dying generation.

Please note that the letters—which are reproduced below— have, since their original composition, been tampered with, souped-up, soured, by a later me *a ghost holed up in Walt Whitman's Brooklyn, trying to write it all away.*

The first letter I wrote that morning:

Dear Simone: July 3, 2004

How's your Fourth of July weekend going so far? Me, I went out for breakfast at Teany, on Rivington Street (you know, the restaurant owned by Moby), and I had a vegetabletarian full English breakfast: tempeh bacon, fried egg, texturized vegetable protein sausages, baked beans, fried bread, fried mushrooms, and grilled tomatoes—and I poured HP sauce over everything. Then I came home, took a nap, woke up, and went out to lunch at Kate's Joint for some vegan comfort food—tofurkey club sandwiches and mashed potatoes and gravy. I'm basically a meat substitute and potatoes kind of guy. And, you'll be reassured to learn, I put my pants on one leg at a time, too, my socks on one foot at a time, my truss on one hernia at a time, and my respirator on one lung at a time. *I felt old even though I felt young.*

Oh yeah, I did organize some papers today, believe it or not, after the wind blew them all over Orchard Street as I was lying on the fire escape in my sleeveless undershirt and boxer shorts, where I'd drug my mattress and slept the night before trying to beat the heat...

God I'm glad to have a few days off.

So, anyway, the reason I'm writing you is I was wondering if you would mind doing me a big favor and forwarding some of Sebastian's *communiqués* this way. As you know my old e-mail went defunct, and I lost everything Sebastian wrote to us prior to June 29 *along with hundreds of other traces, remnants, and orthographic projections of an earlier life* Would you mind?

I'm sorry to keep asking you for favors, you know, like the way I keep asking you to explain one more time the difference between what is it? Oh yeah—blecch!—Vygotsky's zones of proximal development, Maslow's hierarchies of something or other, Gardner's multiple intelligences, Bloom's toxicologies, Occam's razors, Pascal's wagers, Zeno's paradoxes, Jacob's pillows, Shroedinger's cats, Gertel's Bake Shop, Guss' Pickles, Schapiro's Wines, Kossar's Bialys, Yonah Shimmel's knishes, and Blah Blah Blah's blah blah blahs...

I also apologize for copying off your exams, borrowing your textbooks all the time (because I hate to buy them myself—not because I don't have the money, but because I don't like to have such tacky books in my house) and, what else...oh yeah, always asking you to print things for me because I don't have room in my apartment for a printer, even one with a "small footprint," and helping me register for school because it's complicated and on-line and I don't get it, and for finding my reading glasses that are usually propped up on top of my head like Mimi's always were when she used to ask me to help her find *her* glasses, etc.; but then, on the other hand, you're very kind, and I know you don't mind...

The reason I need the material I'm asking you to forward me is because, motivated as I am by an unwavering belief that every child can learn, I'm trying to review everything we've been taught in the last few weeks so I can reach my goal of being a proactive educator who knows how to move instruction.

But I don't want to think about that sort of thing on our four-day weekend.

Tomorrow I'm going to the bandshell down at East River Park where Cat Power will be performing for free, that is if she's not feeling too diffident and high-strung to perform and starts crying and runs off the stage, which apparently is often the case—something I'm afraid will happen to me when I finally get a job and a classroom of my own.

Cat Power, by the way, is hot! Did you see her picture in *The*

New Yorker last year, the one where her jeans are unzipped and you can see some of her pubic hair? Nice article, too, by Hilton Als, who called her performance style "jumpy and perverse, excruciating, and ultimately beautiful," a string of adjectives I'd love one day for somebody to apply to my performance style!

I've been doing some research on the life of Chan Marshall, BKA Cat Power, by the way, and I think I might have diagnosed what ails her (and what has, at crucial points in my life, also ailed me).

It's an affliction of the soul first diagnosed in the middle ages and called "accidie" (Latin, "acedia"): "a state that inhibits pleasure, and prompts the rejection of life; one of the Seven Deadly Sins," according to the *Oxford Dictionary of Philosophy*: "Aquinas associates it with turning one's back on things, through depression or self-hatred, and nicely defines it as a torpor of spirit which prevents one from getting down to anything good [Except — unlike me — Cat Power gets down to something good]. Often it is translated as sloth, which is actually quite different."[40] (At least that's what I keep telling myself, the same as I always told my teachers, and my parents, and my bosses: "It's not laziness, I just feel…torpid…you know, in spirit.")

Chaucer has a few things to say about accidie in "The Parson's Tale":

> After the synne of envye and of ire,
> now wol I speken of the synne of Accidie…

Aldous Huxley cites Chaucer's description in a discussion of the "synne" in a book of his called *On the Margin*, except Huxley calls it a "demon." I've called it an affliction, and would like to call it a disorder, but I can tell you that it isn't included in the *Diagnostic and Statistical Manual of Mental Disorders* (neither is

---

[40] OXFORD DICTIONARY PHILOSOPHY edited by Simon Blackburn (1994): Entry on "Accidie" (p.5) "By Permission of Oxford University Press"

"nervous breakdown" anymore, by the way):

> Chaucer's discourse on [accidie] in the "Parson's Tale" con-
> tains a very precise description of this disastrous vice of the
> spirit. "Accidie," he tells us, "makith a man hevy, thoughtful
> and wrawe." It paralyses human will, "it forsloweth and for-
> sluggeth" a man whenever he attempts to act. From accidie
> comes dread to begin to work any good deeds, and finally
> wanhope, or despair...

But then I guess it's presumptuous of me to think I've diagnosed
Cat Power. I have, though, I think, in my research, finally discovered what the fuck is wrong with me: a relapsing and remit-
ting case of medieval acedia. Even on the cusp of my new life of
"building equity" by "invest[ing] in 1.1 million futures," I'm
lousy with it, mooded, in fact, bynymethed, forslowethed, and
forsluggethed with it, and, now that Chaucer mentions it, I am
feeling a little hevy, a little thoughtful, and a little wrawe. But
that might be the tofu, or the wheat gluten, or the texturized vegetable protein talking.

See You Monday,
Charles

The second letter I wrote that morning:

Dear Ida: July 3, 2004

So the thing is, I'm sitting in a tiny studio apartment on the
Lower East Side of Manhattan (corner of Orchard Street and Riv-
ington, a few blocks from the world of Irving Howe's fathers,
from the old *Jewish Daily Forward* building, from the old Yiddish
Theater District [a.k.a., the Jewish Rialto], from Gertel's Bake
Shop, from Guss' Pickles, from Schapiro's Wines, from Kossar's
Bialys, from Yonah Shimmel's knishes, etc.), correcting essays

written by sixth graders from a school in Harlem where I'm teaching summer school (P.S. 1--, a few blocks from the Harlem Renaissance, from Minton's Playhouse, from Small's Paradise, from the burnt down offices of *Fire!!*, from Striver's Row, from the *Amsterdam News*, from the Hotel Theresa, from the Abyssinian Baptist Church, etc.), and I'm thinking about you because A) I'm taking an "English Methods" class at the City College of New York—alma mater, by the way, of Alfred Kazin, Toni Cade Bambara, Bernard Malamud, Upton Sinclair, Audre Lord, Henry Roth, Yip Harburg, Ira Gershwin, Zero Mostel, Stanley Kubrick, and I could on; can you tell I'm excited?—yes, I'm in New York, and yes, I'm in graduate school again (they say the third time's the charm), going to school for the rest of my life, an idea I got when I was a child, lying on the floor in my parent's bedroom looking at the pictures and reading the captions in my dad's old college yearbook, called the *Entre Nous*—a title that, once I had it translated, I believed was inviting me personally to matriculate, to sign up for all the 101's, and, you know, "broaden my horizons," but this time I'm going to school not to broaden horizons but to get a practical fallback degree, in case my dreams of becoming a novelist, poet, writer/artist for *MAD* magazine, newspaper reporter, playwright, or photographer fall through, and, though I will admit I sometimes find myself humming the triumphant finale of Brahms' "Academic Festival Overture" as I stroll the charming gothic-spired campus of the City College of New York (charming except for the colossal bunker where the education classes are taught, a late brutalist Tower of Babel built, like the Humanities Building at UAB, to withstand revolutions that students would, by the time construction was completed, grow weary of staging), I don't exactly feel inspired to join the glee club, if they have a glee club, or go out for the junior varsity something or other, if they have a junior varsity, or even to wear a sweater (except in class, where the air conditioning is as cold as Florida), but I do smile because even though City College, like UAB, is institutionally, and, at least in its more recent additions, architecturally utilitarian, I feel excited to be starting a new life in the city that I could only dream of living in before, and I smile, too, because every day, on my way to English Methods, I walk by Marshall Berman's office (he's never in—I think he has a joint appointment at the much posher CUNY Graduate Center in midtown, housed, by the way, in the beautiful Renaissance Revival building on Fifth Avenue that was once the B. Altman flagship store) and I stop and look at his nameplate and think about the time I read *All That is Solid Melts Into Air: The Experience of Modernity* for a directed reading with you, meeting you at that big old house of yours and sitting on your porch discussing the book—and other books and everything else—over cigarettes and brandy, and, anyway, my instructor at City College has me working on the kind of corny assignment that neither you nor Marshall Berman, nor I suppose Leonard Jeffries, who still teaches at City, but in an apparently less militant fashion, and without his former entourage of bodyguards and Afro-centric lords-in-waiting, and whose office I also sometimes walk by, would ever make anybody write:

> 1. Name a lecturer whom you consider to be excellent. What qualities distinguish that person's style?
>
> 2. Have you ever known a teacher to take a strong position on a subject in order to prompt your response?

and you—excellent, distinguished, stylish—naturally came to mind...

And I'm also thinking about you because B) I'm using a pencil to correct my student's essays, as you—unlike some of your colleagues, who, you may recall, preferred condor quills dipped in the blood of undergraduates—always used to do when you corrected the essays I wrote for the classes I took with you, but I can't write in the thoughtful symmetrical constructively critical skeptical reassuring hand you wrote in, with its friendly loops and gently probing question marks...

Oops, I just looked at the clock and I've got to go now; Alexis Vasquez needs my help with some misplaced modifiers and run-on sentences (I should talk), and I can't find my Strunk and White anywhere. Also, I need to sharpen my pencil...

I'm back, with answers to questions you'll ask when you reply to my letter [Reader: These are answers to questions "Ida" did ask, when she replied to my letter the day after I sent her mine]: I'll be forty-six Saturday. I've been married for 14 years. I moved to New York from Milwaukee on June 20. We sold our house, got rid of 85% of our possessions, and bid our adieus. My wife (Caroline), currently in Milwaukee attending to loose ends, will be joining me at the end of the month. I am one of 1,500 New York City Teaching Fellows (NYCTF), an alternative certification program designed to fill recurrently vacant positions at "hard-to-staff" public schools. Caroline just landed a nice gig at a fancy not-for-profit think tank kind of an outfit located in midtown that focuses on workforce development (which has something to do with something or other; I've never understood exactly what my wife does for a living).

I'm in the middle of my "pre-service training," attending classes at City College (NYCTF is subsidizing a master's degree in English education), teaching summer school under the supervision of a licensed teacher, and also meeting with twenty fellow Fellows every day at Fellows Advisory sessions led by the Fellow Advisor who advises us fellows, Sebastian—a twenty-four year old tattooed street-wise *wunderkind*, born and raised in Brownsville, Brooklyn, birthplace of Alfred Kazin, Murder, Incorporated, and Mike Tyson, among other colorful figures that also includes, you might not know, speaking of colorful figures, Herbert Blau, former director of the graduate program in Contemporary Critical and Cultural Studies at Milwaukee State University, and, inadvertently, unmoved mover of the cosmological argument of my life; or maybe in an update of the "Aristophanic view" postulated in the famous passage from Joan Didion's *The White Album*, as one of several equally plausible, equally futile stories we "tell...ourselves in order to live" — "the fireman in priest's clothing just visible in the window, the one smiling at the telephoto lens" who will snatch me "back to the human condition" by lifting me off the seventh-story ledge of the Altamont apartment building in Birmingham, Alabama, and then drop me, like the other shoe or a bad transmission, into the welcoming arms of Milwaukee, Wisconsin, "A Great Place on a Great Lake," where I will meet my wife, whose mother will come, once upon a time, to visit from Denver, Colorado, prompting me to take a vacation in New York City, where on a subway train I'll notice an ad for the New York City Teaching Fellows, and carelessly jot down the web address, and ultimately wind up living in New York where I'll try to learn how to be a schoolteacher and attempt to get in touch with old friends from Birmingham and other places with whom, upon starting my new identity in Milwaukee, and even before, I had fallen out of touch, old friends who may or may not have wanted me to get back in touch with them; he'll snatch me back to the human condition, Herbert Blau will, by awarding me the four-year Biermann Fellowship over the (in retrospect, well-founded) objections of other, more level-headed faculty members on the selection committee — who didn't need another posturing would-be Marxist dilettante passing out at departmental parties and never finishing his dissertation...

I seem always (well twice at least, and maybe twice means always), upon moving to a new city with a plan to start a new life, to find myself taking instruction (and not getting my lessons) from one refugee from Brownsville or another, from Herb, and now from Sebastian.

Sebastian never talks much about Brownsville, not directly, except to intimate a childhood so miserable there that he found consolation at school (at school! — now there's a miserable childhood for you), but if you'd ever care to pay a visit to the former Pale of Settlement now 'hood — there've been some demographic changes since the prime mover's boyhood there — Herb provides

some charmingly visceral directions, which are included in his
autobiography,

> As for the news not fit to print, you might have found some of
> it then, more of it now, though it's being printed, if you follow
> this direction: over the Manhattan Bridge, left off Flatbush,
> onto Atlantic Avenue, and straight out toward East New York,
> to where the Long Island Railroad cuts below the street like a
> coronary bypass of the Jewish heart of Brooklyn.[41]

*Reader: Taking a cue from the primus motor cum Aristophanic hook
and ladder man (what caused the uncaused cause and why does he wear
red suspenders? the answer to these and other koans lies, one suspects,
on the other side of the bypass...), I would myself, later, suggest a place
to find some answers to a few koans of my own, in the aftermath of the
horrors of the years 2004-2008 that I can never seem to get around to
elucidating, can only hint at—deferring with far-flung digressions,
sublimated screen memories, bits of popular song, and allusions to Hollywood movies (more screen memories)—without, it seems, the assistance of, say, a memory-inducing decoction of sodium pentothal, like
the serum Montgomery Clift administers—in the cool shade of the pri-
meval man-eating foliage of the late Sebastian Venable's very creepy
backyard in the Garden District of New Orleans—to Elizabeth Taylor
to help her elucidate some horrors of her own in the film version of Tennessee Williams'* Suddenly Last Summer, *a movie that affected me
deeply when I was a boy and I saw it on the Late, Late Show; Montgomery Clift, the high-strung method actor with the ruined face and
the shattered nerves whose body lies buried in the Quaker graveyard in
Prospect Park, a short stroll from the third-floor walkup in the whitewashed "Brownstone Brooklyn" brownstone in Park Slope, where,
prematurely retired from active life in rustic Brooklyn, across the river
from the court at Manhattan, my face not exactly ruined, but blemished
with blotches of creeping and then retreating—ebbing and flowing—
seborrheic dermatitis, and my once simply brittle nerves now*

---

[41] *As If: An Autobiography.*

definitively shattered, I sit in my low-flung mid-century modern up-
holstered chair, a relic of my old house on Newhall Street (both me and
the chair), which I spray down daily with an application of an anti-
allergen formula because I'm allergic to dust mites, and, laptop in lap,
write my own set of directions to a different autobiographical corner of
the County of Kings:

As for the news fit to print, you might find some of it, though it's
not all being printed, if you follow this direction: over the Manhattan
Bridge, stay on Flatbush, straight out toward Grand Army Plaza, to
where Seventh Avenue conks the loud and funky four-lane cross-grid
kink of Flatbush like a lye-relaxer on the Afro-textured hair of the black
soul of Crown Heights, Bed-Stuy, Brownsville, Canarsie, New Lots,
and East New York.

Once on Seventh, be careful to dodge the obstacles popping up like
cardboard cutouts in a police simulation as you run the gauntlet of
young urban professionals playing chicken with eight-cylinder, fuel-
injected Maclaren Model Number WOX14013 Double Strollers (the
Batmobiles of upright perambulators); dog walkers who are unem-
ployed actors by day and/or unpublished memoirists by night walking
freshly-groomed and obedience-schooled haute couture *packs of Cav-*
alier King Charles spaniels, Brussels griffons, and French bulldogs;
wassup rocker wannabes pivoting, ollie-ing, hippie jumping, and
kickflipping the platinum rims of their solid gold skateboards; whole
families on kick scooters and unicycles fanning out in vee formation
like a squadron of fighter pilots or a backfield in motion; idealistic phal-
anxes of concerned young canvassers ambushing passersby with their
earnest clipboards and hopeful entreaties, locked in a more or less ami-
able turf-fight for pavement space, and for your attention, with a trans-
planted shtetl of Chabad Lubavitch hassidim cloaked in tzitzyot and
tallesim waving their lulav fronds like pom poms, asking everyone in
sight, Jew and gentile alike—because, who knows?—"Are you Jew-
ish?"; and old beggarmen who've commuted in on the A train, the C
train, the F train, the 2 train, the 3 train, the 4 train, and the 5, all the
way from the black soul of Crown Heights, Bed-Stuy, Brownsville, Ca-
narsie, New Lots, and East New York, to the white liberal conscience

of Brooklyn, where they sit on upended milk crates perched outside of greengrocers and corner stores, shaking their cans of coins and sing-songing, rapping, toasting, preaching, testifying, stating, asking, "Spare a little change for the homeless?" "Any help will do," "How about a little reparation, white man?" (Not really with the, "How about a little reparation, white man?")

Climb the hill on Second Street to the whitewashed brownstone a few doors down from the Greek Orthodox church whose double-parking congregation drives in via the Brooklyn-Queens Expressway, Verra-zano Bridge, and Holland Tunnel from various post-Hellenistic dias-poras in Queens, Staten Island, and New Jersey, and climb the stairs to the third-floor walkup where you'll find me wheezing and settling into my valetudinarian years; diligently, I apply my vast and compre-hensive home apothecary of powders, pills, potions, tinctures, balms, drops, roborants, elixirs, poultices, purgatives, anodynes, analeptics, restoratives, salves, and homeopathic dilutions to the predominately imaginary complaints that have multiplied since I gave up the ghost ship, resigning, as usual, rather self-importantly over some trampled "principle" or other, tendering another carefully-crafted and cliché-rid-den letter of resignation, quitting another police department, but with nerves this time too unsteady to get myself a steady job.

Relentlessly, I input symptoms at mayoclinic.org and other similar such sorrowful websites I've bookmarked on my also-hypochondriacal laptop; obsessively, I seek confirmation or refutation of my computer-assisted self-diagnoses (confirmation, if the illness or condition doesn't threaten life or limb, and refutation, if it does) by making repeated vis-its, on my wife's very good insurance, but with a ten-dollar deducti-ble—or is it a co-pay? (I never understood the difference; and, by the way, shouldn't the word—a noun after all—be "co-payment"?)—to the examining rooms of a city-wide who's who of distinguished special-ists: a neurologist in Gramercy, an otolaryngologist in the West Vil-lage, a dermatologist in Chelsea, a podiatrist near Columbus Circle, an orthopedist in Murray Hill, an allergist on Park Avenue South, a urol-ogist on Central Park West, a rheumatologist on East 72nd Street, and, closer to home, an ophthalmologist in Cobble Hill and a

*gastroenterologist in Park Slope, at least five of whom—the orthope-
dist, the ophthalmologist, the dermatologist, the allergist, and the urologist—despite their initial skepticism that there was anything
"clinically" or "physiologically" wrong with me, and under my unre-
lenting pressure to "run one more test," finally found themselves worn
down like a lover or a parent and left with no other recourse than to
confirm thirteen actual diagnoses (fifteen if you include deviated sep-
tum and fallen arches): osteoarthritis, osteoporosis, Fuch's corneal dys-
trophy, benign prostatic hyperplasia, gastroesophageal reflux disease,
temporomandibular disorder, tinnitus, a cyst on my left kidney, a cyst
on my caput epididymis, seborrheic dermatitis, lichen planus, and both
allergic and non-allergic rhinitis.*

*The third floor walk-up in the whitewashed brownstone in rustic
Brooklyn where you'll also find me (when I don't have a doctor's appointment or I'm not consulting my Physician's Desk Reference and
collected pharmacopoeias and other* materia medica*) typing my way
through a variety of repetitive stress injuries as I cobble together a
"somewhat fictionalized memoir," aggressively pounding plastic keys
lined up like loose baby teeth on the keyboard of the temperamental red
laptop that I bounce on my knee like a baby, a jalopy, a bingety-bangety
school bus, another flivver, that I believe brings me good luck—"Der
Rosenkavalier" I call it, and sometimes "The Rosy Crucifixion"—with
the lettering on several of the keys—e, r, t, i, o, a, s, d, f, h, l, c, and n—
and all of the punctuation marks (I punctuate a lot), erased, effaced,
obliterated on my remaindered Gateway computer, purchased, when
my mail-order laptop from four years earlier threw a rod, from a pimply
kid at Radio Shack, his voice squeaking like the voice of a cub reporter
or soda jerk circa 1942, who said he knew what he was talking about, a
little red Corvette that has, since the day after its warranty expired,
begun to overheat and, after falling into a swoon, shut itself off every
twenty minutes or so, making it necessary for me (also swooning, and
also shutting down every twenty minutes or so, as I tear out, neuron
by neuron, ganglion by ganglion, the remaining pinkish-gray pieces of
the lateral amygdala region of my brain, where sad memories and easy
ironies are stored, hopelessly, hopefully, furiously revising draft after*

draft of my somewhat fictionalized memoir) to keep clicking "Save" after typing each word and each punctuation mark, so I don't lose anything...

Click: *"Save."*

(So I don't lose anything.)

Splendors and Miseries of Schoolteachers

All that each person is, and experiences, and shall never experience, in body and in mind, all these things are differing expressions of himself and of one root, and are identical: and not one of these things nor one of these persons is ever quite to be duplicated, nor replaced, nor has it ever quite had precedent: but each is a new and incommunicably tender life, wounded in every breath, and almost as hardly killed as easily wounded: sustaining, for a while, without defense, the enormous assaults of the universe:

So that is how it can be that a stone, a plant, a star, can take on the burden of being; and how it is that a child can take on the burden of breathing; and how through so long a continuation and cumulation of the burden of each moment one on another, does any creature bear to exist, and not break utterly to fragments of nothing: these are matters too dreadful and fortitudes too gigantic to meditate long and not forever to worship.

James Agee

My first stop that morning, my first stop every morning in those days *in Upper West Side days, when the first hopeful blush of "I'm going to be a schoolteacher" had faded, replaced with the full dread apprehension that not my coming to New York—and I was always careful to make this qualification—but my coming to New York to be a schoolteacher, had been a mistake* was Fairway, the trencherman's Guadalcanal, "like no other market®," where many a fresh-faced kid just in from the provinces and getting a first foot on the island had fallen and been trampled to death in produce or the pickle aisle. Fairway, that great gastronomic battlefield, where during daylight hours and in the evening until closing time life was solitary, poor, nasty, brutish, and short, and all the clichés about rude, hostile, pushing, shoving, grasping, self-centered, and obnoxious New Yorkers, dispelled of late in the supposed Augustan Age of Messrs. Giuliani and Bloomberg, came flooding back like the return of the repressed, like the ghost of Abe Beame.

But it was five-thirty in the morning, now, *then*, and it was dark *dark and bureaucratic and early to bed and early to rise, and I had started saying things to kids that I'd promised my now-forgotten childhood self I would never say when I grew up*; it would be dark again soon, that evening sun gone done, the sky reddening over the Hudson and then dropping black over the New Jersey palisades, when I would schlep my way home from the ghost ship I was, that morning, preparing to tread (it felt) my way uptown to (it felt, tell the truth, like I was preparing to crawl my way). I was, in those days of, for example, "waiting on line" for "a regular slice," starting to say "schlep" a lot; and, speaking of "a lot," and of things I was starting to say, and things I was starting to do, starting also to spend a lot of time correcting (in green ink, because red hurt the children's feelings the new teachers had been told) all the glaring and unrepentant scattershot of "alots" of my underserved population of schoolchildren. I'd find I'd have spotty success there, or no success at all, because how could anybody—how could I?—convince those moppets, those lovable urchins, to drop the defining, and actually kinda cute, middle school solecism from their repertoire (a gesture or a tic as pre-teen "iconic" as dotting an "i" with a circle), convinced as they were, or as I believed them to be, that their teacher, kindly, but white, kindly, but dumb, and imperfectly educated at non-elite urban institutions, was mistaken about this so-called solecism, was mistaken about how you spell "a lot," as I was mistaken about so many of the other supposed solecisms of theirs, the solecism, especially and ultimately, the background and all-pervading solecism, I feared they felt I felt, of being in America and not being white.

It would be dark again when I schlepped/trod/crawled my way home, seventy-two hours or so after my first stop that morning at Fairway, another tired teacher, "teacher-tired" they call it in the trade, frown-lined and careworn, eyes downcast, schlepping, in addition to my own tired carcass, an unwieldy bundle, secured with duct tape, baker's twine, cable tie, and baling wire, made up of a vast assortment of backpacks, briefcases, suitcases, gallstones (I mean gladstones), steamer trunks, and portmanteaus, bulging comically, all of them, with sheets folded into quires, quires shuffled into reams, reams bundled into bales, and bales gathered into whatever it is bales are gathered into in the International System of Units, an "exaggeration" perhaps—but we will leave it at hell's own surfeit!—of unrepentant student essays to correct, midnight oil to burn, looking like an aged railway porter, as all teachers do at the end of the day, except of course the very youngest of them, who will before their long first year is over start sinking into their own graves, leaning as they fall *into* the fall (I think of a line from James Fenton that I may be misapplying, a little: "Heart be kind and sign the release / As the trees their loss approve / Learn as leaves must learn to fall / Out of danger, out of love"), because otherwise, they sensed, or had been advised, they would break utterly to fragments of nothing, and, in so falling, never know what hit them (teachers get a lot of advice; everybody feels free to advise them: administrators, school "reformers," on-the-make pols, as well as taxi drivers, headwaiters, marketing consultants, education professors, and long haul truck drivers; teaching is the most kibitzed profession in America—except, of course, it isn't a profession, is it?: it's piecework; it's day labor; it's what you do when you can't do so you teach; it's what you do for your sins—the sin of not preparing for another line of work; it is, or it was, or it became, in my case, a kind of morally-indentured servitude). Leaning as they fall into the fall, they shoulder, each evening, new and veteran teachers alike, their tonnes burthen of freight and trudge their *viae crucis* down the streets of Old Jerusalem, down steep and winding stairs across narrow platforms past rat nest and foul smell to stumble over all the gaps they haven't minded, all the consequences of all the earlier incidents of their lives, the piles of wreckage, the piles of debris, and board their respective trains home.

But before boarding my train I stopped first, usually, at the diner around the corner from the stairs leading down to the subway, for one more espresso, just to get me home, the stairs where nearly every day in a little alcove off the first landing I spied an eighth-grade girl I knew, a girl called Francesca or La Monica, I was never sure which one she was, because I was always getting the two mixed up (they both looked, weirdly, identically, like two little Dominican Anouk Aimees), making out with a well-dressed, prep school-attending older African-American boy (he gave off the impression, at least, that he attended prep school; there was, I seem to recall, a school-tie and a navy blazer with a crest on the front pocket, but these might have been the fake trinkets and phony foofaraw of one of those for-profit charter schools with a pretentious, management-studies sounding designation, the Academy for Excellence in Innovation, Success, and Achievement, say, or the Leadership Academy for Achievement in Innovation, Excellence, and Success, or the Achievement and Innovation Academy for Successful and Excellent Leadership, the kind of school where students are called "scholars," and teachers, whose job descriptions are twenty pages long, because they will do "whatever it takes," are called "facilitators," the kind of school where the school day never ends and there are no holidays or teachers' unions and employment is "at will" and the turnover is even higher than at the public schools: the facilitators stay a year in the classroom, and then, if they haven't quit altogether, and once they've mastered the jargon and the talking points and the party line, move into "administrative leadership," where they can "really make a difference"). This was the boy I had heard that Francesca or La Monica's parents had forbidden her to see, because of his age, or because of his race, I was never sure. She would stop her canoodling for a moment when she saw me lumbering down the steps, stopping not out of embarrassment, but out of courtesy, so she could say, "Hi, Mr. Blackwell!," the "i" in "hi" dotted with a circle.

Once I had returned her greeting (glossing over not saying her name, which I wasn't sure what it was, though I had a fifty-fifty chance of getting it right; not that it would have mattered, because this Anouk Aimee never got mad at me if I got her name wrong; the other one did, though; she wasn't as sweet as the canoodling Anouk, wasn't as forgiving; her mother had died and her life had been more difficult; she was sullen and depressed and rolled her eyes at the stupid shit grown-ups say; how could I, a grown-up who said a lot of stupid shit, keep getting these girls mixed up?), she'd close her eyes and open her mouth and lock her lips again on the lips that had waited, patiently, politely, during the exchange of "hi's," of her dark and handsome dreamboat, and smooch unselfconsciously, for hours I imagined, holding tight to love. As I lingered on the stairs and watched the scene for a little longer than might be deemed proper, I recited to myself, very quietly, these lines from Robert Lowell's "Skunk Hour": "...I hear / my ill-spirit sob in each blood cell, / as if my hand were at its throat...."

But it was five-thirty in the morning, then, *now,* and no cart had been overturned at Fairway yet and all the blood from yesterday's skirmishes had been washed away, and fresh sawdust spread to absorb any new hemorrhages, and I had the shop nearly to myself, like in one of those movies where a kid is trapped overnight in a department store or a toy store or barbershop or I guess a museum, but I never saw that movie, just the previews, and things start coming to life; in this case special import olive oil and coffee beans in burlap sacks stuffed in barrels and first-cut beef briskets and kasha varnishkes. I was there to buy my lunch for the day: some bread, some hummus, a plastic box of broccoli florets and carrot sticks, some cut-up fruit, a container of kasha varnishkes, and for dessert maybe a little chocolate or a piece of halvah.

I'd had my coffee already, three stovetop espressos that,

having been reveilled out of bed at roughly the same hour that
Ma Maw's Pa Paw used to get up when he worked in the
coalmines, I had brewed forty-five minutes or so earlier in the
long predawn of the slow dying of the day, brewed in a beat up
old three-cup moka pot that had survived the purge at Newhall
Street, trying not to wake Caroline, grinding the beans as quietly
as I could, with the grinder swaddled in a towel under my arm
to muffle the grrrr. I'd drunk the last demitasse, drained the
dregs of sorrow's bitter cup, all scrunched up like a yogi in my
tiny bathtub, displacing water like an oversized Archimedes,
tipping the thrift-store Stetson I wore in the bathtub, for the fun
of it, to the side of my head, an homage within an homage: get
it? I was doing Michel Piccolo in *Contempt* doing Dean Martin in
Some Came Running; running down all the associations with
"bathtub" I could think of, as a mental distraction, the way pris-
oners of war in old war movies replay whole baseball seasons in
their minds to get through the ordeal of a grueling confinement
in the cooler, or, if they are serving in the Pacific Ocean theater
of war, in the "sweat box," or "the oven" (sometimes they call it
the "sweat box"; sometimes they call it the "oven"); if Caroline
had been awake, I would have made a joke about *Diabolique*,
and/or Charlotte Corday; riffing, riffing, because everything was
a riff to me (or the fodder for one), everything was a joke, or at
least I wanted it to be, thinking it should be fun, that I was in
New York and it should all be a lark, that the company should
be wittier, more brilliant, more "gifted and talented," Robert
Lowell outdrinking "the Rahvs in the heat / of Greenwich Village," say, as "the shrill verve" of Elizabeth Hardwick's "invec-
tive" scorches "the traditional South,"[42] but things were serious,
things were earnest, deadly earnest, like a convention of pam-
phleteers, or the annual meeting of "the Society for the Scientific
Diet, the Association of Positivist Parents, the League for the
Promotion of Worthwhile Leisure, the Cooperative Camp of

---

[42] Robert Lowell, "Man and Wife."

Prudent Progressives, or the Modern Language Association" (I'm quoting W. H. Auden here, except I added "the Modern Language Association"), and, anyway, there wasn't anybody, or, I should say, there was hardly anybody at Peter Minuit Intermediate School who ever showed any interest in getting any of my jokes, which, if they acknowledged them at all, they called corny, like the kids did, and I suppose they were (corny, that is; the jokes I mean); sniffing the aromatherapy oils (sort of the way ladies about to faint, back when ladies used to faint, used to sniff smelling salts) that I'd sprinkled into my bathwater (I preferred medicine-y smelling old man scents like menthol, camphor, and wintergreen; though in happier, hippier, hurdier-gurdier moods, wearing my love like heaven, I reached for the little vials of patchouli, sandalwood, and vetiver that also rested on the bathtub lip; frankincense and myrrh I saved for when I wanted to smell like the little baby Jesus; and mint and anise and cumin for the occasions when I was feeling—woe unto me—scribe-like or pharisaical; and lavender, lilac, and geranium for when I wanted to smell like Mimi), taking long, slow deep breaths and practicing various meditation, guided imagery, and progressive muscle relaxation techniques that I'd downloaded from the Internet, trying to psyche myself up for the day, or resign myself into it.

My breakfast I would have when I got to work: a croissant from the Parkview Diner and a double espresso from the Dominican bakery on Dyckman Street (they called it a double espresso but it was really four shots, and they charged 75 cents for it, serving it up in one of those blue and white Greek diner cups, decorated like little Grecian urns, that used to be ubiquitous around town; this was better economy than the $2.50 double espresso that really was a double espresso that I could have bought at the diner, and would buy later in the day on my way home because the diner was closer to the closer subway), the bakery where, if it were Wanda's birthday, or Crystal's or Nicholas' or Alba's or Rodney's or Lynette's, or anybody else's birthday who had a birthday during the school year, I would buy them a big sticky birthday cake and twelve trick candles, the kind that won't blow out, and ask the lady behind the counter to write the birthday girl's or birthday boy's name on it, and maybe a jokey message.

A special, mass birthday party was held late in June for the children born in what was left of what we used to call summer vacation, a traditional period of play endangered in our cruel and platitudinous (and jargon-ridden) Gradgrind-lite era of school reform, dwindling down in days a little more each year, like the number of independent bookstores, or any kind of store not a nail salon, cellular phone outlet, or a Duane Reade.

I loved to throw parties for my children, I loved to delight them, to make them happy, because they were the kind of kids you wanted to make happy, the kind of kids you wanted to delight. They were beautiful children, sweet and witty, and, in their way, brilliant: gifted and talented even, no matter how relative any of these terms may have been, no matter how Dickensian their surroundings. I adored them; I didn't know how to prepare them to pass all the awful never-ending spirit-crushing standardized tests they had to take, or meet the New York State Common Core Learning Standards for English Language Arts & Literacy, or to spell "alot" "a lot," but I adored them, and they adored me, too, most of them (many of them?...some of them?...any of them?), the sixth graders, at least (excepting the exceptions; and you know who you are), back when I was allowed to teach the sixth grade, my métier, before being punished my last bad year at Minuit for not being "on the same page" as the principal, for not being "data-driven," or "proactive," or a "team player"; punished with a mean and nasty eighth-grade class of mean and nasty duck-assed JDs (excepting the exceptions; and you know who *you* are), some of them ringers, brought in from Central Casting, extras from *The Blackboard Jungle*—and *A Clockwork Orange, Cruel Story of Youth, Los Oblivados*, and *Pixote*—that only Glenn Ford or Sidney Poitier or Sandy

Dennis or Hilary Swank or Michelle Pfeifer or Edward James Olmos (sooner or later every actor in Hollywood takes his or her turn at finding the untapped good), or somebody else with a script, and an agent, and a trailer they could retreat to when things got sticky, could do anything with.

Or, tell the truth, a small handful of very good teachers at the school, brave and caring (and a little methodical), not witty, not brilliant, most of them, or any of them, but brave and caring (and methodical), that I knew, veterans, mainly, with classes way the hell worse than mine; teachers who could rise above the bullshit, above the more fresh hell every day, or at least meet it—the shit, the hell—head-to-head, toe-to-toe; teachers way the fuck better at the craft than I could ever hope to be. They were women mainly (teaching is a woman's game; some men are good at it, but it's a woman's game: a certain type of woman, though—resolute and unflappable; tough-minded, case-hardened. But did they cry at night? I wondered that because I never saw any of them cry during the day): a type of woman resigned, in the new dispensation in which data is king, to the life of a drudge, but finding, apparently, some of them—wresting, you might say, a realm of freedom from a realm of necessity—some fulfillment there, some joy. These were women who'd been granted by god, as they understood her (and there was, it seemed to me, something ickily twelve-step about the things a teacher must do to survive): A) the serenity to accept the things they could not change; B) the courage to change the things they could; and C) the wisdom to know the difference—except most of the teachers I met never really got past A), never really got past accepting the things they could not change, because the things they could not change was a fairly broad category; it included everything in the world. Of course, the only way to get past accepting the things you cannot change, or the only way that I could see (I, who fundamentally, temperamentally couldn't accept anything; I, who was only ever interested in changing things I could not change, and who had never had, nor had I ever sought, wisdom of any kind), the *only* way, as I used to tell my sixth-graders at the end of a long school day (in a slightly different context, but only slightly), after I had marched them, two by two, like ants in the children's song, in fact singing the song sometimes as I marched them down five flights of down staircase to the exit doors: "the ants go marching two by two, hoorah, hoorah...", was to "amscray, skedaddle, put an egg in your shoe and beat it."

But they weren't whiners and quitters and crybabies—like you know who. They went head-to-head and toe-to-toe with the things they could not change; they stood firm, they held fast, they stayed the course. Remember what Billy the Kid said, "It was a game for two and I got there first"; that's what I imagined these teachers saying, grinning sideways, kicking some dust off their chaps, and blowing smoke from the muzzle of their guns, after they'd wrestled a class to submission, or outstayed, outlasted, outdistanced, and out-endured a principal or assistant principal who had been hectoring them, harassing them, haranguing them, because they, the rank and file, weren't going anywhere; *they* didn't have a fucking career ladder; none of them were, moreover, "data-driven," not in their *real* practice—as opposed to the make-believe shit teachers have to play-act to satisfy the Great Chains bearing down on them. (Such a distraction administrators are, such a smarmy, glad-handing, play-acting themselves, parasitical drain.) Nor did they give a fuck about all that Lucy Calkins kind of crap, except to the degree they needed to to keep the principal and his goons off their ass, or to tease out whatever was useful in any prescribed curriculum, to find the wheat in the platitudinous and jargon-ridden chaff; and by the way, these ladies never let any principal, or any goon (or any glad-handing parasitical drain), rattle them. If I tended to employ imagery of the Wild West when I described them, I also, looking east, thought often of this old poem from ancient China, called "The Peasant's Song," that I had read in a footnote in a book of translations of Li Po and Tu Fu that I kept on my bookshelf in the Banana Hut out in Vernon County, a poem that is quoted—without attribution, by the way—in one of Ezra Pound's *Cantos*:

> Sun up, we rise
> Sun down, we rest
> Dig well to drink
> Plow fields to eat
> Emperor, what is your power to us?[43]

They rendered (if I may shift the metaphorics to early Common Era Palestine) unto Caesar the things which were Caesar's, and then they did their jobs. They were valiant; they were courageous; they rose above; and might have asked, though they wouldn't have needed to, "*Principal*, what is your power to us?"

(There is something else I should mention, though, about these gunslingers, these well-diggers, these toilers in the field. I should mention that they were just as inclined to rise above *me*, above my carping and whining and belly-aching, as they were the hectoring and the harassment and the harangues—and the jargon and the contempt and the disrespect and the constant interference [I could go on]—served up non-stop by the administrators in the building: "*Blackwell*," they might have asked, "what is your bleating to us?")

But why, *you* may ask, all the swearing, all the cursing, and all the profanity (yes, I know these are the same things, but people like things in threes), every time I condescend to honor, to give their props to, the valiant and courageous teachers at the Peter Minuit Academy, *profanity that seems to bleed onto the page like blood from the gunshot wound of the bad guy hiding in the rafters of the saloon in Howard Hawks'* Rio Bravo, *the blood that drips in little drops down to the whiskey glass sitting on the bar, alerting Dean Martin that the bad guy is hiding up there; once alerted Martin, playing a drunk trying to get sober, a drunk still fast on the draw, who,*

---

[43] *Bright Moon, Perching Bird: Poems by Li Po and Tu Fu*, Translated from the Chinese by J. P. Seaton and James Cryer, Wesleyan UP 1987.

even with the shakes, shoots the dirty sidewinder out of his nest, so that John Wayne, playing the marshal, can arrest a different sidewinder, a cowardly murderer, played by Claude Aikins, who had, moments earlier, in a different saloon, put a bullet in the belly of an unarmed man and thinks he's getting away with it because he's the brother of a rich and powerful rancher, played by John Russell, who thinks he runs the town, and to some degree does; until John Wayne and Dean Martin (with cute, and also fast-on-the-draw, Ricky Nelson in tow; and, in a supporting role, as the deputy, Walter Brennan, cranky and creaking in a high-pitched voice, stage-limping, and chewing every stick of scenery he can find), until these white hats, a Warner Brothers sponsored coalition of the willing—brawling, blustery, and tall in their saddles— can bring order to chaos, and justice to the wilderness, something that I, brawling and blustery, and to some degree, early in my career, at least, willing, but as far as tall in the saddle goes, slumping fairly quickly, like the general public's idea of a lazy schoolteacher, into the well-worn butt cradle of my Albert Shanker era desk chair (slumping when the administrators weren't looking, that is: teachers aren't supposed to sit, much less slump) wish I could have done with my JDs. Why all the swearing, why all the cursing, why all the profanity, every time I condescend to honor, to give their props to, the valiant and courageous teachers at the Peter Minuit Academy, the teachers who, fast on the draw, could "do something" with the dirty sidewinders, I mean the duck-assed JDs, in their classrooms? (Not that I've attained any height to condescend from; but that's what I do: I condescend anyway, even though I haven't earned it.)

They were heroes, they were heroines (they were heroines, mainly; teaching is a woman's game...); steely and game practitioners, professionals who, out of danger, out of love, didn't take it personal (I took everything personal), and could, as I kept saying, "do something" with the duck-assed JDs they had, by design, or the capriciousness of the job market, fallen in with (they didn't really have duck-asses, by the way, the JDs; they were juvenile delinquents, but they didn't have duck-asses; that was just a joke), heroes and heroines who had the courage, had the heart, had the whatever it is you call whatever it was they had (backbone? true grit? perfect pitch? Unconquerable Soul?), to struggle and search and find something within, and, in so struggling, in so searching, to find the things they needed to to teach the little motherfuckers in their classrooms something, and, in so struggling, in so searching, to love them, even. *To love them, even.*

So why, instead of prostrating my ass—my *sorry* ass—before such nurturance, such charity, such solicitude, such steadfast rectitude, such a *"skill set"* (don't you hate the *language* of success, the language of "strategic human resource management"?), do I curse (and swear and say profane things); why do I sneer? The answer is that, even now, *still* in danger, *still* in love, learning not what leaves must learn (nobody can teach me anything), I do it out of envy, I do it out of shame; I do it because, finally, whether I find himself scratching my ass down south, stroking my chin on the eastern seaboard, cooling my heels in the upper Midwest, or picking my feet in Poughkeepsie, even if on the whole I'd rather be in Philadelphia, or, let's face it (at this point in my career), sailing to Byzantium, I am, if nothing else, a hater; I have coveted everything and taken pleasure in nothing.

Oh, I admired them, or professed to admire them, the brave and caring, admired or professed to admire their dedication and self-sacrifice and tough love and every child can learn; admired, or professed to admire their patience, their "goal-setting," and their small victories—the fucking incremental-ness of it all, the little things that, for some, add up to something bigger. Admired, sort of, but in this case didn't really, didn't, in this case, even profess to admire, but admired, anyway, sort of, grudgingly (sneeringly), their practicality and judiciousness and seasoned knowledge of how and when and where and why to pick their spots, if they ever picked them, which they didn't. They never picked any spots that I can remember because they lived, "philosophically," as a credo (a cliché!), "to fight another day" (if you call that living, which I guess you can, but I didn't and I don't; *I* couldn't live that way; it broke me when I tried, it's breaking me still); they never picked any spots, never lived to fight another day, because, though I could never understand how a teacher (who has, after all, to pay for all of her own supplies, except the $250 "Teacher's Choice" money she is reimbursed, if she remembers to save her receipts, $250 that is only a tiny fraction of the money she has already spent before the first day of school, and an even tinier fraction of the amount she will spend before the Christmas break, an infinitely divisible fraction, in fact, of the amount she will spend before the school year is over), could ever afford to take the long view, they took the long view. (And they remembered to save their receipts.)

Something about the way they carried the things they carried suggested this, suggested they were looking bravely towards a future, suggested they were taking the long view. (I prayed, though, that something like the obverse wasn't true; that because they knew there wasn't a future, that because there was, instead, a sort of murky continuance, merely, in both the workaday and legal senses of the word "continuance" — a creeping in this petty pace, a lot of creeping, a lot of pettiness; pace they call, in the education racket, "scope and sequence" — of the everyday-same "agenda," chalked up on the chalkboard at the beginning of each class, in the workshop model, or balanced literacy, sense of the word "agenda," a.k.a., "flow of the day," consisting of the "do now," the "mini-lesson," the "active engagement," and the "sharing session"; prayed they hadn't, when smack against it — and they were smack against it — resigned themselves to the continuance, to the creeping, to the pettiness, to the scope and sequence, sighing, some of them, in resignation, accepting the universe, or putting a better face on it, some of the others, calling it something else, calling it, I don't know, being "proactive," or a "team player" or a "motivated self-starter," or maybe just being an "adult," calling it "sucking it in," "going along to get along," "picking your spots," and, later, "leaning in"; prayed they hadn't, in a sort of obverse of pinning their hopes on a loss of chains that isn't to be, or a sweet by-and-by that is sweet, perhaps, but is coming neither by nor by; prayed they hadn't resigned themselves to the timeframe, or to the abeyance of timeframe, the timeframe, *sous rature*, that Norman Mailer, in a different context, but I'm borrowing the phrase for this context, too, once called the "enormous present," an enormous present of scaffolding instruction and activating prior experience and modeling reading comprehension strategies and utilizing best practices and positively impacting students and implementing integration strategies and differentiating curriculum...

Or, maybe the context of the Mailer quote isn't so different; maybe I had it wrong; maybe I had had it wrong all along; maybe what I didn't understand was that these teachers were existentialists, that they weren't resigned, exactly, but had made a commitment, a sort of Pascal's Wager in reverse, "to explore that domain of experience where security is boredom and therefore sickness, and one exists in the present, that enormous present, which is without past or future, memory or planned intention, the life where a [wo]man must go until [s]he is beat, where [s]he must gamble with [her] energies through all those small or large crises of courage and unforeseen situations which beset [her] day." Maybe they were hip, and I was square. Let me amend that: I don't know if they were hip or not, but I can tell you with some certainty that I was square; and I can also tell you they weren't hip... The quote, by the way, is from "The White Negro.")

Something about the way they carried, for instance, the enormous key-chains they carried suggested this (that they were looking bravely towards a future, that they were taking the long view), key-chains strung with a thousand baubles, shrunken heads, perhaps, of recalcitrant students ("students with special needs"), or of officious administrators, or whiny Teaching Fellows; a giganticized charm bracelet warding off evil (looking, from a distance, if you looked down a long hallway, like young David's sling and five stones from a brook, dangling from the hand of the soon-to-be king over Judah, and seven years later, king over all Israel...or, flash forward, the head of Goliath itself, bleeding from the neck...or, in deuterocanonical mood, this time getting the gender right, Judith returning to Bethulia, holding by its hair the severed head of Holofernes, also bleeding from the neck).

Something about the way they carried, slung casually over a shoulder, or looped matronly about an elbow, depending on their mood, or their age, their large, Ruth Buzzi-style handbags (big handbags were popular in those days, and big shoes, with long and exaggeratedly pointy toes, menacing accessories that made riding in a crowded subway car stuffed to overflowing with smart professional women on their way to or home from work a dangerous, often injurious prospect), handbags into which they'd slipped, in anticipation of every conceivable contingency, a vast transportable storehouse, a tabernacle, you might say, of gender-specific paraphernalia, the precise contents of which I, who was taught early in life never to look into a lady's pocketbook, or even to ask what was in one, could only speculate on. Something about the way they carried, cradled in the crook of an arm that was pressed against a breast, the way girls have carried their books for as long as I can remember noticing the way girls carry their books, with a closed hand folded over their heart, as they clasped the far upper quadrant of the bundle, almost in a salute (or maybe it *was* a salute—a salute to everything that hasn't harmed them, to everything that has gotten them through; a salute to all the rules they have followed, and the rules they've bent, just a little; a salute to their own verve, their own pluck, their own moxie; a salute, perhaps, to what Zora Neale Hurston described, in *Their Eyes Were Watching God*, as "forgetting all those things they don't want to remember, and remembering everything they don't want to forget," and a salute, maybe, to knowing the difference between the two); the way they carried, in this manner, *all* the books they would need for the day, for the week, for the term, for a long nuclear winter:

grade books, reference books, the *Physician's Desk Reference*, picture books for a mini-lesson, chapter books for a "read-aloud," curriculum guides and self-help books, the ubiquitous Ralph Fletcher (if they were English teachers), and, in the crook of the arm of every new teacher, the very nearly required-by-law Harry Fucking Wong, each book copiously bookmarked, highlighted, and Post-it® noted.

Something about the way they carried, in addition to the bound material they carried, fat bundles of class readings they'd photocopied, collated, and stapled themselves, because they weren't allowed to use textbooks, which you will remember had been ruled "inauthentic" by the demiurges of balanced literacy (or the workshop model or constructivist pedagogy; I get all that shit mixed up), and all those eager to live out the demiurges' dream of a better world, readings they'd had to photocopy, collate, and staple on their own and at their own expense, because a functioning photocopier was only rarely made available to them, and in the occasional instance when one *was* available, they had to purchase their own paper, and then fight each other like yardbirds in chokey to get access to the copier before it broke down and went unrepaired for months; with the administrators watching the melee from behind a one-way mirror, making bets, and taking prurient delight in the bloodshed.

Something about the way they carried, cradled in their other arm, but held lower—as the Statue of Liberty, wading in the harbor approximately 15 miles downstream from the school, in a south-southwesterly direction, holds her *tabula ansata* (The Statue of Liberty, that, once I moved to Brooklyn, I used to see very early every weekday morning, when the F train I was taking to the A train to get myself to work chugged up out of the ground, for a moment, around Smith and 9th Streets, in Carroll Gardens, thinking as I saw her of the appointment I had, about an hour and a half later, with some huddled masses I knew personally, also yearning to breathe free…when the last bell would ring at 3:10 p.m.!)—a thousand student essays to correct, to blue pencil with their green pens in their free periods, back when they still had free periods, before such luxuries, such small mercies, were conceded in the more recent contract "negotiations" (public schoolteachers will, before it is over, lose everything; it is, to paraphrase Henry James, their only logic; more precisely, though, it is the only logic of "education reform").

Free periods that I, playing grasshopper to the lady teachers' ants, used most unwisely myself, as if unaware (which I surely wasn't, having survived in Alabama an almost-Southern Baptist childhood) that "the night cometh, when no man can work" (a night that couldn't cometh quickly enough, I *sometimes* felt); free periods, gone now, lost, conceded, that I, indolent, slothful, profligate, dilatory I, who never, really, ever had a work ethic (I've done *some* work, but I don't have an "ethic" about it), used, not to catch up on my work, but to try to get out of it, to shirk the hateful onus, to crraaaaawwwwwl—I fancied, hallucinated almost, in my desperation, in my riven heart—out from under the weight of the school clocks (this was my fancy), with their Janus-faces and large-print fonts, like they were made to be read, on both sides, by old people, old people who could still read analog clocks, because none of the students at Peter Minuit could read them, clocks that were hurtling me down to my death, I felt, it seemed.

Did I say "hurtling?" Hurtling, if hurtling, in a slowed-down trickling underwater dreamtime sort of hurtling (I used, when I was a child, to have dreams of my school being flooded, and in these dreams I swam underwater from class to class, rescuing girls; schools seemed to me to be underwater places, and places where rescues might need to be carried out; I imagined school buildings as decorative doo-dads in the bottom of a fish tank, for angel fish and black mollies and neon tetras, etc., to swim in and out of), clocks pushing me down and pressing my face to the floor, to the tiny red rocks at the bottom of the aquarium. I sat under a clock in the first row by the door in my class in the days of my dreams of rescuing girls from floods, the days when I first started thinking of being in school as being underwater, when I first started thinking of my life as being underwater, when I first started learning how to be depressed (I think this must have been in the second grade, in Miss Russell's class—she of the unironical ginger bouffant). Under the influence of a picture book I'd loved when I was a few years younger, all about the silly doings of a group of foolish peasants, in something like the village of Chelm, who worried that a pickaxe left by workmen high on a cellar wall would fall on them (for some reason the peasants, who—or is it whom?—you'd think would have lots of work to do, being peasants and all, were always lolling about in the cellar, standing where if the ax fell it would fall on them), I worried that the clock on the wall would fall on me. Perhaps this memory contributed, unconsciously at the time, to the fancy I developed later, the mania, really, that the clocks at the Peter Minuit Academy were bearing down on me, but underwater; lifting me up and then pressing me down again, again and again, but, again, in a kind of slow motion (it wasn't water I was walking through, it was sludge; I was walking though sludge); clocks that never even worked for christ's sake, even if any of the kids could've told time by them, clocks that told, each one, a separate, unsynchronized time that did not fly or creep or even budge or shift its ground, but still, like moving things, made a buzzing sound anyway, like the buzz Emily Dickinson heard when she died, the buzz I heard when I died; but it was also a kind of humming sound, like a third rail humming, or a kind of a rattle rattling, a child's rattle, a death rattle, as each clock's minute hand jerked in place, like something dying *like a rabbit I saw dying on a trail at the Aldo Leopold Center when, a few years later, I came crawling back to Milwaukee, looking for...something, but the naturalists, or the rangers, or whatever they call themselves—Girl Guides, Boy Scouts, Junior Woodchucks, Young Pioneers, I don't know, all prim and khaki-clad and above-it-all and tuned in to the unyielding obliterating inalterable death-ways of nature—that I ran to tell about the poor suffering thing to would do nothing to help the creature or to put it out of its misery;*

*they were prissy and sanctimonious about letting their precious nature
takes it course, unwilling to intervene, like they were the indifferent
god of the deists, or Sebastian Venable watching the flesh-eating birds
devour the baby sea turtles in* Suddenly, Last Summer *because he
wants to see up close the kind of nasty shit god gets up to, or allows
(which is the same thing)* trying (like the rabbit) to move forward,
to move anywhere, to come back alive, to will itself back to life,
to make a progress, to catch up with the needless spinning of the
earth; clocks that drooped and slid to the floor like a cartoon jaw,
or a Salvador Dali painting, that I kept tripping over, righting
myself at the last minute, as I slogged my way through the
sludge, singing the lord's song in a strange land, as little ones in
Babylon are dashed across stones and birds rend and eat the
flesh of newly-hatched sea turtles in the *Encantadas*, and a rabbit
perishes alone and scared in a wood off County Line Road...

Free periods, lost, gone, conceded, that I used, not to grade
papers, or call parents, or "level" my library, or wash my chalkboard (I had the filthiest chalkboard in the school; it was all chalk
and no board, an ever-layering palimpsest that looked like
ghosts might look in the eye of a fly, that looked sort of like the
Milky Way, like faded and peeling hoardings on the scaffoldings
of a wall, of dead "teaching points," old homework assignments,
vocabulary words, Venn diagrams, and names of students who
would have to stay after school[44]), or update my bulletin board
(the student work displayed there was as out-of-date as any
magazine chosen at random at any doctor's office in the land,
but it's always some bullshit magazine, never *The New Yorker* or
The Nation or *Harper's* or *The New York Review of Books*, always
Martha Stewart Living or *Sports Illustrated* or *Details* or *Us* or *Men's
Health*, though if these were the choices I would choose, every
time, *Martha Stewart Living*), but to try to blot out the awfulness

---

[44] Not really. I never kept students after school, except for a few times that last bad
year, but then I'd let them go home after ten minutes because, well, it's pretty boring
keeping kids after school. And, the worst of them, the ones who needed punishing,
oops, I mean "an intervention," wouldn't have shown up for detention, anyway.

of it all, to shake it off, to unwind, decompress, catch my breath, distract myself from the dreariness and tedium and irksomeness of it all, to recover, too, on a personal level, from the damage wrought in the hurricane that had just whorled out of my classroom, a hurricane of exuberance and glandular secretions and life-terror and beautiful narcissistic selfish joy, of tooth-white sneakers and day-glo backpacks and regulation blue and white uniforms; a hurricane that shattered desks and chairs and left a wake of debris behind it, crumpled papers, chewed-on caps of pens, pencil shavings, dried-out highlighters, appliqués of chewing gum, cheese curl crumbs, sunflower casings, lip gloss, in squeezable tube *and* wand-applicator formats, squeezed-out bottles of skin lotion, wadded-up tissues, hairbands, barrettes, clogged-up hairbrushes and Afro picks, and an auto graveyard of marked-up, discarded, ransacked, self-graffitied marbled notebooks, in this case, "Reader's Notebooks" and "Writer's Sourcebooks," *de rigueur* classroom accoutrements of the workshop model, junked and stripped for parts, the rigid outsides of them propped up like A-frames, or place cards, and, strewn about these tented exoskeletons, like autumn leaves scattered around a centerpiece in a *Martha Stewart Living* layout, or animal entrails left over after a divination, the notebooks' variegated high-lighted and Post-it® noted viscera, plucked-out, torn and tattered remnants, shards, and broken pieces of "wonderings," "noticings," "seed ideas," "fix-up strategies," "text-to-self connections," "text-to-text connections," "text-to-world connections," "questions asked," "predictions made," etc., etc., etc., pertaining to the "just right books" they were reading, books that had been painstakingly "leveled" and color-coded after school by their teacher, using the scientific and officially-sanctioned Fountas & Pennell Text Level Gradient™, and, on each torn fragment, or every other one it seemed, the cryptic rune, or Masonic emblazonment, of a Venn diagram (a "graphic organizer" that was the pinnacle of learning in the workshop model); free periods, lost now, gone, conceded (replaced in each teacher's "program" by pointless and interminable "grade level meetings," "professional developments," "in-services," and other such synods, colloquies, and convocations that I can no longer remember the names of); free periods, gone now, lost, conceded, that I used not to catch up on my work, but to forget it, to escape from it; to forget the dreariness, the tedium, and the irksomeness; to forget the what the fuck have I gotten into; to escape the loneliness, utter and abject, of the empty classroom in which I had been left alone (nothing is sadder than a classroom after the children have left; you couldn't wait for the bell to ring, could you? but, once it did, you were alone, you were all alone...) the moment the whorl whorled out (I missed my students when they weren't around, missed them when they were, sort of the way I missed New York even before I left it; missed them then, before I lost them, miss them now that I have), by coming to call on—by making an "intervisitation" with[45]—one of the teachers I admired, while she tried to correct her student essays, plan her standards-based lesson plans, tape her "process charts" to the wall, level her library, wash her chalkboard, or organize her storage bins and her curricular pocket charts, her three-compartment caddies, gusseted portfolios, stackable storage tubs with interlocking lids, organizational utility totes, and plastic storage craft cabinets—god those chicks were organized, and spent a lot of money, their own money, getting and staying organized; or sorted, collated, and stacked endless stacks of sorted and collated paper; they were always, if they weren't sorting things, or collating them, stacking things, like Mimi stacking laundry, smiling as they stacked, nodding politely, indulging the chattering Abraham-Man, the lonely flibbertigibbet who'd come to call, seeking what all men seek from women, or say they seek, seeking succor, warmth, and understanding, seeking reassurance, seeking—finally—love...

They took the long view, and had, for this reason, as I had

---

[45] I kid. An "intervisitation" is when a bad, I mean "struggling," teacher is told to go to a good, I mean "effective," teacher's classroom to see how it's done...

worked it out, something like teleology on their side, or escha-
tology (I never understood the difference); or so it seemed to me.
It seemed to me they must have had something on their side,
some sort of metaphysical apparatus underpinning their apparent composure, their seeming *sangfroid*, but maybe this was another fantasy of mine, another of my fancies (the metaphysical
apparatus, as well as the *sangfroid*). So I fancied they had teleology on their side, a connection to an unfolding plan that was
larger than themselves, and could take comfort knowing, in advance, by definition, *a priori*, that the spots they were so strategically, cannily, and judiciously choosing not to pick, the infinite
dancing flickering quanta of abasement and humiliation, of hectoring and harassment and harangue, of jargon and contempt, of
disrespect and constant interference, would end; that, in the dis-
tant dancing sight lines of experience, it would fade into a blur,
into an oblivion, into a there that isn't there yet, or anymore, or
never was, or ever could have been; that these lines, traced
down, all the way down, to the ground line, to the vanishing
point, would, in something like an eschaton, a last syllable, fade
and dissipate, that they would converge, that they would disappear and dim from view, not here, not there, but somewhere,
into the vanishing point (of time? of history? of *Ding an sich*?), a
vanishing point cupped, like a hand, like the "desired results" of
a "backward design" lesson plan, down, or at, or on, or in, the
fade of the horizon, the hand of god, or history, or graphical perspective, of transcendental idealism, or post-tribulation pre-mil-
lennialism, the hand of balanced literacy the workshop model
constructivist pedagogy data-driven instruction no child left behind race to the top or whatever you call it, the hand that catches
for you all of your distress, your anxiety, your despair, and
crushes it, crushes it all, flicking the bits that remain back into
the superflux; they saw, they knew (or I fancied that they did,
that they must have, else how go on?), that it, that *all* of it, that
everything weighing down on hope, on life, on joy, on making it
to the holidays, on getting through the day, on getting through

a "coverage," or an "observation," or a "debriefing" or a "learning walk," would converge into a trifle on a beautiful shore within a multipoint perspective, imposed on the world, or inferred from it, and accepted (like a grace, like a mercy, like a comprehension strategy, like a fully-vested pension plan), by an adult, who, mature, wise, a team player, struggling within, searching, finding, accepting the universe, putting away childish things, and making an accommodation in an imperfect world, had found, or been granted (like a grace, like a mercy, like a comprehension strategy, etc.), the serenity to accept the things they could not change, the courage to change the things they could change, and the wisdom to know the difference:

> What belongs to frost and thaw
> Sullen winter will not harm
> What belongs to wind and rain
> Is out of danger from the storm.
>
> Jealous passion, cruel need
> Betray the heart they feed upon.
> But what belongs to earth and death
> Is out of danger from the sun.[46]

They took the long view (sounds like the title of a war movie, doesn't it?, like *They Were Expendable,* or the refrain of an old ballad, or like an epitaph) and in taking the long view, in belonging as they did, as I did, for a while, or was trying to, or not trying to *Did I try to be a teacher because I wanted to belong to something? No, I never wanted to belong to something! Why did I try to be a teacher, then? My wife knew I was making a mistake; my friends knew I was making a mistake; I knew I was making a mistake. In for a penny, in, I guess, for a pound…of flesh, sort of, as things transpired (but it felt more like a pound of soul, didn't it?)* to frost and snow, to wind and rain, to earth and death, to dry erasers and process charts,

---

[46] James Fenton, "Out of Danger."

to teaching points and standards addressed, to flexible grouping and proximal zones of development *Did I really even try to be a teacher at all? Wasn't I rather, once I found myself ducking for cover in the classroom, or, attempting, gracelessly, pitifully, to defend myself, leading with my glass chin, telegraphing my…whaddya call them? My pitty-pats, my shoe shins, my haymakers (it was a boxing match, but not as charming, or as colorful, as the argot that I have looked up on the Internet suggests; it was a boxing match, except it was more of a pummeling, or felt like more of a pummeling, the pummeling of a plodder with a lousy set of whiskers, a palooka, a tomato can cosmically overmatched in a fight I couldn't win)* belonging as they did, as I did, for a while, or was trying to, or not trying to, to all the ways we stave off death (and dread, and the alienation of labor), by joining with it, by embracing it, by "leaning in" and making an accommodation, signing a memorandum of understanding, a concordat, a pact of non-aggression, by adjusting to it, by making eye contact, or, if the situation demands, averting a gaze, in rendering, with apparent devotion (resigned and at the same time exultant), to Caesar the things that belong to Caesar (psychologically, it had to trend both ways, to resignation and to exaltation, because everything, as I've already intimated, belonged to Caesar) *Wasn't I, rather, once I found myself ducking for cover in the classroom, continuing to practice pretty much my old trade, the trade not of "youth development practitioner," as they call it at "idealist.org" now (were beginning to call it, then; with "best practices" and "professional standards" thrown in, but at the same low rate of pay), but of youth worker, or the do-it-yourself version of youth worker that I'd cobbled together with materials at hand, all those years ago in Milwaukee? Wasn't I, really, my first three years at Minuit, and in the afterschool programs that kept me from succumbing, utterly, to despair, my last year out, still—reflexively, instinctually, unwilling to let it go—a youth worker, but a youth worker with a necktie and a grade book and union wages (with two "pay differentials" because of my thirty years of schoolin')?* and fanning—heartrendingly—that little light of theirs, keeping the best of themselves for themselves, and for their students (and, unfortunately, in some cases—some burned-out, bled dry, and beat down cases, and you know who *you* are—keeping the best of themselves out of sight and out of mind), they had—somehow, somewhere (not here, not there, but somewhere), squinting their eyes toward a fissure they saw opening up in the distance, toward an aperture or foramen (they saw) unfolding there, a secret Anthropocene, a *longue durée*—set a gaze they could not avert, set it hard and didn't blink.

It was, god bless them, a sort of proud and self-asserting mean mugging against infinity...

They took the long view, and taking the long view, held there, in that embrace—the embrace of the accommodation, the joining with, like a child that is held by a parent who kneels behind it, the parent's hands resting on the child's shoulders, pointing the child a certain way, as a sea-farer points an astrolabe, or a turret gunner points his gun and sights, so the child can see something that its parent wants it to see, something that is far in the distance, like the seven states you can see from Lover's Leap, in Rock City, near the summit of Lookout Mountain, something that can't be pointed to because if you point to it you are pointing not to *it*, but to everything in the world, which is to say, to nothing in the world, to nothing that is not there (they belonged, remember, to frost and snow), and the nothing that is (which may be the point of all beholding)—they saw, even if they couldn't pinpoint it, as I, when I was a child, clinging to the guardrail at Lover's Leap, feeling my vertigo rise, and my heart sink, as I looked into the maw and saw those seven ugly segregationist states glaring back up at me, glinting in the terrible sunlight; saw, even if they couldn't pinpoint it, as a teacher, at the coaxing, at the urging, or the direct instruction of a principal, or assistant principal (administrators are allowed the courtesy, the basic right, of direct instruction), who kneels behind the teacher, the administrator's hands resting on the teacher's shoulders, pinpoints a "benchmark" shining in the perfect tireless symmetry of a "performance metric," a metric that points the way to the self-actualization of Absolute Spirit, which is to say points the way to the self-actualization of Data-Based Decision Making, of Standards-Based Education Reform, of No Child Left Behind and Race to the Top, etc.; taking the long view, held in that embrace, they saw, even if they couldn't pinpoint it, like seeing a constellation that isn't there yet, or hasn't been there for some millennia; saw, in the persistence of vision, as their eyes adjusted to the dark, in a kind of time-lapse photography, but in reverse, but still going forward, something like the point (of vision, of desire), or the convergence of the points, at which the spots and flaps and quarrels and contretemps, etc., all disappear, like bees returning to the hive (there was always a buzzing sound at the school; I liked the sound, some of the time), or schoolchildren disappearing at the end of the day, out of the corner of your eye, out of the corner of your life, after the last bell has rung, after they have been marched down the down staircase and released on their own recognizance to all the influences of their actual lives, the lives they don't see in you, teacher, and the lives you cannot see in them; after the release, a release for me, too, who if I'd been asked would have said I was glad to see them go, that I was rid of something that was tearing at me, that was crushing me, that was cutting my heart asunder; after the release, and before they had flown home, swarmed home, soared home, or flown, swarmed, or soared to the bodega or the candy store or the library or the park or pizzeria, or, I tried not to think about it, to some bad shit that was going to happen to them; or, if they commuted (and many did, to and from the Bronx, using a relative's address as their own so they could attend the "better" schools in Inwood), after they had been released and before they had been funneled into the turnstiles of the IRT and up the long and steep old stairs to the elevated railway, to disappear into a blur there, into the blur they were then, and the blur they will ever be, I, an appalling figure in the school's forecourt, my shirttails hanging out of my trousers, my shoes scuffed up, at least one of them untied, all my raiment espresso-stained, my blazer marked in chalk, as if a tailor had been at me, or a policeman securing a crime scene, waved bye-bye; and watching everything speed away, drain away, blur away *bye Mr. Blackwell bye Mr. Blackwell bye Mr. Blackwell*, against any knowledge I had of myself (which was little, which was scant), or of the world (which was little, which was scant), against the truth of my life, if I could have known it, against what I might find when I got there, if I'd gone there, I prayed to go with them, to be released myself, as they had been released; I prayed to fly, to swarm, to soar,

> ...to be lifted up
> By some great white bird unknown to the police
> And soar for a thousand miles and be carefully hidden
> Modest and golden as one last corn grain,
> Stored with the secrets of the wheat and the mysterious lives
> Of the unnamed poor.[47]

I admired the veteran teachers and tried to learn from them, sort of, but tell the truth, they gave me a pain; you know, with their pluckiness and their stoicism and their code of uncomplaining professionalism, like they were in a fast-talking all-woman (or almost all woman) Howard Hawks film, but from an earlier era than *Rio Bravo*, from the wise-cracking thirties, with the women in trousers, or tailored dress suits, talking on several telephones at once, *Only Teachers Have Tenure*, say, or *His Girl Targeted Instruction*, and had always, at whatever risk—to life, to limb, to nail, to nylon; to heart, to self, to soul—to get the job done, to see it through; they gave me a pain, those hard-boiled eggs, with their grace under pressure (but *did* they cry at night?), and their poker faces, and, if not their tailored dress suits, their tastefully

---

[47] James Wright, "The Minneapolis Poem."

coordinated twinsets; they gave me a pain with their uncomplaining dedication, their perseverance, and self-sacrifice; all the struggling, in short, and the searching and the finding something within, which goddamn it if the something they found within didn't turn out to be, in every single instance, the very "energy and will to struggle and overcome impossible obstacles and do amazing things" that my even-then all-but-forgotten earlier later (old-young) iteration of myself, sketched longingly-wincingly in Chapter One (middle-aged, life-tempered, but still frangible; willing to be lucky in New York), had bragged I was coming to New York to find within *myself.*

They made me feel ashamed and inadequate, made me feel like I was a failure, like I was a dilettante and an interloper, which is what I was; which is what I am: the failure and the dilettante part at least. (I'm not so much an interloper anymore; I'm more of a dropout these days, retired from active life across the country now from the court at Manhattan, in rustic Milwaukee; exiled, like Seneca—I, grandiose Wikipedia-classicist that I am, imagine myself—to Corsica, where, in repose, and in a toga, I write my *Consolations*; or exiled like Ovid—*carmen et error*—to Tomis, to write my *Sorrows*, and my *Lamentations.*)

Not that they tried to make me feel ashamed and inadequate, not that they tried to make me feel like I was a failure and a dilettante and an interloper, although now that I think about it, maybe some of them did, but whether they tried to or not, they succeeded. They succeeded in the sense George Orwell meant when he said, "Mere success seemed to me a form of bullying," except I think he meant it in a different sense...

They succeeded in making me feel ashamed and inadequate and all that other stuff, just like, or sort of like *speak, memory* when I went, briefly, half-heartedly, into the Boy Scouts (being a teacher was like being in the Boy Scouts), briefly and half-heartedly, as I went into everything else I went into (this was, by the way, in, what was it—1969?—a year in which what I really wanted to go into half-heartedly was revolution for the hell of it, so why was I in the Boy Scouts?), and I was made to feel ashamed and inadequate by all the successful self-starters in my patrol, many of them my age, or not much older, crew-cut boys who were for the war and listened to country music, and said they couldn't tell if a hippie was a boy or a girl, and that the peace symbol was the footprint of the American chicken, and lots of other dumbass shit like that, and who were racists, racists who said "nigger," the word I dreaded throughout my childhood to hear, because it meant I was going to be getting into a fight or, more usually, to be hating myself because I was keeping quiet[48]; the word that made a man of me, in the sense that Proust, or Proust's narrator, owns to in the first section of *Swann's Way*: "In my cowardice I became at once a man, and did what all we grown men do when face to face with suffering and injustice; I preferred not to see them; I ran up to the top of the house to cry by myself in a little room beside the schoolroom and beneath the roof, which smelt of orrisroot, and was scented also by a wild currant-bush which had climbed up between the stones of the outer wall and thrust a flowering branch in through the half-opened window," except in my case it was a flowering branch of kudzu, jasmine, or crape myrtle; but who were—despite deeply-imprinted peckerwood tendencies—middle class strivers, go-getters, over-achievers, cracker junior executives (redneck aspirational I called it in an earlier chapter), and had, through individual effort and initiative (god how I hated individual effort and initiative), begun to advance up the ranks beyond Tenderfoot (god how I hated ranks, how I hated advancement), who, notwithstanding the cultural gap between us, and my sneering sense of superiority, made me feel ashamed and inadequate, with their merit badges and their outdoor skills

---

[48] Of course the brave and caring teachers at the school didn't, for the most part, have crew cuts, and they weren't, as far as I could tell, racists, so the analogy breaks down a bit. (Remember, though, that it's the brave and caring teachers I'm talking about here; not all of the teachers were brave, not all of them were caring.)

and their Indian lore. I couldn't even make Tenderfoot: I couldn't tie the knots, not even a square knot (still can't tie a Windsor, or a half-Windsor, can barely tie a four-in-hand, the easiest knot of all); I couldn't memorize the oath, the law, the motto, or the slogan; well, OK, I could remember the motto, but only because of the Tom Lehrer song.

I quit the Boy Scouts within a year of joining. I had wanted to quit for several months before I finally did quit, but I was afraid to tell my father that I didn't want to be a scout, afraid I'd disappoint him and that I'd disappoint the Scout Master, who was a neighbor (this was before my family moved to the fancier house in the fancier subdivision, the split-level that wasn't a split-level), and a friend of my dad's, sort of, a fellow who worked at the plant, which is what they called the dirty, hot, smelly factory part of the American Cast Iron Pipe Company where men who wore boots and said "ain't" did hard work. My father, who wore dress loafers, and spoke Standard English, was the assistant manager of the accounting department, and did something with debentures and accelerated depreciation (I used to picture the old man at work banging on an adding machine, wearing an accountant's visor and a rubber thumb), and always had a funny kind of *noblesse oblige* relationship with the men who made the pipes, and with plumbers and construction workers and gas station attendants. He'd go all colloquial and start talking more southern with these men, more "gall dern," and "sure 'nuff," and "reckon?" (oh yeah, and "rurnt"; when something was ruined it wasn't ruined it was "rurnt"); and sometimes he'd even say "ain't."

By the way, he was very understanding when I told him I wanted to quit the scouts; he was always very understanding.

I quit the Boy Scouts, as I would, all those years later, quit the New York City Department of Education, which I had also wanted to quit for a long time before I found the cheek, or lost the illusion, the Didionic imposition of a narrative thread, that had served as a rein, a check against my letting go (quitting my job was, I would later come to understand, a kind of rehearsal for death), to chuck it all in, to chuck my career in the bin, and my livelihood, and the pension I wouldn't—again—have stayed long enough at the job to be vested in; to chuck, more disastrously (maybe), into the bin, as long as I was chucking, as long as I was in *that* mood, my own identity, my sense of who I was, and what I'd crawled out of, or—remember, I was a sloth—my sense of what I'd crawled down to, crawled slowly; I wouldn't need cheek, this time, though, to tell my father I was quitting something; my father, whom I couldn't disappoint any longer, because the old man was, by then, too far gone with dementia to know or to care that his son had flubbed it again; my father, who would miss the last opportunity he would have to be very understanding of his son.

I quit the Boys Scouts, as I would, all those years later, quit the New York City Department of Education, which I had also wanted to quit for a long time before I did, had, in fact, been wanting to quit since before the Christmas break of my first year out; this was the teaching position I'd wanted so badly, the teaching position, and the opportunity to move to New York, that I had sold my house for, that I had sold, or given away, nearly everything I owned for, the teaching position and the opportunity that I had quit my job for, and it was a pretty good job, the best I ever had, probably, or would ever have again *a job where I could have fun with kids all day without having to have a "teaching point" and I didn't have to carry around a grade book and always be telling kids to spit out their gun;* the teaching position and the opportunity I had moved across the country for, that I had taken a one-way flight for, before we sold our house, and before Caroline had lined up a job in New York, though she'd interviewed for two jobs, and put in her notice at the Milwaukee Nonprofit Initiative, or the Employment Opportunity Council, or the Workforce Development Alliance, or the Center for Strategic Empowerment, something like that, and no one, on one income, can live in New York on a teacher's salary (the single teachers I knew lived twelve to an apartment in bad buildings on bad blocks in bad neighborhoods).

We were coming to New York, and we were willing to be lucky; we were coming to New York, and we *were* lucky. We sold the house less than a month before Caroline joined me in New York. (Caroline was, that summer, selling the house in Milwaukee while I was living in the sublet on Orchard Street, student-teaching in Harlem, and taking my "pre-service training" at City College.) We sold the house at a nice profit, a profit of approximately twenty thousand dollars, even after paying off the agent, all of which we spent moving to New York and, once we got there, at the theater and the Metropolitan Opera and the Café Carlyle, catching Bobby Short's second set (not really; Bobby Short's second set started at 10:30 p.m., and I had to get up early the next day), spent on trips, during school breaks, to London and Paris; oh yeah, and I went alone on a walking tour in France the summer following my first year in the blackboard jungle, mainly in Burgundy and Alsace-Lorraine, but for a little while in Provence, where it proved too hot to walk (see how fancy I was trying to be, complaining, like a Brit, about how hot summers are in the south of France), the whole time trying to figure out a way to quit the job and stay in New York and not have to pay my tuition money back, tuition money that the Teaching Fellows had fronted, with the understanding that if I quit before I'd completed two years of teaching, the minimum tour of duty, I'd have to pay the money back.

Caroline found a job that summer, too, the summer before my first year teaching, just after selling the house, a job that suited her nicely and paid well, a job that still suits her, still pays well. She works it remotely now from Milwaukee, in a lovely office, painted "Pink Shadow," on the ground floor of a Queen Anne-style wood frame house, built in 1898, and perched, like the Dutch colonial revival we had sold almost ten years earlier, on a small hill overlooking Craftsman bungalows and frame houses and, in addition, because this is the South Side where we live now, "puddler's cottages" ("puddler's cottages" are narrow one-story gablefront houses featuring tall windows with decorative pediments and Victoriana scrollwork on the porch or gable fascia that were built in the 1870s and 1880s to house puddlers; "puddlers" were ironworkers who converted pig iron to wrought iron with the use of a special kind of furnace called a "reverberatory furnace," which is not to say that I understand the difference between "pig iron" and "wrought iron," or that I know what a reverberatory furnace is, or what or how or why it is that it reverberates; I did look up "fascia," though—it's a vertical frieze or band under a roof edge), in an also friendly and (mainly) progressive-leaning neighborhood called Bay View, because when the trees are bare, which they are for eleven months of the year, and the fog is out, you can see choppy blue and slate Milwaukee Bay, a frame house that we bought, for a change, and for change (compared to New York), in a buyer's market, when the interest rates were low, and our credit ratings were high. While Caroline tends to debentures and accelerated depreciation downstairs, her feckless, airy-fairy husband, unemployed and unemployable, tends to spiritual matters in a cozy atelier upstairs, my aery, painted "Netsuke," a creamy caramelish color named after the famous miniature sculptures of Japan, and "Picture Gallery Red," based, according to the promotional literature, on the color of the picture gallery at Attingham Park, a country house in Shropshire, England (though when I looked the house up at the National Trust website, the room identified as the picture gallery seemed to be painted in a color that looks to me like "Lullworth Blue"), red because I saw, in The Guardian, a picture of Geoff Dyer's writing studio, and it was painted red, with a green midcentury modern linoleum floor, with specks of yellow, white, and other shades of green, my floor I'm talking about, not Dyer's, like the green midcentury modern linoleum floor at my father's office at ACIPCO, the office where I first understood, sensing, even then, the alienation of the laborer from the fruits of his labor, from the act of producing, and from his species-essence, that I could never like having a job, except maybe, sometimes, when I didn't have one anymore (I think what I miss most about having a job is the whispering camaraderie of dissatisfied employees, the company that misery loves: I loved to complain at a job, and seek out the other complainers and complain with them; I loved to commiserate; it was how I got the fellowship I used to hanker after [I'm pretty much an anchorite, now, and whine alone at the top of my pillar]: "complain," meaning "to lament together," the first and truest, most human fellowship).

I quit the Boy Scouts, as I would, all those years later, quit the job with the New York City Department of Education, which I had also wanted to quit for a long time before I did, had wanted to quit, as a matter of fact, for several years before I quit it, had, in fact, been wanting to quit since before the Christmas break of my first year out, had confessed as much, that I wanted to quit the job—and before Christmas, already—in the e-mails I sent out that first year, the e-mails I sent, desperately, banging on my keyboard, di di dit dah dah dah di di dit, like Morse code from remotest wherever it is that is the most remote from you, a man under siege in those nerve-rattled days of fear and nausea and self-loathing, those days of diminishing returns, days of disenchantment, squatting, in the undisclosed margins, in the excluded muddle, of a new beginning, of yet another brighter green: those days of the new Blackwell, sort of. Days of the new Nixon! I shouldn't kid myself I'm Seneca writing his *Consolations* or Ovid his *Sorrows* or *Lamentations*, or that I've ever read any of these; what I'm writing is more in the line of *Six Crises*, which I also haven't read (who has?), but then I, like Nixon, only ever had one crisis; insecure and self-made men, not that I'm a self-made man, only ever have one crisis in their lives, a crisis they play over and over again like a record on a record player...

A record player like the Mediterranean style console that my old friend from high school Daniel Winfield's little sister Ariadne used to play "Billy, Don't Be a Hero" on, over and over, annoying Daniel, and to some degree me (but I thought it was kind of cute), back in 1974 at Daniel's family's true split-level in Whispering Pines Terrace (or was it Woody Glen Manor?), while downstairs, in a den in a finished basement, with a fireplace and a wet bar and a dart board and snooker table, and all that sort of thing, Daniel and I, two teenage would-be intellectuals, smoked, in my case, by appointment to His Royal Highness the Prince of the Netherlands, St. Moritz filtered cigarettes, and, in Daniel's, a gnarled old tobacco pipe of briar wood, and drank bourbon, both of us, bottled in bond (J.W. Dant was our brand; why that brand and not another I can't remember), and, between sips and puffs, said what I'm pretty sure we thought were smart things about Modern Library editions of William Faulkner and Thomas Wolfe and John Dos Passos and James T. Farrell. Daniel Winfield, to whom I sent, in my first year at Minuit, an e-mail *di di dit dah dah dah di di dit* which will be offered, soon, as evidence submitted in support of my statement that I wanted to quit my job as early as before the first Christmas break of my first year teaching, a relic, this e-mail, an example of—what is my name for it?—"the growing accretion of time lost, fragmented, and digitally preserved," that was sent, approximately thirty years after the two of us drank our bourbon and smoked our smokes and talked our high-fallutin' rot in that long-ago finished basement, to the grown-up instantiation of the blue-eyed boy that I had, so many years earlier, lost contact with. He was, the grown-up instantiation, an attorney-at-law now, living upstate, not far from me, somewhere on the Harlem or the New Haven Line, who had, like me, long since given up smoking (but I believe Daniel still drinks, moderately); an attorney-at-law and old friend with whom I had recently gotten back in touch, sort of, and to whom I sent the e-mail. An e-mail, a note, a relic, composed by a relic, but I couldn't have known that, then, and sent to Daniel Winfield—who hasn't really got a sister; I made that up by conflating, for dramatic effect, Daniel Winfield with another old friend of mine, a friend called Everett Holman, not that either of these are their real names.

An e-mail sent to Daniel Winfield, who had, himself, speaking of the Boy Scouts, been an Eagle Scout at age 12 (this is true), and though always a striver, a go-getter, and an over-achiever, had never been a redneck or a racist, except perhaps in the concealed-carry sense that I suppose it can be said we all are (one of the reasons I wanted to have Daniel for a friend is it was hard to find anybody at my school, or anywhere else in the south, who wasn't the straight-up open-carry kind of racist); a friend, by the way, who, because of his social and academic, and, later, his professional success, had always inspired in me a certain quantum of shame and inadequacy *I have coveted everything and taken pleasure in nothing* because he was, in every respect, a better boy: he could grow sideburns and drive a standard shift transmission and play his trumpet on key (that's where I met him, in the trumpet section of the high school band, although we were seated several chairs apart: Daniel played first trumpet, while I played third) and because he made a perfect score on his ACT (a perfect score!) and I don't want to talk about my score and because he graduated college in three years and it took me nine and because he was well-adjusted and had good mental health (and I...well, you know) and because he was the first to get the hell out of Alabama (he graduated from law school in New York State and was admitted to the bar before I had even completed my B.A.), but mainly, mainly, because he was handsome and well-spoken and well-dressed and girls liked him (he was the first son of a bitch I knew in my own generation to get laid); a friend who, now that I remember it, not that I ever forgot it, stole my girlfriend from me, back in our seedtime, when we were attending UAB (having both chickened out of attending college at the out-of-state schools where we had been accepted).

And, yes, after all my years of flopping with chicks, I had finally gotten a girlfriend. Not a great girlfriend, but a good one. She wasn't, you know, *intellectual* enough for me, and she wouldn't let me go all the way with her, but she would let me go part of the way, which was a big step for me. She'd let me (*partially*) undress her, usually in a car (in my orange Hornet, in fact, shortly before it threw its last rod), parked in the fog, fog in the windows and fog outside (at least that's the way I remember it being: foggy), on a side street perched on a ledge of Red Mountain, with the lights of the city twitching below. She'd let me unbutton her blouse, unhook her brassiere, pull up her skirt, and pull down her panties; then she'd let me touch her, you know...all over. These were the first bare breasts I had ever touched, or seen—in person; and god knows my first vagina. I'd looked at pictures of those sorts of things, after working up the courage to slip through the black curtain into the back room of the 24-hour newsstand downtown, and thumb through the "stroke books," trying to act casual, and, many years earlier, in nudist magazines I'd looked at at the home of my father's colleague from work, Mr. McAdams, "tasteful" promotional literature for the healthy lifestyle of the liberated naturist, in which black bars, to protect their privacy, covered the eyes of the naked cavorters flying kites, playing badminton, and barbequing spare ribs, magazines that were stacked in the open, because there was nothing to be ashamed of, on the coffee table in the McAdams's sunken den, interspersed amongst the canapés, wax fruit, teakwood candle holders, and soapstone Polynesian idols artfully arrayed by McAdams's soigné, and buxom, wife, Evelyn (oh, I had a crush on *her*). She wouldn't go all the way with me, but she'd let me touch her, you know...all over (the girlfriend, not Evelyn McAdams); and, as I touched her, she would return the favor: she would unzip my pants, or unbutton them, because sometimes I wore jeans that buttoned up (these were the nineteen-seventies), and she would reach in and take my penis in her hand and stroke it for an hour at least, because it took me a very long time to come, used as I was to my own right hand. She was patient, though. And she had a good arm.

She was also, as I have already intimated, in her spare time, on the nights she wasn't foggy in my car, foggy, as I would learn later, with Daniel Winfield in his, and with Daniel Winfield, I had it on the authority of a mutual friend, she was going all the way.

She finally broke up with me when, sensing something was wrong, I inadvertently forced a confession, and then she dated Daniel for a few months, until he broke up with her, probably because she'd gotten to be too clingy. Daniel hated that in a girl; he was the kind of guy, you know, like Davy Jones, who just wanted to be free. Like the bluebirds flying by him. Like the waves out on the blue sea. Or (I can't remember), maybe he traded up; he was the ambitious type. But that's all water over the dam, isn't it? Water over the dam. I don't even know why I bring it up:

Hey Old Man,

Four days until our holiday break (one measly week off!). Goddamn this job is hard. I'm crawling with regrets, eaten with second thoughts, laid prostate—I mean prostrate—with Internet-enabled hypochondria, self-canceling *folies du doute*, and agonizing reappraisals, etc. I had a lovely life in Milwaukee, Wisconsin, working with children in informal settings without grade books and lesson plans and standardized tests and "walk-throughs" [later re-dubbed "learning walks"] and other varieties of panoptical surveillance; a lovely life of weekly walks in the country and book-collecting and thrift store and antique store shopping (because I had the space to collect books and vintage furniture, housewares, tableware, knick-knacks, etc., and the treasures I desired could be got on the cheap, and I had the means to cart them home) and I kept a container garden that I planted anew each spring with annuals—lisianthus, nicotiana, dahlias, pentas, zinnias, lantana, marigolds, and moss rose, in the color scheme of yellow, white, orange, red, and peach—and a water feature with papyrus, water hyacinth, and lily pads, and an herb garden and tomato vines and strawberries, a garden in which I fed the birds and cleaned the fallen ailanthus flowers from the birdbath, and chased away the fat raccoons who always ate my strawberries before I could, and splashed around in my water feature; a lovely life with two houses, a town house and a country house, well a town house and a country travel trailer, and though I was sad sometimes, I was replenished and my soul was soothed on those weekends out in Vernon County; a lovely life in which I didn't have to keep going to college and keep passing unending qualifying exams to keep my job, a job in which I am essentially a line worker in an assembly plant, and I didn't have to buy my own supplies and I wasn't all of the time (some of the time, but not *all of the time*) treated with contempt by my supervisors; I had a lovely life in Milwaukee, Wisconsin, but I threw it away, and I threw it away on a whim. All because I had a fantasy of living in New York.

I love my students, and I love New York, but I hate my job. It's a drudgery. And I have I can't even count how many supervisors. And they're all day long spewing jargon, spewing cant, spewing platitudes. And they're grim and earnest and self-important.

Jesus, I don't know, I'm confused. I want out. I want to drop out. Is it possible to drop out? Do people still drop out? That awful election in November depressed me. I'm still depressed about that. I keep thinking of that line from James Wright: "I long to lie down under that tree / That is the only duty that is not death."

Good news is we're going to Paris for a week, leaving Christmas Eve. "A week in Paris will ease the bite of it." The thing is, though, I had to get a new passport and the State Department sends your old (invalidated) passport in the mail with your new one. I also happen to have handy—because I found it while packing last June and for sentimental reasons saved it—my very first passport. Line them up together, which I'm foolish enough to do, and you've got the picture of Dorian Gray. The picture of Dorian Fucking Gray.

Chip

Tell the truth, though: I had been wanting to quit the job for a lot longer than before the Christmas break; I'd been wanting to quit it since at least October (October!), the kindest month of the school year, with the High Holidays and Columbus Day off (where else except New York does the working class get the High Holidays *and* Columbus Day off? or either? though it would have been better to have gotten the High Holidays and *Indigenous Peoples' Day* off, but I took what I could get), and only my second month on the job: my second month (!), not even two whole months, a few weeks really.

These are words I wrote to my Fellow Advisor in mid-October, softening my despair, because I didn't want the FA to be disappointed in me:

> I'll admit I've been a little discouraged—never by the kids, though. It's the administrators who tire me, or the parasitic class of apparatchiks and bureaucratic functionaries, as I like to call them, and the culture of fear they promote; the disrespect they show to teachers, and the contempt they so plainly feel. And all the pointless and avoidable negativity—blecch! And the endless coverages [sic] because of I would imagine teachers who are even more discouraged than I am who keep missing work.

I also wrote, in the same e-mail, because there was *some* softness to my despair (the beauty of the world has two edges), because I wasn't evading entirely the "implacable grandeur" of the life I was living then, the life that was, after all—*amor fati*—mine

> —My formula for greatness in a human being is *amor fati*: that one wants nothing to be different, not forward, not backward, not in all eternity. Not merely bear what is necessary, still less conceal it—all idealism is mendacity in the face of what is necessary—but *love* it.[49]

---

[49] Nietzsche, *Ecce Homo*, Section 10.

the life I had only just begun to despair of, the life I wish now I could have loved: the life, the fate, I *should* have loved (why *couldn't* I love it?):

> The kids are great though—delightful to be around, smart and funny as hell. They're beautiful, man. They really are. I go to gym with my homeroom class every Friday and we have a blast, running and laughing and hopping and jumping. They always beat me when we race and they think I'm letting them win. The gym teacher likes it when I'm there because for once the kids don't drive her crazy with their nutty antics.

Great kids. Always great kids. But always great kids "notwithstanding." I had left behind whole battlefields of great kids notwithstanding ("battlefields" meaning places of employment, "battlefields" meaning "youth-serving agencies") because I couldn't stand the blood and guts (of places of employment, of youth-serving agencies), couldn't stand the strategic planning; the organizational charts; the minutes of the last meeting; the progressive discipline; the fundraising executives and total quality managers; the Executive Directors, Presidents/C.E.O.s, Development Directors, Chief Financial Officers, Chief Information Officers, Human Resources Directors, etc., etc., etc.—all the bumptious, oily, self-aggrandizing administrators and all the bumptious, oily, self-aggrandizing executives; the outcomes pathway and the theory of change; the logic models and Developmental Assets®; the knock your socks off service; or, god help us, god help *me*, the mission statement, the vision statement, the values statement, the impact statement...

Great kids notwithstanding, and there were great kids everywhere, everywhere I had ever worked. I'd left behind so many before only to find a new many more, but not this time. This time when I quit I would hang up my charcoal blazer for good, and my new formula for greatness in a human being...not a formula for greatness, exactly, more like a formula for...something else, would be that of Andrei Bolkonsky, in *War and Peace* (even though I identify more—or used to think I did; no, I still do—with Pierre Bezukhov, who is appalled by Andrei's declaration): "I only know two very real evils in life: remorse and illness. The only good is the absence of those evils. To live for myself avoiding those two evils is my whole philosophy now."

Great kids notwithstanding (and these *were* great kids), I wanted to quit the education department and get myself a steady job (wanted to quit so soon!), for pretty much the same reason I had wanted to quit the Boy Scouts, which is the same reason I wanted to quit everything else I had ever wanted to quit, which is to say everything I had ever wanted to join: because I couldn't tie a fucking square knot! Because I couldn't memorize the oath, the law, the motto, and the slogan (the mission statement, the vision statement, the values statement, and the impact statement). I couldn't tie the knots, couldn't learn a trade, couldn't learn a "skill set," couldn't settle down, couldn't dig in. I couldn't believe in all the claptrap I was supposed to believe in (and it was claptrap; it was pap; it was twaddle), couldn't make myself say the things I was supposed to say. I didn't want to work in "the plant," and I didn't want to work in "the office," which were the only two choices (why do they have to be the only two choices?); and when I had to choose, deluding myself I had a choice, I'd always chosen "the plant," condescending to toil there, "going to the people," like some kind of crackpot *Narodnik* in yet another Russian novel I might have been reading...

This was, of course, all in the past, in the days before I couldn't take it anymore (back when I used to think I could hack it), before I cracked, and one day, in a trance, I walked, like Ophelia, or Blanche Dubois, or Tom o'Bedlam, or that guy in the "Slowly, I turn, step by step, inch by inch" routine, up and down the halls of the ghost ship, murmuring, to no one, to anyone, "No you don't, not anymore," and, without remembering that I'd done it, not knowing I was doing it as I was doing it, doing it before I could stop myself from doing it, like dialing the phone number quickly of a girl you want to ask out on a date, hoping she doesn't answer, or dialing the phone number of a doctor who has the results of a test to give you, hoping *he* doesn't answer, because it's scary to quit a job without having another one lined up, scary to quit a job that you know when you quit it you will never work again, scary to call a doctor, scary to call a girl, I slipped the carefully-crafted and cliché-ridden letter of resignation, in which I expressed gratitude for the "opportunity to serve" and begged to be relieved of my duties, under the principal's door, like a confession of love, or a late term paper, double-checking to make sure the letter had not been wedged under a carpet like in *Tess of the D'Urbervilles* (ever since I read that book as a teenager I have always double-checked to make sure, whenever I slide a letter under a door, and it's kind of embarrassing how many letters I've slid under doors over the years, that it had gone all the way in; I do the same thing when I put a letter in a mailbox; I peer down the chute to make sure the letter has fallen into the bin), and then I gathered together my duffel bag, my briefcase, my gallstone...I mean gladstone, my steamer trunk, my grade book, my pen with the green ink, and my portmanteau, and, opening one of the tall windows in my classroom that required a long pole with a hook at the end, a steady hand, and many years' practice, to open and close it, and, climbing up on the radiator to get to the now-opened upper sash (the lower wouldn't open), I tossed all of that impedimenta (impediments to life) out the window and down into the schoolyard where no children played because their playground was a parking lot filled with SUVs; and with the cat movements of a second story man, I stepped out of the window and slid down a railing to a cornice to a rain gutter to a fire escape to a side street opening onto an alley and a back entrance to a grocery store, which I entered and a few minutes later exited, covered with lettuce and tomatoes and other produce, looking like a bad vaudevillian who'd earned the disapprobation of a rowdy crowd of plug uglies and dead rabbits, which, essentially, is what had happened, and made my way out to broad and roiling Upper Broadway, past the *bodegas* and *botanicas*, past Sal's House of Mofongo and La Reina del Chicharrón, and over to the steps leading up to the Dyckman House; and, looking back once, like Lot's wife, and, I guess it's what I get, turning into a pillar of salt, I paused there for a moment, *almost* motionless (I hadn't really turned into a pillar of salt; the Old Testament, and the New, while allusion-worthy, are not to be taken literally), except one hand was fiddling with my necktie, trying to correct a fucked-up half-Windsor, that, if I'd only known it, was a correctly-tied four-in-hand; I was looking sad and near mad, my doublet all unbraced, no hat upon my head, my stockings foul'd, ungarter'd, and down-gyved to my ankle, pale as my shirt, pale as the ghost of a representative of the Metoac band of Lenape Indians known as the "Carnarsee," my knees knocking each other, and with a look so piteous in purport, as if I had been loosed out of hell to speak of horrors; affrighting, with my foul'd stockings, my knocking knees, and general air of down-gyvedness, the Dominican pensioners still at their games of dominoes, surrounded by pigeon shit, I turned around *slowly, I turn* and started running down Broadway, in the middle of the street, stopping not for traffic lights *step by step* running all the way down, to 190th Street, to 181st Street, to 175th Street, thinking, as I ran, because everything I saw or heard in New York reminded me of a book, poem, song, play, or movie about New York, of Adrienne Rich's poem, "Upper Broadway,"

> The leafbud struggles forth
> toward the frigid light of the airshaft   this is faith
> this pale extension of a day
> when looking up   you know   something is changing
> winter has turned   though the wind is colder
> Three streets away   a roof collapses   onto people
> who thought they still had time   Time out of mind

running all the way down to 145th Street, to 137th Street, and finally to 125th Street *inch by inch* where I turned left and, the curls of my tresses lashing at the lace of my collar, ran crosstown on 125th Street, except I couldn't run very fast because there were so many people clogging the pavement, clogging the street; so many street vendors, so many passersby, so many black people, so many brown people, skin hued black and brown and russet and mahogany and caramel and coffee and bronze and umber, so many white people, skin hued pink and white and beige and cream and ecru, waiting with their luggage for the M-60 to La Guardia that takes forever (La Guardia takes forever, too, if you're waiting for a plane to take off, or if you are circling above, waiting to land), so many pink and white and beige and cream and ecru people gentrifying so many black and brown and russet and mahogany and caramel and coffee and bronze and umber people out of their neighborhood, a slow blur of people, black and pink and brown and white and russet and mahogany and beige and caramel and cream and coffee and bronze and umber and ecru, a slow blur of pedestrians, of long-time residents and gentrifiers and folks headed to La Guardia, a blur of street vendors, a blur of shea butter and hair extensions and kente cloth and cell phone accessories and incense and fragrant oils and jewelry and designer knock-offs and for your reading pleasure street lit and religious tracts and strange preachments and little books to teach your children their math facts and their abc's; panting panting panting I ran on down past Amsterdam, past St. Nicholas, past Frederick Douglass Boulevard and Adam Clayton Powell and Lennox and Fifth Avenue, stopping for a few minutes at the Uptown Juice Bar, near Madison, for some BBQ soy drumsticks, with a piece of sugar cane for the bone, and collard greens and black eyed peas and candied yams and banana pudding, and some bread pudding, too, and, tell the truth, some cassava pudding, too, to give me strength; and then I set back out, downtown and Brooklyn-bound, sleepy and ready for a nap from all that food I'd thrown down, gliding, it felt like, in a dream, sliding like on a sliding board in a fun house, all the way down...down...down: down Fifth Avenue and the Museum Mile to the Pierre and the Sherry Netherlander to the Plaza and over to First past the 59th Street Bridge past Sutton Place and Turtle Bay down to the United Nations and Tudor City and the Queens Midtown Tunnel and Murray Hill and Kips Bay and Gramercy Park and Peter Cooper Village and Stuyvesant Town and the East Village and across Houston Street to Allen Street and the Lower East Side and then across Canal and over to the Manhattan Bridge to Flatbush Avenue, straight out toward Grand Army Plaza, to where Seventh Avenue conks the loud and funky four-lane cross-grid kink of Flatbush, and then, following Seventh, climbing the hill on Second Street, up to the top of my whitewashed brownstone in Park Slope, to cry by myself in a little room beneath the roof, which smelt of menthol and wintergreen and camphor, and was scented also by an ailanthus tree, which had climbed up between the stones of the outer wall and thrust a flowering branch in through the half-opened window; I imagined myself, then, imagine myself now, half-sighing and half-harrumphing, flourishing my quill like Ed Norton exasperating Ralph Kramden, arms flailing, and ink splashing on the ruffles of my sleeve, as I tick the box marked, "neither, none of the above, not any of it" on an imaginary career interest inventory: an imaginary career interest inventory that is of course real, and has made my life a ruin...

A CONSOLATION

But, lest anyone think my last year at Minuit was all bad, which it was, it was all bad, I should mention that there was a consolation, a small and tender mercy, unstrained, dropping, in that desert of human affection, that desert of human solidarity (it's a cliché, I know, but it's true: nobody knows you when you're down and out), like a gentle rain from heaven upon the place

beneath: a second, less precisely Hobbesian class (less Hobbesian in comparison, that is, to the mean and nasty class of mean
and nasty duck-assed JDs that made me forget that my heart had
ever bled for the underserved) of OK, sort of in the middle, not
horrible, not great, but not horrible, eighth-graders, which, by
the way, are the words my urologist, a good one with a nice practice in the West Sixties, near the park, would, a couple of years
later, use to describe my urine flow rate: "not horrible," he
would say, "not great, but not horrible." I had, I could only suppose, been granted this consolation, this small and tender mercy,
because, like god, or a board certified urologist, the principal
never gives you more suffering than you can handle; and, also
like god (I don't think this applies to the urologist, though, unless he's consulting for the "enhanced interrogation" program at
Langley), he gives you just enough relief from your suffering to
keep you (just barely) alive....

Unhappy is the land that needs consolations.

But, every day, by the rivers of Babylon (in my case, the Harlem and the Hudson), I sat down, on the special occasions I was
allowed to sit down, at an "in-service" maybe, or a "professional
development" (teachers are, I will admit, not strictly speaking
forbidden from sitting at their desks while teaching, but they are
aggressively, bullyingly, discouraged from it, in effect shamed
into standing ["teacher-shamed," one might say, when they forget they are "facilitators," and, making "no excuses," will do
"whatever it takes"], which is why, at the Seder, even if they
aren't Jewish, they recline when they eat their unleavened bread
and drink their cups of wine), and I wept, when I remembered
Zion ("The Babylonian captivity" was, in those days, the pet
name I used to describe my forced removal out of the sixth
grade, and into the eighth, out of "gifted and talented," and into
the "general population"); wept, when I remembered the days
before the need for consolations, for small and tender mercies,
when I basked (which might not be the right word; I don't think
I have ever really basked; it just came, that last bad year, to seem

to me that I had) in the gifted and talented program, where things were bad enough, but not as bad as they would get:

> And worse I may be yet. The worst is not
> So long as we can say "This is the worst."

I wept, by whichever river I was closer to, usually it was the Hudson, as I sat during my lunch break or a free period, when I was still allowed a free period, on a crag at Fort Tryon Park that overlooks the tidal estuary (which technically is what the Hudson is at its mouth, but "weeping by a tidal estuary" doesn't have the same resonance as "weeping by a river"); wept, when I remembered my sixth-graders, all of the sixth-graders I ever knew, but especially the halcyon class of my third year teaching (a bad year otherwise; the first year of the new principal; the first year of the clampdown; Year Zero of Data).

They were happy in my classroom, the sixth-graders were; and they flourished. And I was happy, too; and I flourished.

They were happy and they flourished, except, tell the truth (and I feel ashamed, sometimes, when I remember Zion), when their teacher, so kind, so caring, and so understanding, a teacher who never hectored, never harangued, and never harassed, a teacher who never condescended, "best teacher ever" they used to call me, except when this every kid's idea of a favorite teacher ("Mr. B-Well's cool") screwed his kindly caring understanding face up like a butthole and yelled bloody murder at them; except then (and I torture myself now with these memories). I yelled at them, sometimes, and would, immediately, or very soon after, feel bad about it and try to make it up to them with apologies and flowers and candy, like one of those abusive husbands in a made-for-TV movie. I'd yell, but only when they wouldn't, when they *couldn't* it seemed, shut the f--- up, as if they all had flaws in their larynxes or in their throats that produced, autonomically, while they were awake, and maybe even while they were sleeping, a never-ending series of non-stop vocalizations

that made it impossible for them to stop talking even for the duration of for christ's sake a ten-minute mini-lesson, which,
frankly, could get very annoying (the mini-lesson, I will admit,
and the chattering), could get exasperating, could get *very* exasperating.

Except here's the thing, here's the weird miraculous unholy
blessed thing of it: they *would* be quiet, they *would* shut the fuck
up, they *would* stop talking, the darlings (and they *were* darlings,
inexhaustibly, chaotically voluble, logorrheic, even, but still darlings), during the "independent reading" section of the "readers
workshop" that fell in those days, probably still falls—unless
since I made my escape a new transformational game-changing,
though I think the new word is "disruptive," innovation in pedagogy has displaced the workshop model as the new official or-
thodoxy—directly on the heels of the mini-lesson, during which,
in the multiloquent din, I had, forbearing, under penalty of administrative sanction, to instruct them directly, modeled one
(and only one, that was the rule) "targeted reading strategy," a
mini-lesson, that was, of course, in an era of attention deficits,
"interactive," and included a "turn and talk" every forty-five
seconds—that is the rule, too—and not to be confused, as the literacy coaches are at pains to remind teachers, with direct instruction, derided in all modern "learning communities" as, *feh*,
and then you spit on the ground, "chalk and talk," the old, discredited pedagogy (discredited originally, and perhaps heroically, I'm not sure anymore, by well-meaning lefties whose
words and tactics have long since been appropriated, "brought
steadily in each year by the millions into the machineries of the
teachings of the world"), in which teachers were, by law and the
custom of the land, allowed to teach, sometimes even to lecture;
in which teachers were allowed to instruct and (sometimes; not
often, but sometimes) to delight (no, it wasn't all delight; yes,
much of it, like much of life, was boring, but so's the new stuff,
by god; ask any kid; so, by definition, is school, for christ's sake),
at all events allowed to hold forth, some of the time, with just the

teacher talking, which is say, to impart actual information, without a faux-Socratic, near-scripted phony interactive "student-centered" "paradigm," and also without a never-ending parade of Great Chain kibitzers taking a "learning walk" through everything they did; I'm talking about back in old benighted dame school schoolmarm old-school schooldays, before the arrival of the "differentiated curriculum," the "student-centered classroom," and "authentic inquiry-based learning," etc., which I suppose only the barbarism of all the up-to-date data-tested research-approved space-age rot could make anyone, could make me, look back to with fond nostalgia; the days, in short, I'm talking about, before the arrival, and the institutionalization, and the apotheosis, of "excellence." "Why do teachers have to be 'excellent'?" Fran Lebowitz asked on a YouTube video I saw recently, "I never had 'excellent' teachers!"

Unhappy is the land that needs "excellence."

They *would* be quiet, they *would* shut the fuck up, they *would* stop talking during the "independent reading" section of the "readers workshop," because, in spite of all the excellence and the reading strategies and the differentiated and data-driven and targeted and scaffolded and inquiry-based instruction, in spite of action research and curriculum mapping and growth mindsets and ramping up and higher order thinking and on-going assessment, in spite, let's face it, of me, who, frankly, had nothing better to offer them than the claptrap I made fun of, my students liked to read, they actually liked to read; they took pleasure in it: *quiet* pleasure. And in these precious moments of quiet pleasure, of blessed silence

> Heard melodies are sweet, but those unheard
> Are sweeter...

precious still in my memory, the precious moments of independent reading, all the students in the classroom, reposing under a bower in a sylvan glade, I could have believed, their heads

draped in vine-leaves, silently reading books they had chosen
for themselves,

> ...therefore, ye soft pipes, play on;
> Not to the sensual ear, but, more endear'd,
> Pipe to the spirit ditties of no tone:
> Fair youth, beneath the trees, thou canst not leave
> Thy song, nor ever can those trees be bare...

speak, memory some reclining on cushions on the floor, or sitting
on cushions with legs crossed yogi-style, or lying dreamily upon
a spiny radiator, like a fakir on a bed of nails, or perched on one
of the tables that held the little plastic baskets of leveled library,
some sitting at their desks, some on their desks, some under their
desks, some at or on or under my desk (which was available for
languid repose because I was, by Great Chain decree, fluttering
about the room, "collecting data," with pen in hand and a marbled notebook folded under a wing), in the midst of this pastoral
scene, this eclogue, as the children found their "just right books,"
and settled in to their places of repose, the room would in incre-
ments get quieter, would eventually get so quiet that I could
hear, in the hush, and then the silence—I'm not exaggerating—
the sound of the children breathing; a sound that roared in my
heart, like "the aspect of a street in sunlight can roar in the heart
of itself as a symphony, perhaps as no symphony can"[50]; and, as
I lost myself in the ebb and then the flood of their in- and then
their exhalations—it was tidal, this experience; this innocence; it
was gravitational; it was an ocean; it was waves, waves of love,
as I felt it—I would, imperceptibly at first, and then as the sound
grew louder, begin to hear a counterpoint, would begin to hear
the sound of their hearts beating, and then the sound of the
blood coursing through their veins; and then, if I held my own
breath long enough, if I stopped for a second my own heart's
beating, and stilled the blood flowing in my veins, I could hear,

---

[50] James Agee, *Let Us Now Praise Famous Men.*

faintly at first, and then roaring too (because as Kafka said, "Anyone who believes cannot experience miracles; by day one cannot see any stars"), the very emanations of their souls, aural equivalents of the angels that flit like butterflies in Giotto's frescoes in the Arena Chapel, or the brownies in the photographs that fooled Sir Arthur Conan Doyle (that's how I pictured them, pictured what I couldn't see, but heard, but felt), and I was happy, then, in those moments, so happy that I could barely hold back my tears, and sometimes I couldn't, sometimes I didn't; as I listened to the sound of their breathing, worshipping forever their fragile incommunicable tenderness, I would make a "text to text" connection of my own, and mouth the following lines, from a poem of James Wright's that I had memorized once while lying under a tree in my old backyard on Newhall Street, a tree I loved but that a storm would later destroy, a poem called "The Undermining of the Defense Economy,"

> Girls the color of butterflies
> That can't be sold
> Only after nightfall
> Little boys lie still, awake,
> Wondering, wondering,
> Delicate little boxes of dust

Ghosts and Superghosts

But there was one more stop after Fairway Market that I had to make in those days, in Upper West Side days, before I boarded the uptown and Bronx-bound 1 train that would take me to my Golgotha *but it wasn't all Golgotha*. It was to buy some flowers at a market on Amsterdam Avenue, where I was a bulk buyer and had negotiated special pricing. I bought roses, usually, but sometimes chrysanthemums, or sunflowers, in season, and occasionally carnations. I bought three dozen flowers each Monday, keeping them on my desk, in three vases, two of them crystal, the other white porcelain, until Friday, when at the end of the day I gave them away to students who wanted them. All of my students wanted flowers, boys *and* girls, except for this one boy called Andres, who never wanted any.

And then, after getting my flowers wrapped, I doubled back to the 72nd Street subway, even though the 79th Street station was closer, so I could avoid two loud teachers from the old New York that you used to see in movies and on television fighting over a discounted girdle in the basement of Gimbel's, who got on the train at 79th, and who, if I got on the train with them, would have destroyed my will to live by the time the train pulled into 96th Street. They were loud and obnoxious and said terrible things about the students (and about the parents, and about the neighborhood), terrible things that pissed me off because I hated to hear anybody say terrible things about the students (or the parents or the neighborhood), though in a year or two I would say terrible things about students myself, except I wouldn't *say* them, but I would think them. And sometimes say them. They did have delicious old-time New York accents, though, these loud teachers from the old New York; I gave them that; and if I could get them to talk about anything besides the school and the students and the parents and the neighborhood, I got a kick out of listening to them, but not all the way to 203rd Street. Even if they had been witty conversationalists, though, I would still have preferred a solitary commute, easing myself into the day with only my wistfulness and personal despair for company.

All year, that year, and for much of the next, at the approach to the 125th Street station, when the train came up out of the ground to get some air (only to dive back down into its tunnel, like one of those giant worms in *Dune*, or *Beetlejuice*, at 137th Street/City College), providing confirmation that the sun had risen (it was dark when I went down into the subway at 72nd Street), I looked up to see the sun, to squint in its radiance. As I looked up, I noticed, every morning at 125th Street, the "MTA Poetry in Motion" placard bent into its concave slot just above the handrail, jammed next to the New York City Teaching Fellows ad that I was tempted every day to deface, and I read the same oh so appropriate lines that never changed in four years (this I'm not making up; I make up a lot of shit, but this I'm not making up), and might still be stuck up there on that train; I read the words aloud, but very quietly so I wouldn't look to the other passengers too much like the meshuggener I knew myself to be,

> Tomorrow, and tomorrow, and tomorrow,
> Creeps in this petty pace from day to day
> To the last syllable of recorded time,
> And all our yesterdays have lighted fools
> The way to dusty death. Out, out, brief candle!
> Life's but a walking shadow, a poor player
> That struts and frets his hour upon the stage
> And then is heard no more. It is a tale
> Told by an idiot, full of sound and fury,
> Signifying nothing.

And when the train, creeping in *its* petty pace, pulled into my station, the next to last stop on this route, the next to last syllable, I was often the only rider in the car, and as I exited my chest got tight and the old familiar dread took control of my being, and I crossed my fingers and walked the three blocks to the school, stopping for my coffee and croissant, keeping my fingers crossed, and, as I crossed the portals of the school and climbed the steps into the lobby and made my way to the front office, I crossed myself and said three Hail Mary's, or would have, if I'd been Catholic, and prayed, or would have, if I'd believed in God, that I would find my time card in the rack, between the cards of Alvin Barraclough and Edwina Bolaño, because if it wasn't there, it would mean it was on the counter with a "coverage" slip attached to it, and I'd have to substitute for an absent teacher down in one of the lower academies, the "Slough of Despond," I called it, which turned the day for me very dismal, turned it into hell, and gave me great anxiety and very bad nerves until the coverage was done with and I could breathe again, and really, I mean really, appreciate my gifted and talented students (and, later, my OK, sort of in the middle, not horrible, not great, but not horrible students).

Coverage slip or no coverage slip—and it could go either way, because teachers down in the Slough seemed always to be coming down with something—I dutifully punched my card like the dedicated working slob I was, the workingman of the world, and climbed up the five flights of stairs to the fifth floor, lumbered up them really, one hand on the handrail, the other on the handle of my retractable cane, bouquets of flowers tucked under each arm, two under one arm, one under the other, my crammed-up packsack weighing me down and bulging like the hunch of a hunchback (I looked like a hunchback if peeped upon in silhouette; I looked like a downtrodden wretch from a fairy tale who is in need of a charm), huffing and hacking and groaning and hyperventilating, and once I'd alighted, finally, on the last landing, and could pull up my trousers and tuck in my shirt and adjust the straps on my bag, I made my way slowly, very slowly, catching my breath, breath by breath, breathing my way through it, down the long, long hallway to the faculty restroom, because by then I really needed to pee, and then, having peed, I made my way back down the long hallway to my classroom, the farthest classroom from the loo, to drop everything on my desk and grab two of my vases and take them back to the restroom to fill them with water, and then back to my classroom to get the other vase and take it to the restroom and fill it with water, and then back to the classroom to arrange my flowers; then I would eat my croissant and drink my coffee, and brace myself as best I could for the onslaught to come...

I call it Golgotha, but it wasn't all Golgotha, the Golgotha my train had taken me to, not all of it, and it wasn't only the daily beatitude in Independent Reading that served to redeem a small part of it for me; it was, though, mainly that at first, and then, later, only that, and, finally, in the last year of my masquerade, of my long practical joke on myself, the year that everything fell apart and went to shit, not even that.

There had been, for instance, in the beginning and in the middle years, the consolation of the cheerful atmosphere of *bonhomie* of the luncheons I'd begun to sponsor in my classroom, first once a week, then twice a week, then every day of the week, not just for *my* students, but for the students of other teachers, as well— all were welcome who dwelled in "the desert place belonging to the city called Bethsaida": the bread and fishes I fed the multitude were peanut butter and jelly sandwiches, the makings of which I kept, along with bottles of hand lotion and a first-aid kit (all the students on the floor came to Nurse Blackwell with owies and for their skin care needs) in a supply locker in the back of my classroom. I sponsored the luncheons not only because I wanted to save my children from the bullying in the cafeteria, where, I had learned, life was even shorter, nastier, and more brutish than at Fairway Market, but also because their laughter cheered me up when I was down, as did the fun games we played together, and the cheerful *bonhomie.*

I taught them how to play Guggenheim and Botticelli and Ghosts and, once they got the hang of Ghosts, Superghosts. And I purchased a good score of board games and several boxes of replacement dice: the kids, as I've already recounted, were sweet, and where it counted law-abiding, but the fingers of some of them were a little sticky, and not just from peanut butter and jelly, although, as any surface in my classroom would have served to affirm, they were sticky from that, too (I had, I will admit, occasional sticky fingers myself, especially when it came to ballpoint pens, or back in my smoking days, to cigarette lighters; and, in my teaching days, to the scissors and staplers and scotch tape and magic markers and hole punchers, etc., that I "borrowed" from the other teachers, from women teachers, of course, the unofficial quartermaster corps at any school), and they tended, some of my students, to pinch the bones to play at shooting craps, which, being "gifted and talented," they didn't really know how to do, any more than I would have known how to shoot craps at their age, or knew how to shoot craps at mine; they just shook the dice in exaggerated motions, and then rolled them loudly and menacingly down a hallway as they'd seen others do, maybe in a movie or TV show, maybe somewhere in the neighborhood *the only real game of craps, speaking of craps, and you should pardon the digression, that I saw while I was in New York was in a little hidden pocket across the street from the Port Authority Bus Terminal, played by seven or eight wino O.G.s, flash frozen in 1974, and only recently brought back to room temperature; these interesting-looking throwbacks were decked out in Sweet Sweetback velour and in hats like the hats that Huggy Bear used to wear on* Starsky and Hutch *(there were also a couple of out of place looking white dudes in the party, decked out in threads sort of like Don Knotts' in* Three's Company *after the Ropers got their own show); the scene looked staged for tourists and flâneurs, but when I was out on any of the long and restless strolls—my learning walks—that my feet seemed always in the mood to take me on (even when swollen and receiving auxiliary support from my retractable cane), I was forever walking in on similar such anachronous slices of time-frozen Old New York, Johnny Casey, little Jimmy Crowe, Jakey Krause, the baker, who always had the dough, pretty Nellie Shannon with a dude as light as cork, except, though I always had an eye peeled, I was never able to see hidden in any pocket anywhere I looked the stickball game I'd always hoped I'd see one day; once when my students were ribbing me for being corny and square and a hick out-of-towner, I told them, "aw, go and play a game of stickball why don'tcha," but they had never heard of stickball—or Johnny Casey, or little Jimmy Crowe—and they ribbed me further for talking about such boring ass old school stuff, and so I retorted, funnily, I thought, "so's yer old man," but the kids just looked at me kind of blankly and one of them said, "what does that even mean?" and then it was time for Independent Reading, and everybody got busy questioning, visualizing, inferring, determining importance, synthesizing, employing fix-up strategies, and making text-to-self, text-to-world, and text-to-text connections...; these haints of Old New York would appear just when I had given up the city to Starbucks and Urban Outfitters and American Apparel and Barnes and Noble and Rite Aid and Duane Reade, etc.; later on, though, to confound things, I started feeling nostalgia for Barnes and Noble when the Lincoln Center branch closed down, which, by the way, how could that store close down? It was always mobbed, which I know because I stopped there frequently to pee when I was in the neighborhood; they had one of the nicer toilets in town, because it was always being cleaned—always—which meant you had to wait to get in, and while waiting try not to pee your pants, which I will admit, with my prostate gland, I sometimes did a little—peed my pants...a little.*

Our favorite board game was Pictionary, though Mancala and Yahtzee had almost as many followers, and on occasion large and raucous games of Monopoly were organized—epic and unfinishable games (some of them are still going on) that sprawled across a couple of dozen mismatched desks the boys and girls would pull together to form an uneven table that would almost accommodate all the players, a game in which we used real money (just kidding about the real money). I would only agree to play Monopoly as long as I didn't have to be the banker, which the children, typecasting me I felt, were always wanting me to be (because, I worried, they thought I *was* a sort of a banker, you know, since I so obviously pined for the banking model of education; but they didn't really think I was a banker; I just felt old; old and white, and, by comparison, rich [and corny], sort of like the father in *Mary Poppins* before Mary Poppins gets a hold of him, and was projecting; or else maybe, in my soul, I constituted, now that I think of it, a sort of a mishmash of the two, a mishmash of Mary Poppins and the banker-daddy). I set, in addition, one other condition that would have to be met before I would play Monopoly: I had to be the iron (since replaced, I have read, with a cat), not that there was ever any fierce competition for the pleasure of wielding that token, but I made a big deal of wanting it, of pretending that it was a hot commodity that everyone would be fighting over, and intimating that I would have a tantrum if I didn't get it. Before I rolled my dice, I blew all over them, loudly, exaggeratedly, and shook them in my hands for a good three minutes, exasperating some, inspiring others (to steal the dice and pretend they were playing craps), and then, finally letting them fly, I would holler, in southern-drawled Damon Runyon, sounding something like a hillbilly Sheldon Leonard, "Seven come eleven baby needs a new pair of shoes," and the children, moaning, would retort, invariably, and in unison—*and* in laughter; there was always a lot of laughter, alot of it, even—"*Cor*-ny!"

You must understand that the underserved populations at the high-needs school where I facilitated were never allowed any playtime. Their recreation, and the profits of Princeton Review, and the approved list of all the other Supplemental Education Service "providers," consisted of test prep—during school hours, after school, and on weekends, "studying the conventions of the genre," as the "literacy team" called it. They had gym for one forty-five minute period once a week, and there was no recess. Their playground was used as a parking lot for teachers, administrators, and staff, which always pissed me off, not only because adults had expropriated sacred real estate—a playground, for crissakes!—from children, for selfish and banal and eco-unfriendly purposes, but also because they owned a car at all (about half of the teachers, a few of the staff, and *all* of the administrators, every single one of the administrators), which you don't need in New York, you really don't (of course the administrators would have to have cars, and they would have to be big ugly gas-guzzlers: Lincoln Leviathans, Ford Fracases, Cadillac Colossi, BMW Behemoths, and Buick Brobdingnagians). New Yorkers with cars irked me (so, by the way, did New Yorkers with bicycles, scooters, skateboards, and prams), except I guess for Ms. Doris Ornstein-Taylor, an ESL, or ESOL, or ELL (they kept changing the name of it) teacher I knew, who owned a Saab and lived in Park Slope and gave me a ride home sometimes, or unless they kept them parked in garages and only used them, their cars I'm talking about, not their bikes or scooters or skateboards or prams (which I'm having fun picturing, though; especially, for some reason, the scooters), to get to their summer homes upstate or in the Berkshires or the Hamptons (or if they lived in Brooklyn to the Fairway in Red Hook), which is something Caroline and I planned to do one day (keep a car in a garage so we could drive to our summer home upstate or in the Berkshires or the Hamptons; and, once we moved to Park Slope, so we could drive to the Fairway in Red Hook, because neither Key Foods nor Met Foods was cutting it, though the lady who ran the Met Foods kept a big friendly cat that I liked to pat; Key Foods, though, had no redeeming qualities, none; and joining the Co-Op was, for me, out of the question, completely out of the question), when we still thought I could keep my job; when we still thought I could learn how to stand it.

But I was never going to keep my job; I was never going to learn how to stand it; not I, who, in comparison to the stoical brave and caring (and methodical) teachers who had learned how to stand theirs, was like the holocaustal baby in the C. K. Williams poem called "The Rampage," a poem that I sometimes thought of then,

> a baby got here once who before
> he was all the way out and could already feel the hindu
> pain inside him and the hebrew and the iliad
> decided he was never going to stop crying no matter what
> until they did something he wasn't going
> to turn the horror
> off in their fat sentences...

For me the job was and would always be a fat sentence—a misery—that "bowed" me, simpering wretch that I was (and "ill-provided," though middle-aged and not "young," as in the bit from Melville I'm interrupting quoting C. K. Williams to quote here, so there's no excuse), hard "to the brunt of things." It's a mixed blessing for me, now, but "never again," since I slid my notice under the principal's old and peremptorily massive door, would I "know," as Norman Mailer once put it, "in the dreary way one usually knows such things," but for reasons that are obviously different from Mailer's, "what it was like to work at a dull job or take orders from a man one hated," but this was more than a dull job, more than taking orders from a man I hated, though it was a dull job (or the part of it I hated was, the part where there were no children around; I tried to save my sick days, a merciful ten per year, for days of in-services and professional development and teacher conferences [talk about Golgotha!], days the students had off), and I did take orders from a man I hated, but how can anybody explain to anybody just how miserable, how alienating to all human yearning, to any bright hope—how bad, how dreary—the job at Peter Minuit Intermediate School truly was? *And why would anybody care?* I couldn't even explain it to the other teachers who worked at the school, teachers who seemed, incredibly, not to know how bad and dreary their jobs were; teachers who seemed, incredibly, not to know how bad and dreary their lives were. It would, of course, have been wrong, then, would have been presumptuous (is wrong and presumptuous now), of me to say such a thing, had I said it, which I guess I have (now), or to think it, or even to feel that way, but I was feeling all kinds of bad ways then (and, frankly, feel all kinds of bad ways now); I was, after all, unlike the pros (and they were the pros), only playing at being a teacher, but then one of the things wrong with me was I thought everybody was only playing at what they did, which is to say playing at what they were, at who they were, which of course they were, which of course they are (some of them, the method actors, are just very deep in character), but all I wanted was to say honestly to people, first at the high school I attended, and later at all the colleges I went to, and then at every job I ever hated, but with a particular sense of urgency at Peter Minuit Academy, was the thing that Anton Chekhov said was all *he* wanted to say to people, not that I would compare myself to Chekhov, but then I guess I sort of am, implying I see things others don't, which I don't, I'm just being presumptuous, just being a hater: what Chekhov said was, "All I wanted was to say honestly to people: 'Have a look at yourselves and see how bad and dreary your lives are!' The important thing is that people should realize that, for when they do, they will most certainly create another and better life for themselves. I will not live to see it, but I know that it will be quite different, quite unlike our present life. And so long as this different life does not exist, I shall go on saying to people again and again: 'Please, understand that your life is bad and dreary!'" But you can't really say that to people, can you? One can barely stand to say it to oneself.

I found myself, sometimes, getting angry, unfairly I knew (these were the salt of the earth, but had, for me, lost their savor), at the teachers who could stand it; I found myself getting angry at *all* the thick-skinned people of the world, angry at everyone who could stand it; and angrier, still, guiltily angrier, at the patient uncomplaining ones who stuck it out anyway, for the sake of the children, or because they had signed something on a dotted line and were whatever the sacrifices going to see the thing through, forgetting in the face of all that sacrifice the beautiful lustrous wisdom of W.C. Fields, wisdom that I had long since acceded to, "If at first you don't succeed, try again. Then quit. There's no use being a damn fool about it."

Some of the time I thought something was wrong with me because I couldn't stand it, but more often I wondered if something wasn't wrong with those who could, if they weren't the alienated ones, not I. But it was me, wasn't it, that something was wrong with? I was the alienated one, wasn't I? Smug, complacent, self-satisfied in my self-loathing, nodding knowingly, as a teenager, staying up all night in my bedroom on Willow Way, scribbling, "yes!" in the margins at the passage in *Tender is the Night* when Nicole Diver shakes "her head right and left, disclaiming responsibility for the matter," and says to Dick, "So many smart men go to pieces nowadays," and Dick answers, "And when haven't they…Smart men play it close to the line because they have to—some of them can't stand it, so they quit."

There was something wrong with me, wasn't there? I was kidding myself, romanticizing things, lumping myself in with the smart men of all those years ago (the smart men of today are proactive, entrepreneurial, and have a prescription if the wires get crossed, or a twelve-step program). Oh, there was something wrong with me. I went to pieces, it's true, and couldn't stand it so I quit, but not because I was smart and had to play it close to the line, but because I was dumb and self-deluded, the little C. K. Williams baby who decided he was never going to stop crying no matter what.

But *that* baby stopped crying, didn't it? Which I guess is the point of the poem. That baby stopped crying like the boy trapped in the barbershop in the Philip Levine poem stopped crying. He stopped crying like all the babies in all the poems and in all the stories and all the lullabies (and all the confessions, spiritual autobiographies, *cris de coeur*, advertisements for oneself, and *apologias pro vita sua*) stop crying, like all babies eve-rywhere stop crying, except, of course, at a restaurant or in a movie theater or on an airplane, but I didn't want them to stop crying, except at the restaurant or the movie theater or on the airplane, didn't want that to be the point of either poem, of any poem, didn't want to hear that anybody's life had just begun, or that it was ending; I didn't like beginnings, or endings, just the muddle, as Philip Larkin called it, though I believe I read some-where that Peter De Vries said it first.

He stopped crying, the baby who got here once, as we all stopped crying, or most of us, all of us who got here once,

> and looked up and said all right
> it's better now
> I'm hungry now I want just to sleep

But I wasn't sleepy; I'd had a lot of coffee. And I couldn't eat; I was too nervous. I never ate anything all day at work except that croissant I bought for breakfast, dunking it in my giant cup of espresso. I always ended up bringing the broccoli and carrots and hummus home and eating them for dinner, or leaving them in my desk and forgetting about them until the broccoli started stinking. Sometimes I ate the fruit, or a small bite of the bread. The kasha varnishkes I usually wound up tossing or giving to a science teacher I knew, until I gave them up altogether once I found out the onions are fried in schmaltz (I was trying very hard to be a vegan).

I guess, realistically, though, teenage me would have been better off if, instead of staying up all night reading *Tender is the Night*, and vowing the next morning to go to pieces someday, I had stayed up all night with Kafka:

> In the fight between you and the world, back the world

But if adult me had known, later, much later, positioned as I was, cheek by jowl with the world, in its headlock, going toe to toe with it, that I would, within a few short years, having wriggled and scooched myself out of the fray, find myself, in my lonely decampment, moved to write a book about all that fight, about all that hopeless fight, I might have wanted to include as the book's epigraph, alongside Kafka's precept, a passage from John le Carré that I had jotted down one morning on my long commute uptown, in one of my vest pocket Macguffins, as, squeezed in the tiny orange patch of subway bench that I had wriggled and scooched (always with the wriggling, always with the scooching) a boney butt cheek into, I read a bouncing-on-my-knee folded-over copy of *The Constant Gardener*, reading this book when I should have been dashing off a lesson plan, like the other teachers in the car, the proactive ones, to have on my desk when the ghouls came in to check (teachers without lesson plans on their desks are sent to the rubber room, get a letter in their file, have to report to the principal every morning to show Cap'n that their mind is right and they have prepared a lesson plan formatted in approved style),

> They did this to me but I have remained who I am. I am tempered. I am able. Inside myself there's an untouched man. If they came back now, and did everything to me again, they would never reach the untouched man. I've passed the exam I've been shirking all my life. I'm a graduate of pain.

But I had never graduated from any pain. I'd been fudging my CV my whole life. The objective correlative to my suffering, lavish and self-aggrandizing, baroque, rococo, lying figuratively now like a deflated anticlimax, in a pile outside in the rain in the parking lot playground of Peter Minuit Academy, was neither objective, nor did it correlate; the correlative was incommensurate to the pain, the pain was incommensurate to the correlative. I had failed another Master's Comps, shirked another exam, the exam I would continue to shirk all my life.

353

Knowing this, and ashamed of myself for the foulness and the hatefulness of the small and squalid daydreams that propelled me then, that kept me in trim, I paused sometimes, in the early days of when I couldn't stand it and I quit, and, only after nightfall, in the privacy of my mind, only in my head, though, but not even there, I wondered, wondered if the brooding pain I nursed and fed and kept alive with shortcake and violet biscuits and tinctures of wormwood and powdered mandrake root would have been commiserate, would have earned me a *cum laude*, if, and here's the if that shamed me, *if*, I sort of almost fantasized *only in my head, though, but not even there, somewhere in a primitive preserve of the brain stem, in some small place near the top of my spine where thoughts that later get expressed or never get expressed begin or die, where they aren't even thoughts whatever they are just images and feelings of love and hate and rage and fear and something's wrong*: if something awful had happened: not to me, of course, not directly, but to somebody I knew, somebody I cared about, somebody I loved even, but wasn't *too* close to, during my tenure at Minuit (and there was something that you will read about below that sparked the particulars of this latest stirring, this latest outrage, in my fitful oblongata), something awful, something calamitous, something terrible occurring off-stage, in the Greek style, not, as I say, something that would have happened to me, not directly, or in my line of vision, but something near me, off-stage, and out of earshot, something that is reported on after it happens, by a chorus of children perhaps, or of brave and caring classroom teachers, in matching twinsets, or a chorus of support staff, the lunchroom ladies maybe, spatulas in hand, or the custodians, leaning on the handles of their dust mops (and then, to satisfy the crowds seated in the *theatron*, the bloody results are rolled in on a wheeled platform for the audience to inspect, a *tableau mordant*): something the knowledge of which could break a heart legitimately, and make a man fall honestly and commensurately to pieces. Something awful and honest and terrible and commensurate and real and sublime, sublime in the Longinus or

Edmund Burke sense of the word, not poor little put-upon me, sad and getting my feelings hurt, experiencing an emotional derailment, suffering from the alienation of my labor, and feeling a feeling of powerlessness, or "sence of injur'd merit," a Mommy and Daddy don't understand me in a world I never made, but something awful and honest and terrible and commensurate and real and sublime, something dreadful and heartbreaking, something grievous, something exquisite, something Greek, a catharsis, sort of, which is to say, because the end of all stories, even if the writer forbears to mention it, is death, someone dying, as Virginia Woolf said, in order that the rest of us should value life more: something like if a student, god forbid, a student I had known and loved and tried to help and taught some things to, had, shooting off his mouth, or getting involved in something he shouldn't have gotten involved with, or in the wrong place at the wrong time, if such a student had gotten himself shot, offstage, and was killed, let's say, *let's just say*, in a drive-by shooting, and had died in the arms of another student from the class, a kind of pieta, as I pictured it, as three other students, their faces contorted, looked on in agony in the chiaroscuro of a red dusk somewhere in Harlem, or Inwood, or Washington Heights, somewhere in Region 10, which is the kind of thing that *could* have happened to one of my students, less likely with my gifted and talented students, more likely with the JD's, but I didn't love those students, or maybe a couple of them, a little, but at any rate the effect wouldn't have been the same.

This thing I'm describing, the agony, the pieta, the whole tableau, did happen, though: a child did die. It happened, off-stage, to the student of another Teaching Fellow I knew who taught at another school, a Fellow in my cohort, a Fellow in my advisory group, a Fellow who, if the narrative you are reading now had been more elegantly structured, would have been introduced earlier in the text, as a kind of literary foil—younger, braver, and wiser than me; and then, the punchline having been set up, the details would have been revealed of how the foil had, when tested, proven himself to be patient and uncomplaining, an authentic graduate of pain.

He was gallant, this other Teaching Fellow, this foil, and he was, in addition to being a Teaching Fellow, a poet, a sort of a Wilfred Owen, as I fancied it, of alternative certification for service in high-needs schools (except, god bless him, he survived the war), who might have functioned, moreover, in addition to functioning as a foil, as a sort of rival poet, if I had been a poet, which I wasn't, though I sometimes wished I had been, and if he had been my rival, which he wasn't, though I will admit I did feel rivalrous with him, sort of, not in the early years, when I first met him, but many years later, sort of, when I read on the Internet a brief account the "rival" had written of how he had acquitted himself (admirably, self-deprecatingly), after many struggles, and a couple of actual physical assaults on his person, in a much more difficult classroom than any classroom I ever knew, a stickier theater of war, and left the field honorably,

> My first six months of teaching middle school in Harlem were brutal. I could not consistently control my classroom. I was physically assaulted twice and tried to resign three times. Each of the three mornings I arrived with a letter of resignation, one of my kids encountered me coming into school and interacted with me in a way that crushed my will to abandon them. The third time I arrived two hours early to avoid such an encounter, but a kid on the basketball court saw me and came over to sing the theme song to *Welcome Back, Kotter*. I had been out of school for over a week with pneumonia and had realized I didn't just love the kids in theory but in practice. Once I dedicated myself to the necessary disciplinary practices of an inner city middle school, my students revealed themselves as perceptive, engaged learners. We read Hemingway and Salinger and excerpts from *Inferno*. We covered basic curriculum and reading strategies, and their standardized test scores leapt. By the beginning of my second year, my classroom transformed into a happy, safe learning environment, and my supervisor could assign troubled kids to my class so that we could

practice social interventions, often successfully. I absolutely
love teaching college classes, but I'm never going to love students as intently as I loved my Harlem kids.[51]

Yes, I felt just a little rivalrous, sort of, when I read the account
this poet who loved his Harlem kids had written, as I'd felt many
times before in the presence of other poets I had fallen in with,
poets who had also loved the people, places, and things they
loved, loved them *intently*, as a poet loves.

I had mixed feelings about poets: I liked, for instance, the way
they said the things they said, but envied their saying them so
well; liked their sideway slant, the way they snuck up on things;
admired their turmoil, but felt threatened by all the exaltation,
the flowing robes and the fine chiseled features, the fine-tuned
feelings, a certain *hauteur* of feeling things *better* than everybody
else, of feeling them smarter; of naming things other people
didn't know needed naming; a desire to be vatic; and of having
a *sympathy* to life I couldn't acquire, or in some cases a detach-
ment from it (something else I couldn't acquire); a moral sanction, often, to be hurt, and to thrash around a bit; or to hurt
others; or to hover, aloof (there are many different kinds of poet,
having to do, perhaps, the bio-reductionist in me suspects, with
variations of chemical imbalance, imbalances that benefit the
race, if not the spouses and friends and lovers of poets: "It's terrible, Bob," Robert Lowell once wrote to his editor, Robert
Giroux, "to think that all I've suffered, and all the suffering I've
caused, might have arisen from the lack of a little salt in my
brain"); and a tendency, sometimes, some of them, of a certain
age, or temperament, or training, to accept the universe (we're
back to that), and to trip off into it; to love *everything*, or feel a
"communion" with it; a belief to seek and find meaning where
there is none, or when finding none, to *make* meaning, to conjure
it, summon it, flush it out into the open; or maybe it wasn't

---

[51] "An Interview with Matthew Henriksen," http://www.bookslut.com/features/
2011_07_017953.php

meaning they were after; maybe they didn't need for things to *mean*, but rather for them to *signify*, to leave a message; I think of Orpheus, in the Jean Cocteau movie, listening to the car radio and writing down the announcer's phrases, or, in the play, to the horse's stamps ("Orpheus hunts Eurydice's lost love," or is it "Eurydice's lost life"? Does it depend on the translation? I could look it up but I don't like resolution).

No, I can't explain what bothers me about poets, or what delights me; I sound foolish trying; it must, therefore, not be bother but envy, yet another instance of it: "A hater is a hater in everything," as Charles Coburn says in *The Lady Eve*, except he says "mug" and not "hater." I was a hater in everything. And a mug. (Oh, and by the way, except for sneaking up on things with a sideway slant and saying them well, and having a sympathy to life, very few of the mixed feelings delineated above applied to my rival poet, but he was a poet, the rival poet was, and the mixed feelings carried over.)

But maybe rivalrous isn't the word to describe how I felt. I think I felt envious; I think I felt trumped, out-classed, coming up short. Yes, that's it, coming up short: I felt like a self-made man in the presence of an aristocrat, sort of the way Norman Mailer felt sparring with Robert Lowell in *The Armies of the Night* (I think the sparring was all on Mailer's part). "Lowell's shoulders had a slump," Mailer wrote of his rival, "his modest stomach was pushed forward a hint, his chin was dropped to his chest...One did not achieve the languid grandeurs of that slouch in one generation...." Desiring this man's art and that man's scope *I have coveted everything and taken pleasure in nothing* I envied this "rival," this foil, as Mailer had envied Lowell, envied him, in my case, perversely, sickeningly, I'm sure, to normal people, because this poet/Fellow had, on his battlefield, earned his red badge of courage, vicariously, of course, but still: a student he had known and loved and tried to help and taught some things to, had, shooting off his mouth, or getting involved in something he shouldn't have gotten involved with, or in the wrong place at the wrong time, gotten himself shot, off-stage, killed, in a drive-by shooting, and had died in the arms of another student from the class, a kind of pieta, as I picture it, as three other students, their faces contorted, looked on in agony in a red dusk somewhere; it was Harlem, in the case of the Teaching Fellow/Rival Poet's student:

> Going into the public schools, I had no ideas about changing lives, but I saw it happen. Of course, in a place like Harlem trouble isn't merely nagging at the kids' heels. It's a big fucking storm cloud even on the sunny days and it's in every shadow, too. Near the end of my second year, one of our students got killed in a drive-by shooting, a twelve-year-old. One of my students held him while he died as three more watched the life go out of him. I went to the wake. A few young teachers who worked with the same group of students had unofficially designated me as the mentor of the group, but I had no answers for them and could offer no consolation. I had a breakdown, left the school at the end of the year, and couldn't get it together as an adjunct for a couple of years. We'd been trying to intervene with the student who was killed, and I can say with certainty that I could have taken actions that would have probably prevented his death. I don't blame myself, but I'm not willing to skew an experience to fabricate happiness. Without my wife…I probably wouldn't have come back from that darkness. Now I still get to teach Dante but also I get to come home at night and be a poet and a daddy.[52]

I envied this Teaching Fellow, envied this poet, in a way, because losing a student in the way he lost his, having something awful, something terrible, etc., happen to a student he knew and loved and had taught things to, he had earned *his* breakdown. Because, you see, if you have a child in your class get killed god grants you grace, or something like it, after the horror, after the

---

[52] Ibid.

ordeal (yes, this was a terrible thing to say, to think, to feel, but I was feeling terrible things then, and thinking terrible things, and saying them); you are justified; you have passed your test; you may quit your job, leave it behind, get the fuck out of there, and people will understand; they will understand if you fall to pieces; and they will watch in admiration as you put yourself back together. A dead kid is, in the moral balance, commensurate. A dead kid gets you off the hook, and you may retire honorably.

Here is something else my rival wrote, "rival," I think now, in the sense of "the rivals of my watch," partners who live by the same "rivus," or stream, and use it, both of them, for irrigation,

> When you teach in an inner city school, you have to create an aura to survive the day. When you go home, you turn into someone else, because you can't carry the grief and stress around with you. Now I don't have to separate my roles. I'm the same person when I write poetry and when I teach. My daughter doesn't see a persona. When we read books or watch videos I don't set myself outside the experience. We have a strong connection through language and music. We go to the park and I talk to her about trees and birds, as I do with my poet friends, only I stay away from abstraction and sarcasm because she can't share in that with me. We look at nature and interact with each other on a more instinctual level, which I prefer. Children see the world with an awe that stands apart from purpose. A child's awe contains all the sadness and beauty I need to experience, so I don't have to grieve or hope.[53]

But I could never get out of my aura, or the someone else I had turned into; I couldn't get out of my grief, out of my stress, out of my hope; I was—and am—all persona, all role, all abstraction, all sarcasm, or almost. I pray now, though, down by my rivulet, for my own (qualified) exemption from grief and hope, for my own transport to the sadness and beauty I need to

---

[53] Ibid.

experience. But do you have to have a child to do that? Do you have to grow? ("Lord," Melville asked Hawthorne, "when shall we be done with growing?" —I am Melville in this analogy, the rival poet Hawthorne.) Do you have to cover basic curriculum and reading strategies? Do standardized test scores have to leap? Do you have to dedicate yourself to the necessary disciplinary practices? Does a student have to die so a Teaching Fellow can value life more? Does a black or brown student have to die so a white Teaching Fellow can value life more?

And is this (growing, covering basic curriculum and strategies, etc.—accepting things, getting over them, getting over life and death) what the C. K. Williams poem is about? Is it a closely observed rendering, one moment of many, the passing of another comprehensive examination, in a life of always growing, of always covering basic curricula and strategies, in which everyone stops crying?

I want the poem to be about the horror and the fat sentences, no growth: hindu pain and hebrew and iliad pain.

I want it to be about how the baby "was going to keep screaming / until they made death little like he was," little like in my envy, in my rot, I have made the death of a black child in Harlem, and, as you shall see, the death of a black child in Milwaukee, two more black children whose lives matter—as plot devices, as metaphors—in books written by sad and sensitive white people about sad and sensitive white lives lived, in my case, abstractly and sarcastically: a white life lived, in my case, in shame and self-exculpation, self-exculpation masquerading as self-excoriation, somewhere in the aura of the middle class, in the aura of the white middle class.

But then, for all my envy and my shame, for all my self-excoriation and self-exculpation, for all my rot, I might still have, if I'd thought about it, reassured myself that if *I* had wound up with a dead kid in my class, *I* (so sad, so sensitive) wouldn't have been able to stand it; *I* wouldn't have been able to cope: to suffer, to heal and then move on...

Except, this isn't true. I had known a child who'd died. I'd known a child who died in Milwaukee, Wisconsin. And I had stood it. I had coped. I had suffered. I moved on.

But the death occurred a few years after I had known the child, after I had been close to him, I mean, so I was spared... something (white people are always spared...something). The boy was 9 and 10 when I knew him, and he was a teenager when he died. I almost always lost kids when they entered their teenage years, not to gunfire or some other tragedy but to their putting away of childish things, childish things like looking up to me, finding me amusing or fun or interesting or admirable. I didn't seem like such a cool guy anymore when the kids who used to admire me turned 14 or 15. The scales fell from their eyes. I seemed, then, to their teenage selves, old and corny, a relic of their early youth.

But still, a child I had known had died, a child called Nathanial. I had gone to the funeral and seen Nathanial's brother wail and cry and come very close to crawling into the casket with Nathanial's body. I had seen Nathanial's mother cry, and in the beautiful cheekbones of her face I saw the beautiful face of her dead son living—living, loving, shining through: alive. This was a boy I had tried to teach long division to, but couldn't, and a mother I had tried to teach to read, but couldn't. This was a boy who came to see me every day after school, every day (he never missed a day), and one time he asked me what I did at night after I left the youth center, what I did before I went to bed, asked me, specifically, if I used this time to "set my plans." Such an old-fashioned, such a Biblical sounding expression I remember thinking at the time, something I have never forgotten, and I've never forgiven myself for getting over the death of that boy, for accepting it, for moving on.

The morning after Nathanial died, his mother called very early and left a message in my voice mail. She left the message in my voice mail because, I supposed, I was the only staff member she knew at the youth center and I guess she assumed her son still came to the center to see me. The message was, or the part of it I remember was, "Nathanial won't be able to go on the field trip today because he died." And I stood it...

At the funeral I kept looking at Nathanial's brother, after he sat down and regained his composure, looking a little embarrassed, but mainly sad and tired. He was handsome in his grief; he looked grown sitting beside his mother, looking somewhere, I couldn't tell where, both of them looking somewhere, I couldn't tell where. The room smelled like church. I know it was air-conditioned but the way I remember it it was hot as Alabama in there and the ladies were fanning themselves with church fans that had Bible verses printed on them. Nathanial's auntie took the lectern when the minister asked if anybody would like to come up front and say anything and she told everybody to get in church. That was her message, "Get in church," and she kept saying it; she'd say some other stuff but then she'd come back to her refrain, "Get in church." People listened hard, and some of them said "yes," and "that's right," and "tell it, sister." I don't know if any of them afterward got in church, anyone who wasn't already in church, I mean, but everybody seemed to understand that somebody must say something and several people did. A lot of people knew Nathanial, a lot of adults, not just family members, and they all said sweet things, true things based on what I knew about him. Nathanial had outgrown me but had found new adults to help him set his plans. I was listening, but I kept looking at his brother, whom I didn't think I had ever met before, but kept thinking that I knew him from somewhere.

The service ended and I went to say something, I didn't know what, to Nathanial's mother, whom I hadn't seen in I didn't know how long, and then everybody headed out to the parking lot, just standing around out there, not getting in their cars, just kind of standing there, smoking some of them, squinting in the sun, those who were facing in the sun's direction, because the sun was bright that day, and then Nathanial's brother, who I noticed was looking at me now, walked over and asked me, "You still carry around that baseball bat? Is it in the car?"

We looked at each other for a moment, and I remembered that I did know the young man, had met him, but hadn't been introduced, had spoken, in a dreamscape of Milwaukee, I don't know how many years earlier. I was walking through Nathanial and his brother's neighborhood that abutted my neighborhood, crumbled into pieces off to its side, on my way somewhere. My head was lowered, as it always was when I walked; that's how I walked. I was carrying a baseball bat, my Louisville Slugger that I'd brought up from Birmingham, its sweet spot resting in the hollow between my neck and shoulder. It was a heavy bat, and I had to choke up on it, but I could usually get at least a single with it if I didn't swing too soon or too late. I was on my way to the youth center to drive a bunch of boys and girls in the youth center van (the van that a wheel fell off of one time, but no kids were in the van, and I was driving slow, but, still, a wheel fell off) to play some baseball at a park in a "good neighborhood" across the river, where we could have a diamond of our own, with a pitcher's mound and a backstop and real bags for bases, and, because my head was down, I didn't notice that up the road about a block and a half away, two boys I'd never seen before were watching my approach; one of them was maybe fourteen or fifteen, a tall fourteen or fifteen, and the other was a much shorter few years younger. They were hanging out on the sidewalk in front of a corner store that had the words "Meat Deals" painted on its window; there was a torn and peeling billboard falling off the side of the building, an advertisement for Kools or Olde English 800. The boys were drinking canned sodas, drinking them with straws, the kind of straws that bend with a little accordion in the middle. The cans were wrapped in napkins. When I was close enough to the youths for them to speak to me, the older boy grinned and said, "Hey man, this is a rough neighborhood, but you don't need no baseball bat." I startled, and then I laughed and explained why I was carrying the bat, and the young man said, "Let me ask you something. Have you been to Europe? I mean did you spend a year in Europe, you know, when you graduated from college? I mean, what I'm asking is, You been to Europe ain't you?"

I had been to Europe, but I was resisting a strong urge to explain about how strong the dollar had been when I was there, and how it had taken me nine years to finish college, and how I'd failed my master's comps when everyone else had passed theirs, and about the trouble I'd had with abyssal aporias, but replied, instead, "Yeah, I've been to Europe, but not for a year. I was there for six months, but it was before I finished college." The young man shot a glance at his companion and said, softly, "See."

And then the boy kind of leaned back on his heels, and held his arm out at a funny angle to his body, and so, involuntarily, did I, and the two of us, adult and teen, looked at each other for what seemed like a very long time. I was squinting in the sun—it was a sunny day, like it would be a few years later at the funeral. We looked at each other across a vast crevasse filled with weeds, tall blue chicory that flowered in cracks of the pavement below our feet, and then, after a while, the boy said, "It was nice talking to you," and tossed his empty soda can in a trash bin and walked on down the road, the other boy following behind him.

And then the sun went behind a cloud and the cloud swelled big and dark, and then it burst, and the game was called on account of rain. I took shelter under an awning, and a little later, when it was clear, I headed for home.

THE END

ABOUT THE AUTHOR

CHARLES BLACKWELL was born in Birmingham, Alabama, in 1958. He was educated at public schools there and at the University of Alabama at Birmingham, the University of Wisconsin-Milwaukee, and The City College of New York. He was for many years a youth worker in Milwaukee, Wisconsin, and, briefly, a public schoolteacher in New York City. He is currently living in Milwaukee.